Woodworkers
Career and Educational
Source Book

Published by
Guild of Master Craftsman Publications Limited
166 High Street, Lewes, East Sussex BN7 1XU

Prices quoted are correct at the time of going to press

Typeset by FotoDirect, Brighton
Printed in Great Britain by Hillman Printers (Frome) Ltd.

ISBN 0 946819 23 8

CONTENTS

Alan Peters, OBE

I often recall the comments of my well intentioned teachers back in the late 1940s. They continually extolled the virtues of working hard at school in order to gain meaningful employment later. I recall also their utter dismay when I chose to leave on my 16th birthday in order to grasp the opportunity of a 5-year cabinetmaking apprenticeship with the late Edward Barnsley. In doing so I was forfeiting any chance I had of gaining my School Certificate and with it any chance of meaningful employment, which was narrowly defined as a job to provide a good salary and social respectability – keeping hands clean and shirt collar white. It was considered the essential aim for any pupil whose intelligence was average or above.

My only allies then were my parents and my woodwork master. The latter I sensed was not held in any great esteem by his colleagues in the staff room, but he was, nevertheless, a constant source of inspiration to me.

At times, too, I contemplate what might have happened had I not chosen, in 1948, a life of making things and living with dust and polish under my finger nails. Could I possibly have achieved the level of satisfaction and pleasure that has come if I had been working full-time in an office? Even a design office?

Now, in the 1990s I would like to think that these prejudices against manual work have largely disappeared. But, sadly, old attitudes die hard and while design is considered an acceptable area of study, the crafts are still viewed with suspicion in many circles and considered a career option only for the least gifted in our society.

So what constantly gives me great pleasure, and what I find so encouraging and exciting today is that, despite this continuing prejudice, despite there being far less opportunity for pupils to experience the joy of making things and acquiring craft skills at school than there was 20 years ago, more and more gifted young people are moving into manual and, more particularly, craft occupations from choice.

And this is happening against the background of industry and commerce moving towards a 30 hour week with retirement at 55, 50 or even earlier. It is encouraging that so many reject this soft option – the company car and other perks that go with it – for a life as a self-employed artist or craftsman, which will inevitably mean a 60 hour week or more and never the time or the inclination to think about retirement.

Fortunately, as the schools (by and large) neglect their duty to teach manual skills in their current flirtation with design/technology, more and more opportunities are opening up in further education, and this is particularly true in the area of furniture.

At long last many of our colleges up and down the country are bowing to pressure, often from the students themselves, to recognise the need for courses directed towards the studio/workshop end of the furniture industry. This book, I am sure, will help to identify those excellent courses that now exist both at degree and other levels.

It was William Morris, as leader of the first craft revival back in Victorian Britain, who said man's greatest need beyond food and shelter is to gain pride and satisfaction from the work he or she does.

He and others spoke of the day when every small town and large village would have its resident furniture maker and potter, not to replace industrial production but to provide an alternative.

Now, in the 1990s, the ideals of the Arts & Crafts movement have never been closer to realisation. But we should always remember that a life in the crafts is not solely about personal fulfilment. It is also about service, and about enriching society by the objects we make.

There is – justifiably – a great deal of concern about the deforestation of the world, particularly the wholesale destruction of its rain forests. Some people want to blame woodworkers for that. If it is making you think twice about a career or hobby in woodworking, read on.

It is true, rain forest is being destroyed at an alarming rate. That is important because the so-called lungs of the earth are probably responsible for nearly a third of the world's oxygen supply and contain many species of plant and animal life still to be categorised. Apart from being important in their own right, that diversity of life might well contain substances which could be useful to mankind.

But let's put the timber trade into perspective. In 1987 the world (including the producing countries themselves) bought 71,350,000m³ of tropical wood as timber, panels or veneers. Ten times that amount was simply burnt off because it was in the way of rapidly expanding populations.

Britain imports most of its timber. In 1989 it imported 90,000m³ of mahogany from Brazil. A mahogany tree produces an average of about 3m³ of top quality timber, so about 30,000 trees were felled to supply Britain's demand. Say two mahogany trees grow per hectare, which is about right – rain forests contain over 600 species of categorised trees of which 40 or so are used for the timber industry – so 15,000 hectares were required to grow the trees. There are 2.47 acres per hectare and 640 acres in a square mile. An area just over 7½ miles by 7½ miles in total supplied all of the UK's needs for mahogany with less than one tree per acre being felled.

Brazil is currently using around 12½ million m³ of its forests as timber each year. More than 11 million m³ it uses itself. The rest is exported. But 172 million m³ becomes fuelwood.

If the world stopped buying tropical rain forest timber today just as much of the forest would be destroyed tomorrow – possibly even more because land now being preserved to supply the timber industry would suddenly lose any value in timber terms and would probably be felled to make way for cattle grazing.

More than 90% of tropical rain forest destroyed each year is simply burnt to make way for farmers, cleared for mineral extraction or flooded to provide water for the fast expanding populations of the third world where the forests grow.

Every time you eat a can of South American corned beef you are doing more to threaten the rain forest than if you furnished your entire house with Brazilian mahogany. By buying the corned beef you are telling the peoples of these areas that the land is more valuable for grazing cattle than it is for the production of trees. And it is no good telling those people they are harming the global environment. Their concern is how they are going to survive the next month, never mind the next 100 years.

Because relatively few of the rain forest species of trees are used for timber, the forest does not need to be destroyed for the extraction required, although it often is for ease of access. Forest management is needed and a longer term view of a renewable asset, which wood is.

Unlike coal, oil, steel, plastic, aluminium, or practically any other raw material, most timber will replace itself as a usable raw material within the lifespan of a human being, and tropical wood grows particularly quickly.

There is a misconception that trees in rain forests are hundreds of years old. They are not. Rain forests are efficient and old trees aren't. Tropical trees usually stop growing after 80 years and seldom live more than 120 years. Then they fall down and rapidly decompose.

It is this relatively quick growth which makes the rain forests so efficient at refreshing the air. Growing trees break down a thousand times more carbon dioxide (liberating the oxygen and building themselves from the carbon) than do mature trees.

Timber is Green in its use of energy, too. Production of a tonne of aluminium uses 20,000Kw/hours of electricity. Steel uses 3,800Kw/hours. Wood uses 435. That means savings on the fuels burnt to create electricity and less pollution from their burning.

The majority of Green concern is for the rain forests, and rightly so. But the rain forests are not the only source of material for the timber industry. Britain itself produces fine wood and a look at the list of contacts in this book will identify some sources of this timber.

Britain was once practically all forest. Nowadays it has only 9% coverage, but there is a growing awareness of the demand for indigenous timber and more trees are being planted than are being felled.

The same is happening elsewhere in the world. Europe has, on average, a 20% covering of forest, much of it softwood, which is well managed and replanted as a sustainable resource. In the USA where, admittedly, vast areas of temperate forests have been felled in the past and left cleared because the land was wanted, much replanting of forest areas is now taking place. In a 2,000 mile stretch of forest from Maine to Louisiana annual growth is exceeding felling by a million cubic metres. This is hardwood, some of which is giving British woodworkers chances to discover timbers they had not previously known. Further north, in Canada, policies of sustaining forest land are also being followed.

So be proud to use timber or to enter any of the industries mentioned in this book. Enjoy working with the material. Revel in its warmth and natural beauty. The more people who use timber the more interests will be concerned to make sure the supply of it is maintained.

And if, in working the material, you make a mistake and have to throw a piece of wood away, be happy that at least this material will rapidly biodegrade to return to the ground what it has taken out of it so that more wood may grow. This is nature's way of recycling.

Young trees in a sustainably managed tropical rain forest.

One of the fascinations of woodworking is that it embraces so many different individual crafts, each calling for specific skills and appealing to particular interests and talents.

Except in exceptional circumstances, few of the crafts lead to the making of fortunes. But all of them provide the means for a satisfying career and a never-ending love affair with a material about which there is always something new to learn.

A particular advantage in favour of woodworking as a career is that it offers the opportunity of becoming self-employed to those who master their craft. Skilled hands need never be idle and traditional craftsmanship is coming into its own again as a reaction against the monotony of mass production. But whether they remain in employment or become their own bosses, most woodworkers choose woodworking as their hobby. There is always so much to make; so many other woodworking skills to acquire.

Brief descriptions of the main woodworking crafts are given here in alphabetical order. But if you are really keen to find out about a particular craft, speak to the craftsmen themselves.

You or members of your family may already know local craftsmen who would be glad to have a chat with you. If not, search them out for yourself. Look them up in the *Yellow Pages*. Telephone them, write to them or call on them. If you call on the off chance, they may not have time to speak to you there and then. But they will be impressed with your enthusiasm and initiative and arrange to see you at some more convenient time.

Remember that craftsmen are proud of their skills and glad to talk about them to those who are interested. And not only will you find out what you want to know about their craft, the likelihood is you will be given useful advice on how to go about entering it.

You may even, if you have a mind to, be allowed to make tea in their workshop in your spare time and see at first hand just what the craft entails.

In the case of firms, as distinct from individual craftsmen, the man to seek out will usually be the Works Manager or Works Foreman. However you contact them, make the point immediately that you merely wish to find out something about the craft in question and could they spare a few minutes to talk to you about it and perhaps allow you to look around the workshop.

Have no qualms about making approaches of this kind, either to individuals or firms. As they have done for generations, many older people tend to think that those younger than themselves are lacking in self-reliance. Your proving to them otherwise will come as an agreeable surprise.

One other way in which you should be sure to

surprise them is by taking the trouble to write a 'thank you' letter shortly after your visit. Not only is this a simple matter of courtesy, it is also a good way to ensure they keep you and your name in mind.

If you have suitably impressed them, when next they need an apprentice they may well get in touch with you.

BOAT BUILDER

Boat builders will always be needed in our island home, both for business and leisure pursuit. Largely located near the coast for the building of bigger boats, the leisure crafts industry can be found almost anywhere.

This trade requires great accuracy in the reading of drawings and the fashioning of wood. A great number of boats use plastic in their construction, but at the same time timber is used in making the mould. Both hand and machine tools are used and all sorts of site conditions will be experienced. A considerable amount of work in wood is found in the fixtures and fittings of the boats.

CABINET MAKER

This is skilled work which requires more attention to detail at the bench than some of the other wood trades. You may work from the sawn material, using hand and machine tools to bring the job to fruition. At present great use is being made of prepared materials reducing the amount of hand work. Timber used will be soft and hard and experience will be gained in many areas of the furniture industry, including the making of reproduction furniture – ie furniture made to the exact design of much of the well-accepted work of past cabinet makers. You need to have a feeling for wood and a genuine desire to attain perfection.

Many college-trained students graduate to this area to gain experience before setting up on their own. Most aspire to becoming their own bosses but the initial costs are high, even if suitable premises can be found.

CARPENTER AND JOINER

Apprenticeships are still available which cover both trades and generally you would be accepted as an apprentice, leaving a final choice until a later date and after some experience of these trades.

The **Carpenter** is usually found working on building sites of every kind. He would be responsible for everything associated with the use of timber on site – shuttering for concrete, door linings, floor and ceiling joints, flooring of every kind, staircases, doors, cupboards and wardrobes are some of the many jobs. Some little knowledge of wood as a working material will be helpful.

Maintenance and repair work will also be a feature of the job, often demanding knowledge of traditional work in the matching of woodwork.

The apprentice must be fairly strong, able to work in all sorts of site conditions, in fair weather and foul. His work may take him far afield from his home base and often to heights well above his own.

The **Joiner** will be skilled in the making of windows, doors, cabinets and fittings of all kinds. Although many of the fittings these days are ready made in factories, much of the maintenance work will require particular skill in the use of tools and in the making of joints.

Careful reading of drawings and attention to detail will be necessary, not only from the need to obtain accurately fitted work but also to watch the costing of each job.

CARVING

There are still opportunities within furniture firms for those who want to take up carving, although furniture with hand carving on it is expensive. Simple shapes and mouldings are almost exclusively produced by machines these days, but more complex work can only be produced by hand.

Unlike machines, which produce virtually exact copies of a pattern each time they produce it, each example of hand carving is unique. That is what gives it its attraction and its value.

Carving can be learnt at college or with the few companies that are still offering apprenticeships.

Carving is often an important part of restoration work, not just on furniture, but on sculptures, panelling and even the structural timbers of buildings and other structures, such as boats.

If your work is good and your style appreciated you might be able to make the transition from carving as a craft to sculpting as an art form.

FURNITURE MANUFACTURING

Although the industry manufacturing furniture in the UK has undergone a considerable contraction in the number of owners of factories in the past 20 years, there are still hundreds of businesses taking in trainees each year at all levels. And the training given can include a lot of instruction on hand tools and bench practices as well as the use of the sophisticated machinery in the industry today.

The industry takes on around 500 trainees each year who want to learn how to make and/or design furniture. It now also recognises that trainees do not have to be school leavers. Older people are also considered. And the qualities of the individual are more important than their academic qualifications.

FURNITURE RESTORER

This is a trade which requires great skill and patience together with a love of beautiful things. It is normally a step taken by those who already have woodworking skills.

The apprentice will be trained to refurbish

valuable antique furniture, paying great heed to the protection and retention of vital colour, patina and polish. Often a part will need to be replaced or a repair made, demanding exact matching of the timber and precise fitting.

The training is specialised and demands a knowledge of the history of furniture itself and an intimate study of finishes of the past. It's not a job for everyone, but it's the type of work which will be found to be completely absorbing.

Usually jobs will be found in small firms specialising in this work – furniture restorers and ecclesiastical restorers. There are also small workshops with just one or two workers.

MARQUETRY

Marquetry is the art of making pictures and designs using wood veneers. It saw its heyday in 12th century Italy, although earlier inlay work is known.

Today marquetry, and its cousin, parquetry – produced in the same way but to geometrical patterns – is undergoing somewhat of a revival, although almost entirely by amateurs because of the time it takes to produce good quality detailed work. A few cabinetmakers are still producing intricate marquetry work on expensive furniture.

Most marquetry on classical pieces of furniture was cut using a fine saw, but veneer was much thicker in those days and now most cutting is carried out with a craft knife, although both hand and machine fretsaws are sometimes used.

Much of today's marquetry is not used for elaborate decoration of furniture but purely to make up pictures.

A veneer – or more than one, sometimes – is chosen as a background. Another piece is placed over that and the two pieces cut together. Cutting a piece on top of the background leaves a hole in the background of exactly (if you get it right) the right shape and size for the piece cut out. When all the pieces have been cut they are stuck together on a board using PVA.

MUSICAL INSTRUMENT MAKER

A highly skilled trade demanding a good knowledge of wood and an understanding of music. The use of beautiful woods, their decoration and finishing

add to the attractiveness of this job. Attendance at a school will often be needed prior to an apprenticeship. Competition is considerable but the rewards are attractive.

The work is largely a hand skill, working at the bench, demanding considerable application and patience. There are one or two schools of training, although few companies specialise in this work. The repair of musical instruments is an interesting aspect of this craft.

MUSICAL INSTRUMENT REPAIRER

There are many who aspire to the making of musical instruments, but very few whose only income is from this exacting work. No less exacting and skillful is the work of the musical instrument repairer. All the skills present in a successful maker must be present in the successful repairer, as new parts have to be made, but with this is coupled the ability to solve problems, make tools and jigs and to be inventive as no two repairs, restorations or maintenance tasks are exactly the same. The work is varied, exacting and highly skillful as the responsibility for a valuable instrument rests wholly with the repairer.

The skills are very rarely learnt by being apprenticed to an experienced repairer. The usual route is through a course of training at college.

It is important that this specialist course is aimed at producing a person who is highly skilled in hand tool techniques through the hands-on task of repairing musical instruments.

An interest in music is desirable but a willingness to work to high standards is more important.

PATTERN MAKER

The making of moulds for grey iron, SG iron and other metal castings, also plastic, necessitates the making of a wooden pattern. Very accurate drawings made to allow for shrinkage in the casting material, demand a skill in reading and finally an attention to detail in working wood.

This work involves benchwork, including carving, wood turning and the use of band saw, circular saw and planer. Some experience in mathematics and technical drawing will be found useful.

Many engineering works – making articles both large and small – have a pattern shop. They are pleasant places in which to work. They are generally located in the industrial areas of the country.

POLISHER

This trade is one where it is possible to be apprenticed in a modern factory or in a small one or two man workshop.

The factory polisher will often use machinery and spray plant of a hand or automatic kind. The polish will be highly volatile material used under very strict conditions of safety. On the other hand, smaller concerns may be using hand-applied polishes from the modern polyurethanes to French polishing carried out in the traditional way.

Preparation of the work to receive the polish, together with strict attention to clean conditions, matching of colour and polish will be necessary. Learning to repair and improve polishing will often be called for. Once again, it's a job for skill and patience, but a highly rewarding one.

SEAT WEAVING

Seat weaving is a craft suited to people of all ages, able-bodied and the disabled, who wish to enjoy the satisfaction of working with their hands and without having to lay out large sums of money on tools and equipment.

Each material used in seat weaving has its own working methods and patterns. With rush there is only one basic pattern – four triangles, each apex meeting the other three in the centre of the seat. The weaving method is simple: each coil goes round each corner of the seat in turn. The expertise comes in twisting the rushes smoothly and adding new ones to form one continuous coil, and in keeping the edges of the triangles straight. Artificial or fibre rush, sold in ready coiled lengths, is easier and less expensive for the beginner to work with.

Open-work cane seating can have a few variations of pattern utilising the basic method of 'sewing' each strand of cane through the holes in the four sides of the seat frame, and interweaving the strands across the seat. Close caning (where each strand lies against its neighbours throughout the work) allows a greater variety of patterns, but the method is more intricate.

Seagrass seating can be woven in the rush pattern, or more usually to give a chessboard or chevron effect. Danish paper twine is specifically used on a particular design of contemporary chair, though it can be woven into other patterns provided that the seat frame is suitable.

SHOP FITTER

A more specialist job, where the apprentice finds himself working mainly on fitting and fixing work associated with places of business like shops, banks, restaurants and public houses.

This work will be carried out in hard and soft woods and in small and large buildings. Often the work will have to be carried out after normal working hours, when the premises are vacated after the close of the day's business. Often, too, considerable skill and patience will need to be exercised. Inside work in workshops making the fittings will have to be undertaken. Working happily with others will be of importance.

UPHOLSTERER

This is a trade where training in a highly mechanised factory or a small family concern may be found.

In the large factory, much of the work will entail the use of machinery, with pre-cut fittings and coverings. The better area to train is where much of the work involves making individual sets of furniture and repairing and restoring older pieces.

Skill and attention to detail are the hallmarks of success. Many upholsterers also tackle the supply and making of other house furnishings, such as curtaining and drapes for four-poster beds.

WOOD MACHINIST

The wood machinist is a key man in the woodworking industry. He sets up the machines for cutting timber accurately to shape and size. Many different types of plant will require the machinist – from furniture manufacturers to builders, tool makers, prefabricators, timber mills and others. The apprentice must have a leaning towards machines since great accuracy in the setting up of cutters and equipment will be needed.

The job calls for sharp tools and finely finished work with a minimum of waste, all to be carried out in safety. Planers, thicknessers, mortisers, lathes, boring tools, hinging machines and shapers will frequently be experienced.

Many modern plants, particularly those producing fitted furniture, will be using highly accurate equipment often controlled by computer. The use of safety equipment should be compulsory since the work is noisy and dusty. Physical fitness is essential and the apprentice must resign himself to standing for most of the day.

WOODTURNER

Located in both the larger manufacturing plant and the small two or three man firms, this is an interesting trade with continuing variety.

Large companies requiring repetition work in quantity will need people skilled in machine setting, since automatic wood turning lathes will be used. A knowledge of timber and an ability to read drawings and to sharpen and correct cutters will be necessary.

Few companies will offer work on the hand lathe. There are, however, firms who specialise in woodturning and offer quantity and one-off jobs, the latter requiring hand skill.

Many people have set up small companies to carry out individual work employing one or two people. This is perhaps the best way to work, but opportunities are limited.

Individual woodturners, apart from producing utilitarian domesticware, components for shop fitters and small builders, might also produce individual items for collectors and galleries. This latter aspect has now become important. Many amateurs produce work of a high standard.

Woodworking*today*

The official journal of The Guild of Master Craftsmen

The leading woodworking magazine for all woodworkers!

E ach issue brings to you the experience of worldwide top designers, craftsmen and leading authorities.

A full year's subscription to *Woodworking Today* incorporates most aspects of working in wood. It is a magazine you will be proud to own and will often refer to.

Cabinet making, turning, carving and joinery are regularly featured with news about tool and machinery development, exhibitions, books and competitions. Latest designs and new techniques will improve your work. In each issue of *Woodworking Today* you will find easy-to-follow and rewarding projects.

Woodworking Today embraces a broader world of woodworking uncovering such projects as making bows and arrows, lettering, pyrography, cricket bats, musical instruments, to name a few.

If you would like full details about *Woodworking Today* subscriptions simply complete the coupon below or telephone — 24 hours (0273) 477374 quoting reference 65GWC

YES! I would like more details about Woodworking Today subscriptions

Mr/Mrs/Miss/Ms _____ Initials _____ Surname _____

Address _____

_____

Postcode _____ Telephone _____

Guild of Master Craftman Publications Limited
Castle Place   166 High Street
Lewes   East Sussex BN7 1XU   Telephone: Lewes (0273) 477374

65GWC.

Parkin Loy

Parkin Loy was trained at Loughborough College during the early 1960s when design was very much influenced by Edward Barnsley who, at that time, was still Consultant Adviser in Design. Parkin Loy's first teaching appointment was at Bradfield School, Sheffield, as a teacher of 'handicraft'. After five years he was appointed Head of Faculty of Design at Wisewood School, also in Sheffield.

In 1974 he and his family moved to the north of Scotland. He taught Technical Education at Tain Royal Academy, specialising in wood. Since those days he has been appointed Principal Teacher of Guidance, with emphasis on careers education and schools/industry liaison. He is still involved in the teaching of technical subjects.

He also offers private tuition in his purpose-built studio for anyone interested in woodturning or cabinet making. One-off commission work is a speciality at his country studio on the outskirts of Tain in the Scottish Highlands, using mainly air-seasoned local hardwoods and a variety of exotics.

A question often asked by pupils in our school workshops in the 1990s is: "Why do we have to do so much sketching and writing about our models? My brother/sister never had to do all that, and their work was more complicated." I suppose the answer has to be that there is far more emphasis on the design process and, therefore, the practical ability of our young people will perhaps be more limited than in the past.

I would, however, be concerned if these sentiments were taken no further. What has happened in England and Wales over the past 10 years and in Scotland over a slightly shorter period is that time has been cut quite dramatically in all schools for technical subjects because of the demands on timetabling to produce a broader-based curriculum. This has resulted in all schools working to more or less the same guide lines. The better school courses of the past have in many cases been watered down while the schools where very little initiative in designing was apparent have been dragged into the new methodology.

My greatest concern is not for the latter category but for the schools in which standards have been forced to drop. Some educationalists would question this statement, but when one considers that a number of HM Inspectors in technical education have given up their position in the past few years, to say nothing of the hundreds of technical teachers in the British Isles who have left the teaching profession because of disillusionment, there would appear to be something seriously wrong.

However, one of the most rewarding statements from pupils is still: "Is there any way I can get more training in cabinet making?" Even though the courses have changed so greatly in our schools, the basic human requirement to produce something of character and value is still there. It is interesting to note that pupils less frequently ask technical teachers about courses for design and theory.

So what is the problem? Possibly in the past 30 years there has been too little emphasis on the designing aspect. To attempt to rectify this, the state system of education has gone to the other extreme of enforcing a design process.

What is needed is a fair balance of design, theory and practical work – I would suggest more practical work than is apparent at the moment. Most schools use the latest technology in their technical departments, but there is a great difference in manual skills between using a computer keyboard and working at a bench or machine. In some examination systems it is possible to get a good pass without nearing completion of the project. How can a design be evaluated if it is not seen through to fruition?

Many employers have commented to me on a lack of practical skills from recent recruits to industry. We are tending to produce a lot of pupils with great ideas, but very little practical know-how to see the ideas realised.

Further Education

So, as well as the craft and design, or craft, design and technology courses in our schools, what should next be done if the pupil wishes to take some finer element of woodworking as a career? Let us consider some of the possible avenues open to such young people.

When considering my own background I remember with considerable gratitude the help and example of my own woodwork teacher. Like myself, he was a Loughborough-trained man who had direct contact with the Barnsley tradition of cabinet making. He took two of us to the Loughborough College Exhibition. I shall never forget the impact that single day in my secondary education had upon me – it was more use than months of classroom work. So if there comes the chance of seeing quality work, find the time to examine it.

Our schools nowadays have excellent guidance systems in which a considerable amount of work is covered in connection with careers. Many pupils will have worked through 'Micro-Compass' and the JIIG-CAL (Jobs Ideas Information Generator – Computer Aided Learning) scheme and hopefully found them of considerable assistance in career choice. Always remember, however, that even though the guidance staff in the school have a particular concern for their pupils, there are probably many other members of staff who will be glad to give advice. If a pupil feels that a certain member of staff is very approachable, why not discuss the problem with him or her?

I would suggest the above points are initial steps at school. Most schools have a careers officer with whom most pupils will have contact. These people, who are often responsible for a number of schools, will be able to offer up-to-date, sound advice on training possibilities generally, but should also have excellent knowledge of local employers. The careers officer will be in a position to let pupils have details of colleges specialising in cabinet making courses (see the directory section of this book). Always consider the fact that good GCSE's (in Scotland 'Standard Grade') passes in English, Mathematics and Physics will probably be required as well as evidence of good craft skills. Art and Technical Drawing (Graphic Communication) will also be of considerable help.

The opportunity of work experience can be a great advantage to all pupils. If you are fortunate enough to live in an area where there is a reputable cabinet maker, have a talk with him or her. Ask them if they could help in the field of work experience. Don't just leave it to your guidance/careers teacher, show initiative and enthusiasm. Employers are usually very pleased to communicate with pupils who are keen. Work experience can give the pupil a taste of the 'real world' and, of course, give some idea of whether or not this is a sensible proposition for him or her. Never forget that work experience can sometimes lead to a full-time job with that particular employer.

Evening school/college classes can also help in encouraging the student develop more skills and experience working with older people. Such classes can be excellent and offer qualifications. Unfortunately, the school-type evening classes all too frequently have high numbers of budding Chippendales or KD (knock-down, also known as self-assembly) fanatics who will demand a considerable amount of tutor time. Remember that in a two hour evening class containing just 10 adults you can only expect 12 minutes for yourself – in reality the time is likely to be less than this. And you may well be paying for that time.

Sometimes students are unaware of the variety of privately run courses, very often available throughout the year, which are run in the British Isles. Such courses can offer excellent value for money. Their great advantage is that often only one or two places are available per course which means that individual tuition is normally available and hands-on provision is guaranteed.

Courses of this nature are well advertised in the woodworking magazines and can also be seen in the pages of this book. Many people embark on the smaller private courses because of the amount of time wasted while waiting for tutor help when larger numbers are involved.

These smaller concerns are usually run by dedicated craftsmen or women who not only receive income from such work but also enjoy passing on their expertise to craftsmen and women of the

"The opportunity of work experience can be a great advantage to all pupils."

future. Course fees are usually reasonable. All safety equipment has to be provided by the director of the course and meals will normally be available. Some of these organisations can offer accommodation on site or within a few miles of the workshop/studio.

Such courses can be an excellent way to learn new skills or modify existing ones together with visiting new areas of the British Isles – very often students will incorporate a holiday and a course. I have known visitors from Canada fly to Scotland for one of our courses – and take in a few rounds of golf while they are here.

It is worth remembering that if you are fortunate enough to obtain an apprenticeship with a furniture manufacturer, part of the training may well be in collaboration with a local college. The same principle often applies if you are a student at college studying some aspect of furniture manufacture. Part of the course is likely to be in conjunction with a local furniture manufacturer.

So far I have attempted to illustrate the variety of tuition/training available in connection with cabinet making. Great pleasure and achievement can be gained from such pursuits, but what about the business/economic side of this for anyone envisaging a career in cabinet making?

The college courses will very often incorporate the necessary business organisation – keeping records, basic business law and marketing. If this is the precise area in which you are lacking, there are numerous bodies throughout the British Isles who can assist with this, such as local colleges and training agencies. Local careers services will have details of the nearest course to suit you.

Many flourishing businesses have been started through word of mouth recommendations and, later, advertising. Choose what the scale of business may be – all clients have to be able to trust and depend on your judgement. First impressions count a lot and last for a long time. The first two years of setting-up in business can be very worrying – cost of premises, general overheads, plant, materials, insurances, business rates, etc. Up-to-date advice can be obtained from the addresses given in this book.

Sometimes there will be the possibility of grants or loans, depending in part on financial projections and, of course, the area in which you are working. You should see the chapter headed 'Money' for more advice in this matter.

Details of college courses/prospectuses are listed in this book. However, the importance of a broad-based education cannot be over-emphasised. The necessity to change ideas and direction is becoming more apparent as we move towards the year 2000. Very few people follow the same career for the whole of their lives any more.

There is a great requirement in the late 20th century for craftsmen/women of individuality and integrity. Craftsmanship has always been a basic need in the development of our society. This will continue to be the case. It is our duty to continue these high ideals for the benefit of future generations.

Jeremy Broun

Jeremy Broun trained at Shoreditch College covering the traditional making techniques in wood, metal, ceramics, basketry and bookbinding, which gave him the grounding for his later creative work.

His wide range of interests include composing and playing music – he plays the cello, guitar and synthesizer – and it was this that led him on to working in wood when he made a classical guitar for himself at the age of 17.

On leaving school Jeremy Broun became a teacher and for six years worked full time in secondary schools in London, Glasgow and Bristol. In 1972 he was a founder member of The Dove Centre of Creativity, near Glastonbury, and the following year he set up his own small but innovative furniture design workshop in Bath. He is still there, working both speculatively and to commission.

He has exhibited extensively and won numerous awards, the latest being for a video he made. He has set up a business called the Thinking Hand Video making videos on woodworking.

If you enjoy the smell of wood shavings, can design and make a superb piece of furniture "by hand" and think that by setting up a workshop on your own the world will then beat a path to your workshop door to buy everything you make, you may be living in the wrong century.

While British society holds great reverence for the craftsmen of yesteryear and a lot of people seem to want to believe that if you can find good craftsmanship at all today, it has to be produced with yesterday's tools by some little old man with a pencil behind his ear, the reality is that pure hand work is rarely paid for today and that "designer makers" use machines for economic necessity before anything else. In fact, if it weren't for the revolution in power tool woodworking many would not survive their first week of business.

The lot of a designer maker producing modern work (and not copies or derivations of the past) is tough, but immensely satisfying – what can be more satisfying than creating potential antiques of tomorrow rather than regurgitating copies of the past? However, few survive without the back-up of teaching or some other income. That is no admission of failure, especially in the early years.

If financial security is paramount become a carpenter, joiner, re-production maker or restorer. Don't work for yourself but be an employee and just enjoy working in wood, taking your pay packet at the end of the week. There are numerous and varied opportunities within the woodworking industry for just that.

What kind of madness drives people like me to go against the grain and set up on their own making their own style of work which sells to a very limited market?

The answer is that it is immensely satisfying for me to design and make a new piece – a piece that has never existed before – for a client who could quite easily spend his money elsewhere and to receive a letter a few weeks later saying how thrilled he is living with the piece each day. And, indeed, to meet another client, completely out of the blue, who bought a speculative piece nearly 20 years earlier and who, when I ask to buy it back from her, flatly refused. (This happened to me just before writing this piece).

Of course, this is the cream on the cake. To survive over the years all kinds of work has to be taken on just to pay the bills, let alone pay for the tools and machinery. In my case, although I spent many years solely as a practicing woodworker, I ought to say I do not make furniture full time now. I prefer to divide my energies between woodworking, writing and making educational videos on woodworking and design (and occasional lecturing). One of the reasons for this diversification is that making furniture became too solitary and limiting for me. Now I have an excellent mix all in the same field and those many years of sheer hard graft seem worthwhile. No experience is wasted.

I set up a tiny furniture workshop in 1973 with no capital. The bank simply would not lend money without collateral.

I used mainly hand tools until I could afford carefully chosen machines. The climate was very different then as there were a handful of makers such as Alan Peters and John Makepeace and a few unknowns like myself. They were pioneering years for the craft revival which was to come about in the late '70s.

Today, being a designer maker seems to be trendy with all sorts of opportunities and back ups to get started, and a glossy image to wrap it all up in. But sustaining a livelihood is more difficult and I think it is worth considering a few points before you embark on this career.

Probably the most important aspect is your temperament, given that you have a potential craft skill. The skill can be learned and there are several ways of acquiring it whether it be a course of study or workshop experience, or combination of the two. At the end of the day you may be better suited to go and work for someone else because self employment is tough.

You must be able to work long and hard. Much of it is repetitive work. You must be able to make personal decisions and endure the heat when things go wrong, as they surely will at times. And there will be nobody to pass the buck on to, or even talk to about these problems. You have to have a burning desire to set up on your own, for whatever reason. Nobody is asking you to. In my case I simply wanted to make furniture that I had designed and no opportunity existed other than finding an empty workshop and just doing it on my own. There was no encouragement, backing or guidance from anybody else and I threw up a secure teaching job at the time to do it. If you really want to do it, you will do it.

It is an advantage to have a training and ideally to mix this with work experience in a reputable workshop. Colleges such as Rycotewood are able to offer both. I know a few competent makers who have taught themselves but they do tend to be the exception. It is a slow and painful process just taking the information from books.

The buzz for me is designing, but I did not originally train as a designer. After gaining 'A' level Woodwork at school I trained as a Crafts teacher at Shoreditch College specialising in woodwork. I

consider this gave me an excellent vocabulary for designing because I learned how to handle wood, metal and other materials in a disciplined way. The bench-based craft experience gave me the confidence to explore my own ideas, perhaps as a mild rebellion against "tradition". Being told there was only one way to work this amazing material, wood, seems restricting now, but at the time it gave a solid base. In my opinion the pendulum has swung the other way now. Truly integrated courses are thin on the ground.

If I had to choose between a design training or a craft training I would recommend the latter because understanding the character and limitation of wood by handling it, and all the processes and techniques is not only a more marketable skill (you can take on bread and butter work such as fitted wardrobes and kitchens) but the weird and wonderful ideas you conceive have more chance of standing up when they are made. In fact, the broader the materials handling experience the better.

> **"I have known a few competent makers who have taught themselves, but they do tend to be the exception."**

The nature of a craft training need not be too rigid as the diversity of woodworking trades can overlap and serve as a solid base (ie joinery, cabinet-making, pattern making, etc).

One essential skill is the ability to draw, which is particularly useful when communicating with a client over a design. Sketching enables quick feedback and establishes what the client does or does not want at the start. I find it amazing how few people can actually sketch freely and spontaneously. I learned to draw before I knew how to cut tight joints.

Very closely linked to temperament and skill is speed. Probably the most common complaint among employers who have taken on a new college graduate and trained them up to their particular workshop operation is speed, or lack of it. Time costs money and when a price is quoted on a job it has to be made to a deadline.

If you are self employed it is a crucial factor which goes hand in hand with skill (in fact, self employment is the teacher of speed whether you like it or not). But speed without skill and vice versa is disastrous. It is something which I think most colleges fail to teach and is also closely affiliated to method.

There are quick and slow methods and in woodworking training there tends to be a preoccupation with "the right way" to do a particular thing, which is often the slow way because the method was adopted a century ago.

A self employed designer maker will be forced to look at quick ways of doing things but he/she must do so without sacrificing quality. If you want to learn what speed is about go and work in a furniture factory, or be a site carpenter on piece rate. Craftsmen are notoriously slow-and-careful. It is the quick-and-careful ones who survive and it is fundamentally a mental attitude.

To the enlightened reader it will be realized that an important challenge to a designer maker (who really has a great opportunity to produce something new and better) is to consolidate all these factors in a piece of furniture – skill, method, production efficiency, economic use of materials – and to constantly question what you do. It's actually called "design" and there's a lot more to it than that, but space prevents me from enlarging on it here.

Regarding a workshop, how you find one, set it up, finance it and run it space here is also limited other than to say you can survive in a limited space to start with.

A small workshop is easier to heat and will cost less to rent. It forces you to keep it tidier. And large commissions still have to fit through average doors.

Keeping your overheads down is vital. You will need a range of hand tools and essential machines such as bandsaw, circular saw, planer thicknesser and router (depending on what kind of work you will do). Check whether you need planning permission. Country workshops are cheaper than city ones. Sharing a workshop keeps costs down.

The main hazards with a workshop are fire risk, noise and dust. You should have a dust extractor and for insurance purposes you will have to sweep shavings up at the end of each day.

Your two best business friends will be your bank

manager and accountant and you should tell the Inland Revenue what you are doing. Borrowing money may be necessary but do so carefully and only when you really have to. Keep regular books right from the start.

It is said 50% of advertising pays. But nobody knows which 50%? You cannot expect the world to know about you unless you tell it, and that includes sending out reminders from time to time.

Your image is important and a good business card and stationery is essential. Inexpensive colour postcards are good initially to use as a brochure. Don't try to run before you can walk but build up gradually. It is a slow growth business in any case. Try and exhibit your work or use any opportunity for exposure – editorial in your local paper, for example.

Designer makers work in isolation (even co-operatives) in so far as they do not enjoy the benefit of a consolidated group with a union behind them. This makes it difficult to price work and sell it. At the end of the day you are your best salesman. You have to be. It took me many years to realize not to turn up at a gallery or client's house with wood-shavings in my hair. Young people today seem far more conscious of "image", but there's got to be substance behind the gloss.

The question is, why, in a nutshell, should Jo Client come to you as a designer maker for a new chest of drawers rather than go to the local MFI store, Habitat or indeed junk shop? There are lots of reasons but the one overriding factor is that more and more people are becoming disillusioned with unimaginative look-alike high street furniture and that the price gap between "hand made" and "quality" mass produced furniture is closing.

There is clearly a need for individual, superbly designed and made furniture. A huge problem is in the public not knowing about designer makers and the service they are able to give. In a word, it is called education and if you set up as a designer maker you will also be involved in the education business – that of educating clients (they don't always know what they want and, like you, they are capable of changing their mind).

You need to be able to offer something special. Just making something that looks different, as though it is screaming to be noticed, is not enough. Furniture design is mostly about solving problems, about function, aesthetics, structures, materials, environments, etc, etc. Beyond meeting a client's immediate needs, you have to give more, I believe.

Whereas a few people over the past two decades who commissioned my work vaguely talked about "heirlooms" it may be that in the 1990s a lot more will do so if the throw-away society is more seriously challenged by the "green" issues. Timber is a precious commodity and should be handled with care. The designer maker has a great challenge ahead to do just that.

A final word: if you are seriously thinking about becoming a designer maker, try to find an opportunity to work for someone else before you set up on your own. Learn from their mistakes and experiences (but naturally they will want hard work from you).

Although you need to be quick-and-careful, do not be in a hurry to set up on your own. The strong oak tree grows slowly.

Samuel Chan was sponsored at college and later given a chance to exhibit in a London studio. He was even offered a job before he had applied for it. You might say he was lucky, but opportunities are open to all students who are prepared to take them. Chan's story is an inspiration to all.
Reproduced by permission of Woodworking magazine.

Most people who are offered a chance to carry on studying with what was the London College of Furniture (it is now the City of London Polytechnic) do not turn it down. Samuel Chan did.

He had already been at the college for two years and had gained his Diploma. The chance to stay on is afforded to few, but he does not regret the decision he made in 1984. There were only half a dozen places on offer and a lot of competition for them. But Chan, who came to England with his family from Hong Kong when he was 14, chose instead to go to Middlesex Polytechnic.

Chan had already gained his Diploma in Furniture Studies from the London College, having left school with 'O' Levels in woodwork, metalwork and design technology.

At the beginning of the new academic year in 1984 Chan started a three year BA course at Middlesex Polytechnic. Three years later he picked up an honours degree in furniture design.

That was not the end of his full-time education, though. From Middlesex he went on to Buckinghamshire College of Higher Education, a leading furniture design and making college in the heart of the furniture making industry in High Wycombe (see the list of private colleges) to become a Master of Arts in Furniture Design & Technology.

Chan was sponsored for his Masters by timber merchants Albert Isherwood, who had seen his work when he exhibited at the Direct Design Show. The company were impressed and offered him financial help during his studies. Chan's research for the MA was, in the light of his sponsorship, into the possibility of a timber merchant entering the furniture design and manufacture market, combining the different aspects of the businesses and so producing furniture at a lower cost. The sponsorship came to an end before Chan finished the course and the final term of study was spent without the merchants' patronage.

Chan's furniture designs are a pleasing mixture of the Oriental and the Occidental. They were already earning him a reputation as a designer before he finished his full-time studies in 1988.

While at Buckinghamshire, Chan produced a dining suite of sideboard, table and chairs. The chairs, in particular, have the look of that turn of the century Scots genius Charles Rennie Mackintosh about them and you could be forgiven for wondering if Mackintosh has influenced Chan's designs. Chan says not. He is not surprised there are similarities, though, with the Oriental influence showing in both designers' work.

The Chan suite grew from the sideboard. Chan believes in the functionality of furniture design and wanted to show the hinges on the cabinet doors because they are entirely functional. With the knobs, a pattern of three squares was created. It was a strong design feature which he carried through as three holes in the backs of the chairs in the same right angle configuration. On the table the three holes appear again, this time with the top of one of the legs also standing proud of the table top. The work is in Cherry. Chan likes to use British woods because it reflects the Western influences on his Oriental designs.

The aesthetically pleasing work combines with a practicality of construction which allows for ease of manufacture and strength of the finished item. This ease of construction is exemplified in a laminated chair he made from constructional birch veneer.

Chan is now working for an interior design company in north London. A project of his is St George's Hotel, a new luxury hotel on Hyde Park Corner.

The company he is working for is called Ezra Attia Associates. It is named after the man who owns it and who 'discovered' Chan in the way a movie mogul might have discovered a young film star in the 1930s.

Chan, having gained his BA Hons degree and working towards his Masters, exhibited at the now defunct Direct Design Show. A small section of the show had been set aside for students. Space in this section was less expensive than in the show proper. Ezra Attia saw Chan's work, liked it and suggested the student should give him a call.

Chan finished his MA course, took a couple of months off in Australia to visit his girlfriend, and, 12 months after receiving the invitation to do so, called Attia. That was on a Friday. He was asked to come in for an interview the following Monday and on Tuesday he started working with the company.

As well as working for Ezra Attia Associates, Chan won a shop fitting contract in his own right, at a shop called Watsons, in Shaftesbury Avenue. The shop is selling tartan and wanted plenty of storage space for the different weaves, so Chan designed box con-

> **"You have the rest of your life to work, but it's not easy to go back to full time education."**

struction fittings. He also made exciting use of parquet, managing a red carpet effect up to the counter, encouraging the customer into the sales area. But he went further. The parquet forms the centre part of the desk, flanked by mirrors. The resulting effect is of being able to walk right through the desk, which prevents it becoming the usual barrier between customer and sales staff.

Chan does not make furniture any more, although he does still design it. He has now teamed up with Patrick Stronarch, a former student of the John Makepeace School, at Parnham, Dorset (see Private Colleges).

Chan's designs are exhibited in a Chelsea Gallery, which came about as a result of him showing his work at the British Contemporary Furniture Show. It was at the show that he met Stronach. It was also there that he was approached by an agent who wanted to display Chan's work in the Chelsea shop. Now there are various examples of his chairs in the studio. The dining chairs are on sale for £350 each, but Chan hopes to sell them in lots of 25 or more, when the price comes down to £228 each. It is this work he hopes will keep Patrick Stronach busy. One of the laminated chairs has already sold

to a Dutch collector.

Chan is not worried that he no longer makes the furniture he designs. "Some people can express themselves best on the workbench and some people can express themselves best through the drawing board," he says.

He is, though, critical of some designers who have little practical experience and he is grateful for the two years he spent in the workshops of the London College of Furniture. "I can look at some people's designs on the drawing board and see a joint isn't going to work, or that a structure can't be produced easily."

That combination of skills, along with his business studies, has given him a depth of experience which he is sure he would not have gained from the London College of Furniture alone. It is why he has no regrets about his decision to go to Middlesex.

For the future Chan still thinks it could be a good idea to combine the various aspects of timber merchanting, furniture design, manufacturing and distribution, along the lines of his MA studies.

He idles with the idea of setting up such a business of his own. But, he says, running his own business is not paramount. "The pinnacle of my achievement would be to design good quality furniture. I don't mind if I am famous or not. If I could design furniture using the full extent of the timber I would be very happy. It's not so important whether I set up my own company or work for a company which has the same approach."

Chan recommends a craft and design career. "I would say it's a good area to get into and the best thing is to go to college. You have the rest of your life to work, but it is not easy to go back to full time education."

Just to take up the point of starting with a foundation course, it can present problems with getting a grant later. If you are going from a degree foundation course to an HND course in furniture making some authorities do not see it as progressing and will not give a grant.

City and Guilds and the National Council for Vocational Qualifications

Training continues to undergo a good many changes, which can be confusing for employers and trainees alike. Employers still ask how many 'O' levels a qualification is equivalent to, even if the training for it is so different from the old 'O' level that the two simply don't equate. That can leave trainees questioning the worth of the qualification they end up with.

The government is trying to introduce a national standard on training through the National Council for Vocational Qualifications (NCVQ). This has led to some confusion itself.

The NCVQ is not an examining body. It does not set exams, it does not mark them and it does not issue certificates. What it does do is assess the training of other bodies, such as City & Guilds. It requires training to be modular and progressive and requires certain elements and standards to be reached before it will approve courses.

Once it has approved a course and the qualification, the certificate awarded carries the mark of approval of the NCVQ and will say that the qualification is to one of four standards. Level one is the most basic and level four an advanced standard. Level one roughly equates to a pre-GCSE standard and level 4 is at Higher National Diploma level. There are moves now to create a fifth level for professional qualifications. The accreditation with the level achieved means an employer can look at a certificate, whatever training organisation it comes from, and know what level of training the person has received.

So far, 230 qualifications have been accredited by the NCVQ as National Vocational Qualifications at stages 1, 2, 3 or 4. Clearly there is some way to go, but gradually more qualifications are being assessed and brought into line with the NCVQ requirements.

One of those requirements is that trainees should be able to continue to build on what they have achieved so far by adding more units to their training so they can progress on to whatever level their potential can achieve.

There might be a small amount of confusion added by a Certificate of Pre-Vocational Education (CPVE), which is designed to give youngsters staying on at school a chance for a broad introduction to working life, including some work experience with a company in the field the youngster is intending entering. The idea is that the person gets a feel of where their education is leading them in work terms. That might reinforce his or her intention to continue on that route, or it might change his/her mind. The CPVE works with both City & Guilds and BTEC, which, under other circumstances, are competing training bodies.

These government-led changes in shaping training are designed to bring education and industry closer together.

Once, of course, they were totally managed by industry through apprenticeships, but apprenticeships are hard to find these days and, in any case, people do not expect to be a trainee for six or seven years anymore. Training is now largely in the hands of schools and colleges outside of industry and the government and industry felt the training was in danger of failing to reflect what industry required. Hence the changes which have taken place during the 1980s.

That does not mean that well-established and respected institutions like City & Guilds are any the worse for the changes.

The City & Guilds of London Institute, more widely known just as 'City & Guilds', is Britain's largest technical certificate awarding body. As an independent organisation operating under a Royal Charter, it works closely with leading industry bodies, The Department of Education & Science, the Training Agency and the National Council for Vocational Qualifications.

The value of its qualifications are recognised and understood by employers throughout the United Kingdom and in the other 70 countries in which they are available.

City & Guilds schemes cover all the main sectors of industry and the public services in addition to the timber trades subjects described in this chapter.

Qualifications for people in the Timber Trades
Courses which work towards a Craft Certificate are normally about 900 hours long and are often covered by part-time day release over two or three years or block release. Evening and full-time courses may also be available.

A City & Guilds Craft Certificate qualification is available separately for Furniture, Carpentry & Joinery, Machine Woodworking and Shop fitting. The following schemes are of particular relevance to Timber Trades.

Furniture Craft Subjects Scheme No 555
The Craft scheme is split into two parts. Part I (normally one year on a block or day release basis) gives an overall introduction to the subject and is suitable for trainees from all sections of the Industry. Part II (normally two years) is made up of 12 modules, namely:

Timber Preparation
Metal and Plastics Preparation
Upholstery and Bedding Preparation
Finishing Preparation
Carcase and Wooden Frame Construction
Metal and Plastics Construction
Modern Upholstery and Bedding Construction
Traditional Upholstery
Modern Finishing
Soft Furnishing
Hand Made Furniture Construction

Modules may be selected to suit the needs of the individual. For example, Timber Preparation, Carcase and Wooden Frame Construction and Traditional Finishing might be the choice of those wishing to become cabinet makers.

About 800 candidates enter for Part I examination each year, with varying figures for each of the individual Part II options.

Carpentry & Joinery Scheme No 585†
Carpentry and Joinery attracts the majority of wood-working candidates. Each year there are about 5,000

candidates for the Craft Certificate from about 250 different examination centres taking this subject. The scheme covers Tools and Workshop Procedures, the Use of Materials, Construction Items and Procedures, Safety and Communication.

Machine Woodworking Scheme No 586/606†
Machine Woodworkers are employed in a great number of different industries using large wood-cutting machines. This scheme attracts about 900 candidates each year and there are about 60 centres offering this subject. Some of the machine wood-workers are sawmillers, and optional studies are provided for their particular needs, although the number of such people is small.

Shopfitting Scheme No 587†
Shopfitting attracts roughly 250 candidates each year for courses of study and related examinations. It is intended for students employed as shopfitters and, as with all schemes, it has been designed to be complementary to the training and experience they will get in their employment. It was developed at the request of the National Association of Shop-fitters and it emphasises the variety of materials used by that trade.

Stringed Keyboard Instrument Manufacture Scheme No 563
The scheme was designed in conjunction with the Institute of Musical Instrument Technology. The syllabuses and associated examinations are designed for the following specialisms:

Action Finishing and Regulating
Harpsichord Tuning and Toning
Pianoforte Tuning and Toning
Pianoforte Repairing and Reconditioning

The purpose of the scheme is to provide a sound understanding of craft processes and an apprecia-tion of related science and technology. Centres offering 563 subjects include The Royal National College for the Visually Handicapped.

Yacht & Boat Building & Ship Joinery Scheme No 245
This scheme is intended for students undergoing

training or employed in ship joinery and boat building. Its purpose is to provide a sound understanding of craft processes, an appreciation of related science and technology and an introduction to a study of the marine craft industry. The Part I and Part II Certificates are related to the needs of all trainees who expect to become craftsmen in the industry. The Part III Certificate recognises an advanced understanding of craft processes, technology and related science, a broader knowledge and understanding of boat building and ship joinery craft practice and an introduction to industrial organisational studies.

Special Schemes

Some centres have devised their own schemes which are validated by the Institute. For example, several special examinations in Furniture Craft are available under the 564 scheme covering areas such as cabinet making, furniture restoration and modern and traditional chair making.

Higher Qualifications (Master Craftsman)

The progressive pattern of City & Guilds Certificates combined with the recognition of practical skill achievement leads to the award of the Licentiateship of the City & Guilds of London Institute (LCG).

The achievement of this award, which corresponds in status to the Master Craftsman in Europe, should be the aim of all skilled workers. It aims to help those who are looking to their future and wishing to add to their initial experience, either by additional studies or by reaching positions of authority and responsibility in which their technical expertise is an essential or desirable qualification. – for instance, starting and managing a business of their own, becoming teachers or instructors, or being responsible for the supervision of people, processes or products. The LCG has been awarded to a number of applicants who have specialised in Timber Trades.

† This qualification has been accredited as part of the National Vocational Qualification.

Course Enquiries – UK

Within this guide, schools and colleges are listed stating the courses available. You should contact them directly for further details of the schemes which interest you. Alternatively, or in case of difficulty, write or telephone – quoting the subject in which are interested – Division 14, City & Guilds of London Institute, 46 Britannia Street, London WC1X 9RG. Telephone: 071-278 2468.

Course Enquiries – Overseas

The City & Guilds '800' series schemes, including Construction, has been especially designed to meet the needs of students overseas. For details, write or telephone – quoting the subject in which you are interested – to Division 25 (International). The address and telephone number are the same as for UK enquiries.

Whatever you do when you are studying or training, you will need money. It is easy to get carried away with enthusiasm for a new career or course, but unless you can find a source of finance for it, you could be disappointed.

Every kind of study costs something. You may have to pay yourself, but you will be able to get help from a range of sources. This chapter is extracted from *Second Chances*, a book produced by the Careers & Occupational Information Centre, Moorfoot, Sheffield S1 4PQ. It tells you about some of the bodies which might help you finance what you want to do.

What do you need money for?

Course fees

With very few exceptions, you will have to pay fees to follow your course. These can vary from a few pounds for a local authority evening class to about £2,000 a year for a full-time postgraduate degree course.

Exam fees

Some courses end with exams that have separate entry fees. GCSEs and Standards cost about £16, and A-levels/Highers in the region of £20 to £34, depending on the board.

Materials and equipment

You may need to buy equipment for your course. Even if you don't, you will need books, pens, paper and other general stationery supplies.

Dependants

Children don't stop needing new clothes when you start studying. If you have to support someone else, you need to budget carefully.

Travel

Remember that you'll have to get to the place where you're studying. This might mean bus or rail fares, or even the cost of a bicycle. If you have a car now and want to keep it while you're studying, remember that it will still need tax, insurance, petrol and servicing.

Some courses include field trips or study abroad. These may not be covered by a grant – if you get one.

Living

As well as all expenses for your course, you still have to live – food, rent or mortgage, community charge, electricity, gas and so on all have to be paid

for. And you can't study all the time. You'll need some money for entertainment and leisure.

National Insurance contributions

When you're a full-time student over 18 you don't get any credits for National Insurance, but you may want to pay voluntary contributions (see below) to make sure you're still eligible for benefits. If you're studying full time and are being paid by an employer at the same time you will have to pay normal National Insurance contributions.

If you are doing a course lasting less than 12 months which is not part of your job, you may be able to apply for training credits.

Look at leaflet NI125 from your local social security office.

If during any tax year you are not entitled to credits or you do not have to pay National Insurance contributions as an employed or self-employed earner, you may be able to pay voluntary class 3 contributions (about £4 a week in 1990/91).

Pension contributions

If you have worked for yourself you may have your own pension scheme. If you've worked for a company, you may be part of their scheme. All schemes are different, but many will allow you to stop paying while you are a full-time student and start again later on.

Check carefully what the regulations are for the scheme you're involved in, and think about keeping up the payments. They will be another item to budget for.

Community charge

Community charge is the 'poll tax' which has replaced rates. It is paid by everyone, not just those who own houses. The size of the charge varies from area to area.

Full-time students (undergraduate and postgraduate) and people on Income Support can get an 80% rebate. Part-time students are not given the rebate automatically, each case is looked at individually.

Money and course choice

Find out what financial help you are eligible for before you start – before you waste a lot of time applying for a course which you won't be able to afford. It might lead to disappointment, as you realise that you can't do what you want. But it's better to have this disappointment now than halfway through the course, when you're seriously in debt and have given up a secure job to study.

Welfare benefits

The whole system is complicated, and what follows is only a general guide.

Income Support
The 21-hour rule

You may be entitled to Income Support if you are 18 or over and your course is part time and does not take up more than 21 hours a week – not including time for your own study.

You should get Income Support if for three out of the last six months before starting the course
• you've been registered as unemployed and have been receiving Unemployment Benefit or Income Support

or
• you've been getting Income Support or sickness benefit because you are sick or incapable of work

or
• you've been on a YT programme
You may study during the three months provided it is a different course and the adjudication officer decides you are available for work. If you are 18 you can study up to 12 hours a week; if you are 19 or over your course must not be considered full time by the college. But
• if the course is less than 21 hours a week and the college call it a full-time course, you won't get Income Support
and

• if you're found work, you'll have to give up the 21-hour course immediately.

Full-time courses

If you're a full-time student, you can normally only claim in the summer holidays. It's up to an 'adjudication officer' to decide whether the course is full-time, from evidence from the college.

But you can claim all the year if you're studying full time and:
• you're a single parent or single foster-parent
• you have a disability which would make it very difficult for you to get a job in a reasonable period of time.

Open learning

As long as you're available for work and take a job if one is found for you, you can get Income Support and study through open learning. But you don't get benefit for weeks spent on residential study.

Savings

If you have savings above the set limit (£6,000 in 1990-91) you won't get Income Support. If you have some savings (£3,000 - £6,000 in 1990) your Income Support will be reduced. And savings of a dependant or spouse may also reduce your benefit.

Mortgages

If you have a mortgage, you can claim 50% of the interest for the first 16 weeks, and then the whole of the interest. If your savings exceed a set limit (£16,000 in 1990) you will not be entitled to this benefit.

Housing Benefit

Part-time students getting Income Support can get full Housing Benefit. This is all of your rent and 80% of your community charge.

Unemployment Benefit

To get this you must be available for work and have a National Insurance contributions record in two recent tax years. Full-time students can only get this benefit during the summer vacation. If you are unemployed and available for work but cannot get Unemployment Benefit you can claim Income Support instead.

Benefits for people with disabilities

If you have a severe disability and need a lot of care, you can claim Attendance Allowance. It can lead to other benefits, so if you think you are eligible, you should claim.

If you have severe walking difficulties or are unable to work, you can claim Mobility Allowance. This can also help with other benefit claims.

You can claim invalid care allowance if you spend 35 hours or more each week looking after someone. But the person must be getting Attendance Allowance. You can study part time, but not full time, if you get Invalid Care Allowance – and you won't get it for study periods like summer schools.

More information

The best way to find out more is to ring one of the free 'phone lines. You will be connected to a regional centre – not your local office – and an experienced official who should be able to answer your queries.

England, Scotland and Wales: Contact Department of Social Security Freeline 0800 666555 between 8.30 am and 4 pm. There is an answerphone service outside this time.

Northern Ireland: Contact Department of Health and Social Services, Freeline 0800 616757 between 9 am and 4.30 pm.

Look at A guide to Income Support (leaflet SB20) and Income Support: new rules (leaflet SB22), A guide to Housing Benefit (leaflet RR2), Attendance Allowance (leaflet N1205), Mobility Allowance (leaflet N1211), Invalid Care Allowance (leaflet N1212). These are available from your local office of the Department of Social Security (DSS) – the address is in the 'phone book.

Northern Ireland: Contact Department of Health and Social Services, Upper Newtownards Road, Belfast BT4 3SF. Tel: 0232 650111.

Look at National welfare benefits handbook.

Training Agency programmes
Youth Training (YT)

Most people who go into YT will do so straight from school at the age of 16 or 17, but you can join it later.

You will either be employed on a full wage or until then will receive an allowance of at least £29.50 a week if you're 16 or at least £35 a week if you're 17. If you're not employed you have to pay the first £3 of your travel costs and the rest is paid for you.

The equivalent in Northern Ireland is the Youth Training Programme (YTP). The training is organised slightly differently but the money arrangements are exactly the same.

Contact your local Careers Service – the address is in the 'phone book.

Employment Training (ET)

This is a programme intended to help people return to work after unemployment. Training normally lasts for up to 12 months. It is carried out by a Training Manager (a Managing Agent in Northern Ireland). You must normally have been unemployed for at least six months to be eligible.

While training, you receive an allowance equal to the benefits you received immediately before starting training, plus a 'training premium' of £10 a week.

Your National Insurance contributions won't be paid, but you may get credits for them. Travel costs over £4 a week are also paid. Trainees who are single parents can claim help towards the cost of childcare, and this will be paid direct to the child-carer.

It is important to remember that Employment Training, like Youth Training, is mainly designed to train you for a specific type of job. About 40% of your time will be spent doing training designed to help you gain a qualification.

As with YT, you can become an employed trainee and receive a full wage while continuing your training.

Contact your local Jobcentre, the address is in the 'phone book.

Your employer

Your existing employer, if you have one, may be willing to pay your fees or make a contribution to your other costs if you take a full- or part-time course. You may have to agree to stay with your employer for a set time.

Sponsorship

Some companies and some of the armed forces will sponsor you to take a course even if you haven't already been working for them. For example you could do two years of a degree, working for the company during some of your holidays, then have a whole year with the company, return to college and finish your degree, and then work again for the company for an agreed time. Getting the sponsorship for these 'sandwich courses' can be very competitive.

Sponsorships usually range up to £1,000 per academic year, and you can usually get £2,750 a year in sponsorship without losing money from your grant, if you get one.

For more information on companies offering sponsorships look at *Industrial sponsorship and the Universities' Central Admissions Scheme*, free from UCCA, PO Box 28, Cheltenham, Gloucestershire GL50 3SA. Tel: 0242 222444. This covers university sandwich courses but only tells you how to apply.

Grants

Most students finance their studies by getting grants from their local education authority (LEA), Regional or Islands Councils (Scotland), or Library Boards (Northern Ireland). There are two kinds:

- discretionary (which the authority does not have to give)
- mandatory (which it does have to give if you are eligible and you are accepted for a designated course)

Discretionary grants

Grants for further education (usually up to A-level or equivalent), both full- and part-time, are always discretionary. Each LEA, Regional or Islands Council, or Library Board, has a different policy about giving grants. The best plan is to get in touch with yours as soon as possible to find out if you're eligible.

Broadly speaking, LEA's etc will give discretionary grants for

- Access courses designed to lead on to higher education
- full-time A-level/Higher courses or those at a

similar level, such as BTEC National Diploma
- full-time GCSE or Standard grade courses (but grants for these are rare)
- City and Guilds courses

Who gets a discretionary grant ?

LEA's etc can give discretionary grants to anyone. Most, but not all, set residence conditions and some may only give you a grant if you study at the institution nearest your home.

Discretionary grants may be competitive, so your past exam results or other experience may be considered.

How to apply

Wherever you live, you should apply as early as possible – spring at the latest for a course starting in September or October.

England and Wales: Contact your LEA (see Chapter 15). You will be directed to the right person to see or to write to, and be sent a form to complete.

Scotland: In Scotland grants for non-advanced courses are discretionary and are paid by Regional or Islands Councils.

Look at Guide to students' allowances, free from Scottish Education Department, Awards Branch, Gyleview House, 3 Redheughs Rigg, South Gyle, Edinburgh EH12 9HH.

Northern Ireland: In Northern Ireland you will be eligible for a discretionary award as an adult student over 18, but awards are few in number. You will, however, have your fees paid for you, and you may gain a lodgings grant if living away from home. There are also two allowances; for single parents and dependants.

Look at Grants to students, free from Department of Education for Northern Ireland, Scholarships Branch, Rathgael House, Balloo Road, Bangor, Co Down BT19 2PR.

How much is a discretionary grant ?

A discretionary grant must be the same amount as a mandatory grant if you are attending a designated course but do not satisfy the other conditions for a mandatory award.

Otherwise the size of your grant is up to the LEA, Regional or Islands Council, or Library Board. It may decide to pay only part of your fees, and it may not pay maintenance as well as fees, depending on its local policy.

Mandatory grants

These must be paid by an LEA, Regional or Islands Council, or Library Board, to anyone who is following a 'designated' course and who satisfies certain conditions. All the courses are higher education – post A-level/Higher – and are full-time or sandwich courses. The only exceptions are a few part-time teacher training courses. Grant regulations are decided by the DES (SED in Scotland) and may be revised each year.

Designated courses lead to
- a first degree from a university or the CNAA
- a Diploma of Higher Education
- BTEC Higher National Diplomas
- an initial teaching qualification, including the one-year Postgraduate Certificate in Education or Art Teachers' Certificate or Diploma
- a University Certificate or diploma course lasting at least three years
- certain other courses designated as 'comparable' to first degree courses.

For a list of designated 'comparable' courses contact your LEA, Regional or Islands Council, or Library Board.

Look at Designated courses, free, Department of Education for Northern Ireland (DENI), Rathgael House, Balloo Road, Bangor, Co Down BT19 2PR. Look at Guide to students' allowances, Scottish Education Department (SED), Awards Branch, Gyleview House, 3 Redheughs Rigg, South Gyle, Edinburgh EH12 9HH.

Part-time teacher training courses

These are normally designated to attract mandatory grants; for confirmation contact your LEA, Regional or Islands Council, or Library Board.

For general information contact Teaching as a Career (TASC) Unit, Elizabeth House, York Road, London SE1 7PH or, in Scotland, the SED (address above).

Who gets a mandatory grant ?

Mandatory grants cover fees and maintenance. Even if you have a place on a designated course, you may not get a grant. If you don't get a mandatory grant you can still apply for a discretionary one.

The main conditions for a mandatory grant are:
- you must have been living in the British Isles for three years up to 1 September before the start of your course. For example, if you wanted to start a course in October 1991, you would have had to have been living in the British Isles since 1 September 1988. Temporary employment abroad, however, would not disqualify you
- you haven't stayed in the UK wholly or mainly for full-time education
- you must apply to the LEA, Regional or Island Council, or Library Board, in writing before the end of the first term of your course
- you haven't, in the opinion of the LEA, Council or Board, shown yourself unfit to get a grant
- you haven't already done various types of higher education

According to the regulations, you are not eligible if you've attended part or all of a full-time advanced (post A-level/Higher) course lasting more than two years. But attendance of less than six months is usually disregarded by the LEA, Council or Board. If the course was longer than six months but less than two years, the period for which your grant is payable may be reduced. If you have completed a first degree at the Open University you will not be eligible for a mandatory grant for another first degree, even though you didn't have a grant for the OU course.

If you have taken an advanced course before, even if it was abroad, consult your LEA, Regional or Islands Council, or Library Board.

You should get a mandatory grant if your previous study was:
- a course at a long-term adult residential college for which you were entitled to a DES bursary (SED in Scotland)
- a course leading to a 'specified' qualification for entry into higher education. So if you have spent a year studying A-levels or Highers, or on an Access course for which you got a discretionary award, you should still get a mandatory grant for a degree or 'comparable' course.

Other specified qualifications include:
- a foundation course credit of the Open University

- ONC/D or BTEC National Certificate or Diploma
- attestation of fitness of the Scottish Universities Entrance Board
- certificates of completion of a full-time art, music or drama foundation course lasting two or more years
- European or International Baccalaureate.

How much is a mandatory grant ?
If you have to attend the course for more than 30 weeks and 3 days (25 weeks and 3 days for Oxford and Cambridge Universities) you get extra money for each additional week. If your course lasts for 45 weeks or more, the grant covers any continuous period of 52 weeks, made up of the basic grant figure plus the weekly rate for the extra weeks.

You may also be eligible for extras:
- weekly payments during vacations if you would suffer hardship without them – but this is at the LEA's, Council's or Board's discretion
- an allowance if you have to maintain a home for dependants while you are away studying
- money for additional costs incurred if you have a disability (excluding travel costs).

Independent status
Most grants for younger students are reduced by an amount which the parents are intended to contribute. Adults can avoid this and qualify for 'independent status' if one or more of the following applies:
- you are over 25 before the start of the academic year your course starts
- both your parents have died
- you have been married for two or more years before the start of the academic year
- you have been supporting yourself for three years before the academic year

If you are over 26 and have earned (or received in taxable benefits) a fixed amount in the three years before your course starts, you are eligible for an additional sum.

Money for dependants
You can count your spouse and children as dependants, but if they have any income this might affect their status as a dependant. Allowances for children

depend on their ages.

Additional points: If you or your spouse have any income, your grant will be reduced, though you are allowed a certain amount of income without losing grant money. After that, your grant will be reduced £ for £. If you do not have independent status, your parents will be expected to contribute to your costs and your grant will be reduced.

Special cases
There are special arrangements for:
- sandwich courses
- part-time teacher-training courses
- single students with dependants
- students with a disability

Appeals
If you think you haven't been given the right grant, or should have got more money, you can appeal. First write to your LEA, Regional or Islands Council, or Library Board; if your appeal is turned down you can go to your education department (DES, SED or DENI). It isn't a legal appeal, but the education department may contact the LEA etc if they feel that all circumstances haven't been considered. It is very rare for the department to overrule an LEA so make your original case as sound as possible.

Bursaries for adult residential colleges
If you are going to one of the eight adult residential colleges you may be eligible for a bursary.

England and Wales: Bursaries are paid direct by the DES. Apply through the college concerned by completing and returning a form by early July of the year in which you want to study. The college will do the rest.

Look at Adult education bursaries, from The Awards Officer, Adult Education Bursaries, c/o Ruskin College, Oxford OX1 2HE.

Scotland: The scheme is run by the Scottish Education Department. Contact Scottish Education Department, Awards Branch, Gyleview House, 3 Redheughs Rigg, South Gyle, Edinburgh EH12 9HH.

Northern Ireland: The scheme is run by the Department of Education for Northern Ireland.

Postgraduate awards

England and Wales: If you want to do a higher degree or a course designated as being at postgraduate level, you can apply for a grant from either the education departments or the research councils, depending on your subject and where you live.

There are two kinds:
• bursaries – calculated like mandatory grants
• studentships – based on a higher rates of grant because they cover the full 52 weeks of the year.

All are competitive, and you have to have a very good first degree and excellent academic references. If you are aiming for a research degree in arts, sciences or social sciences, you also need a clear outline idea of your research topic.

DES awards are given for postgraduate study in three areas:

1) designated professional and vocational courses; to qualify, you generally have to be under 40
Look at Postgraduate awards 1, DES, Elizabeth House, York Road, London SE1 7PH.

2) studentships in the humanities, either for a one-year course leading to a qualification or for a course of research lasting up to three years
Look at Guide to postgraduate studentships in the humanities, The British Academy, Postgraduate Studentships Office, Block 1, Spur 15 Government Buildings, Honeypot Lane, Stanmore, Middlesex HA7 1AZ.

3) studentships and fellowships in information science, for advanced courses or longer periods of research in librarianship and related areas
Look at Postgraduate awards 3, DES, Elizabeth House, York Road, London SE1 7PH.

Student loans

The government plans to top up students' finances with a loan for all full-time students gaining a place in higher education, except postgraduates. It will be over and above the present means-tested maintenance grant and the parental contribution. Over time the amount of the loan will be increased and the grant and parental contribution will be held steady.

The introduction of loans will be a major change in the funding of higher education throughout the UK and will have considerable implications on adults considering a return to study.

For more information as it becomes available: Contact the DES, SED or DENI.

Career development loans

Career development loans have been introduced by the Department of Employment and some commercial banks to help people who want to undertake vocational training and are prepared to finance themselves.

Training can be full-time, part-time or use open or distance learning but must last at least one week and no more than one year. The course must be suitable to the work you want to do in the future, and you must agree to work in the EC after completing the course.

You can borrow between £300 and £5,000 from three banks (Barclays, Co-operative and Clydesdale) to cover up to 80% of course fees, plus books and materials and in some cases living expenses. You don't start repayments until three months after you finish your course.

The government pays the interest until then. The amount of the repayments is fixed when the loan is agreed and remains the same throughout the loan period.

For further information contact your jobcentre, a branch of one of the banks taking part, or ring 0800 585505 for a career development booklet which includes examples of loan repayments.

Educational trusts and charities

There are some charities and trust funds which make payments to students. Any grant is usually small (around £75, although some are as high as £5,000) and may be aimed at a particular age, often under 25. They are worth looking into, but don't be too hopeful. You may be able to get help if you meet financial hardship during a course, but funding for a whole course is rare.

There are some directories of charities which might give grant aid. You should find them in larger libraries.
Look at The charities digest
Look at Directory of grant-making trusts
Look at The educational grants directory
Look at The grants register
Look at Education yearbook.

Trade unions

The General Federation of Trade Unions Educational Trust make grants of £100 a year. Aid is given for full-time study in a course nominated by the recipient's trade union. Larger individual unions or branches may have similar arrangements. To find the education officers of the major unions: *Look at Education yearbook*. Contact GFTU Educational Trust, Central House, Upper Woburn Place, London WC1H 0HY. Tel: 071 387 2578. Contact your union branch convenor or shop steward.

Other sources

If all the above fail, don't despair. You might also try:
- part-time work during the course (evenings and in vacations)
- loans from relatives, employers or other individuals
- bank loans – other than the career development loans mentioned above
- hardship funds attached to the institution where you are studying

Starting Your Own Workshop

If you want to set up your own business, or to form a partnership or company with other woodworkers, a good place to start is at your local Department of Employment Offices or Jobcentre.

There is a whole range of literature available explaining the business training courses available, tax arrangements necessary, financial help available and so on.

If you are unemployed, and have been for at least eight weeks, and have £1,000 of your own money to invest in starting up your business, the Enterprise Allowance Scheme gives you a guaranteed income of £40 a week on top of whatever profits you make for a year. That can make a lot of difference to the cash flow of a small business in its first year. The scheme also offers business training and advice.

If you are not sure how to go about starting up a business on your own the government makes available £1,000 worth of training free through the Business Enterprise Programme (BEP). It says with training you are three times more likely still to be

in business after two years than you are without it.

If you are happy about starting your own business but are finding it difficult to raise the cash, the government's loan guarantee scheme might, help although you have to pay for the privilege – 2.5% of the sum guaranteed.

The guarantee normally covers 70% of the loan up to £100,000. The Loan Guarantee Scheme does not automatically mean you will get a loan. You still have to put your business plan to a bank and they have to approve it. But, if they know they can recover 70% of the loan no matter what, it might tip the balance between getting a loan and being unable to go ahead with your project. Work out the cash flow carefully to take into account the extra cost of borrowing.

If you need to borrow money, look around. The amount of money you will be able to borrow will vary not only from bank to bank, but also from branch to branch. In business everything is negotiable – and that includes the cost of borrowing and running a bank account. Do not be fooled into believing that bank charges are fixed. Once again, they will vary not only from bank to bank, but also from branch to branch.

Raising money does not have to involve borrowing. An alternative is to take on partners, either as partners in the business or as shareholders. There is a tax relief available for people investing in small businesses and there are government schemes available for raising equity finance (selling shares) from the government, especially in development areas. The Scottish and Welsh Development Agencies will be able to give you more information of such schemes if you are moving into their areas.

More information

The following organisations can give you more information.

Educational Grants Advisory Service: Help is only given to people referred by bodies which are members of the service such as college student advisers, student unions, advice services and certain LEA's. The service advises on sources of financial help for study with particular reference to educational trusts.

Contact Student Adviser, Educational Grants Advisory Service, Family Welfare Association, 501/505 Kingsland Road, London E8 4AU. Please do not telephone.

National Union of Students: The NUS grants department can help with specific cases or put you in touch with someone who can.

Contact Grants Department, NUS, 461 Holloway Road, London N7 6LJ. Please enclose an sae.

Citizens' Advice Bureaux: Your local Citizens' Advice Bureau has expert knowledge of the financial side of studying, and can advise you about courses, eligibility for grants and the general impact of study on your life. Contact your local CAB – the address will be in the 'phone book.

Libraries: Larger reference libraries will have reference books and, although they may not be able to answer specific enquiries themselves, will direct you to someone who can. Ask at your local branch – the address will be in the 'phone book.

Education departments: The three education Departments should also be able to help: Contact The Department of Education and Science, Elizabeth House, York Road, London SE1 7PH; The Scottish Education Department, Gyleview House, 3 Redheughs Rigg, Sough Gyle, Edinburgh EH12 9HH; The Department of Education for Northern Ireland, Rathgael House, Balloo Road, Bangor, Co Down BT19 2PR.

Further Reading

The educational grants directory (latest edition 1988), £12.50 inc p&p from Directory of Social Change, Radius Works, Back Lane, London NW3 1HL. Tel: 071 435 8171.

The Grants register 89-91, £65 plus £1.50 p&p from Macmillan Distribution, Globe Services, Brunel Road, Houndmills, Basingstoke, Hants RG21 2XS. Tel: 0256 21002.

Directory of grant-making trusts (1989 edition), £49.80 inc p&p from Charities Aid Foundation, Publications Department, 48 Pembury Road, Tonbridge, Kent TN9 2JD. Tel: 0732 771555.

The charities digest 1990, £9.95 inc p&p from Family Welfare Enterprises, 501/505 Kingsland Road, London E8 4AU. Tel: 071 254 3618.

National welfare benefits handbook 1990-91, £5.95 inc p&p from Child Poverty Action Group Ltd, 1-5 Bath Street, London EC1V 9PY. Also available from bookshops and your local library.

Sponsorships 1991, £1.95 plus 55p p&p (cheques only, payable to COIC) from Dept CW, ISCO 5, The Paddock, Frizinghall, Bradford BD9 4HD.

The adviser's handbook 1990, £10.95 inc p&p from The Newpoint Publishing Company Limited, Newpoint House, St James' Lane, London N10 3DF. Tel: 081 444 7281.

Education year book 1991, £52.50 inc p&p from Promotion Department, Longman Group UK Ltd, Westgate House, Freepost, Harlow, Essex CM20 1YQ. Tel: 0279 442601. Also available from some bookshops.

THE ROYAL ENGINEERS

Although the Royal Engineers are not the only branch of the Army to employ carpenters and joiners, they employ the largest number. Every man who joins receives comprehensive employment training. Priority is given to the skills needed for combat and operational duties and subsequent training is directed towards those skills which will prepare a Sapper to take his place in an engineering construction team.

Every Royal Engineer is trained first as a fighting soldier. This training is completed in the initial 10 weeks of service and follows a similar pattern for all recruits to the Army. In the following nine weeks, every Sapper learns the skills of engineers in battle and should then gain his qualification as a Class 3 Combat Engineer. On doing so, the Sapper is ready to join a squadron.

Once a Sapper has acquired some experience of an operational unit and has seen other tradesmen working in the field, he can decide whether he wishes further training for any other employment. Selection will depend on aptitude and recommendation and usually requires him to serve for a minimum of six years. Those opting for training as a Carpenter & Joiner will be trained at the Royal School of Military Engineering at Chatham to a standard recognised by City & Guilds and the Trade Unions.

Recruits who already have civilian trades experience, or hold certificates such as City & Guilds, may be exempted from employment training.

Apprenticeships

The Army offers some 380 apprenticeships each year at the Army Apprentices College, Chepstow, the majority of which are for all employments in the Royal Engineers. The Charter of the Army Apprentice College, Chepstow, is to train soldier tradesmen who will be the main source of further artisan Senior NCOs, Warrant Officers, Clerks of Works and Specialist Commissioned Officers in the Royal Engineers. Competition for places at the college is keen and applicants have to pass the selection tests for their particular employment. Those aiming at technician trades should be studying at least Mathematics and English at 'O' level standard. Boys are accepted between school leaving age and 17½. Apprentices spend two years at Chepstow. They may leave any time in their first six months. After that, they are expected to serve for a minimum of three years having completed training at the college.

The apprentices receive some general education but the majority of their education is in support of their specialist training. In addition to trade tests, the apprentice craftsmen are entered for their respective City & Guilds of London Institute craft certificates with opportunities to gain advanced craft certificates at later stages in their careers. The majority of apprentices leave with qualifications recognised by civilian institutions and the Trades Union Council. Apprentices may do private study to resit or improve their educational qualifications. The college facilities are excellent with laboratories, classrooms and workshops.

The Carpenters & Joiner Employment

The Carpenter and Joiner courses at the Royal School of Military Engineering are at two levels, initially at Class 2 and after further experience, at Class 1. The Class 2 course lasts 30 weeks and aims to train a student to become a skilled tradesman capable of producing a high standard of work with minimal supervision, given adequate briefing and the right materials and tools.

The main objectives of the carpenter & joiner are:

- to construct, maintain, modify and repair those parts of a building requiring the use of timber products using hand tools or woodworking machinery as necessary.
- to manufacture, erect and strike timber forms for concrete beams, slabs, columns and walls.
- to construct, erect, maintain and strike arch supports, dead and raking shores for buildings and excavation timbering for construction or operational use.
- to erect, maintain and dismantle trestles, ladder and tubular scaffolding up to two storeys.

- to strengthen existing buildings for operational use using timber products.

Having qualified at Class 2 level, and after a period of working at his trade and gaining suitable experience, a soldier may be considered for training at Class 1 level. This course lasts 18 weeks and aims to develop the scope and skills of a tradesman which he learnt at Class 2 level and to give him technical supervisory skills. By the end of the course the student will be a very highly skilled tradesman capable of exercising technical supervision in his trade.

Class 1 Objectives

- to improve and expand the skills at Class 2 level
- to interpret, from working drawings, those main components of a building requiring the use of timber or timber products and to set them out
- to select those fixtures and fittings in a building requiring the use of timber or timber projects from standard designs
- to interpret working drawings of timber form-work for concrete structures, check that form-work is safe for use and detail the method of erection and striking
- to select standard designs of timber formwork for precast concrete members
- to quantify, plan and specify the above works and provide technical direction to less skilled tradesmen employed on these

In all his work, the carpenter & joiner, in addition to using the basic hand tools, will use portable machines for use in the field. He will be trained to operate and maintain static woodworking machines in the workshop, including circular and cross cut saws, overhand planers, thicknessers, mortise machines, tenoners, dimension and band saws as well as machines for sharpening, setting, grinding and brazing. He will be trained in identifying, selecting and using soft woods and hard woods, laminates and manufactured sheet products, ready made joinery, external wall and sheet coverings, insulating materials, adhesives and preservatives.

The likely production tasks are many and varied

but include the production of formwork, setting out and construction of timber carcassing, laying and fixing floors, walls and roofs. Standard joinery tasks include the manufacture, installation and repair of doors, windows and stairways, partitioning of buildings, and planning, preparation and repair of sectional formed huts and internal systems.

THE ROYAL MARINES

Although part of the Royal Navy, the Marines are a military corps functioning primarily as commandos and amphibious specialists. They are famous for their versatility and physical fitness. The Technical Wing includes Armourers, Artificers, Illustrators, Drivers, and so on. It is under the Specialist Training Wing that we now find the Carpenter & Joiner under the new mantle of Assault Engineer.

After the initial Commando Training, and usually a spell in a Royal Marine Commando Unit, the Marine can volunteer to become an Assault Engineer (AE). After the AE training he has the option of taking the additional qualification as a Carpenter & Joiner. To become a Carpenter & Joiner he must first pass a basic qualifying course lasting 13 weeks. Following the completion of this and after a suitable period to gain experience and complete the AE 2 course he can again volunteer to complete his Carpenter & Joiner training by completing a course which lasts six weeks. At the end of the course he qualifies for the City & Guilds of London Institute Carpentry and Joinery Craft Certificate 585.

Having upgraded he will have become a skilled tradesman capable of working without supervision and, using his own initiative, producing a high standard of work given the right materials and adequate tools. Should the Marine be a candidate for promotion, he could be selected for a Junior Command Course. If he passes this course and becomes a corporal he could find himself as a carpenter workshop manager, responsible for the Carpentry & Joinery requirements of the Commando Unit.

Assault Engineer (Carpenter 3) Course Aim

The aim of the course is in 13 weeks to train an AE 3 to do the following:

* read and produce a technical drawing used by fellow members on his course
* use confidently and with skill all hand tools and power tools in use in a carpenter's workshop
* make all types of common joints used in woodworking
* sketch elementary carpentry fixtures found in the building industry
* recognise timber defects and the uses of which timber can be put
* carry out simple practical construction work
* prepare surfaces for painting and finishing on wood, metal and similar surfaces

- be conversant with the Factories Act Regulations relevant to his trade
- use and maintain carpenter and joiners' tools and equipment
- carry out hand working of timber, setting and marking out, planing materials to a flat surface and given size
- make all types of common joints used in woodworking
- prepare surfaces for all types of finish
- have a knowledge of uses of plywood, hardboard and synthetic materials
- prepare simple dimensioned sketches and drawings
- recognise defects in timber and select suitable wood for prescribed work

- be able to glaze
- be capable of carrying out any of the following tasks:
  - (i) erect, under supervision, timber buildings with lintels doors and windows
  - (ii) make moulds for pre-cast concrete work and also make and erect formwork for small concrete work
  - (iii) construct a solid frame door, the frame to be plain and rebated with skeleton frame-jamb linings. Construct battened and ledged doors, simple parallel glazed doors and flush doors. Hang all types of door
  - (iv) construct both casement and sash type window frames and be able to install them

Training Objectives

A Carpenter must be able to:
- calculate areas and volumes
- read a technical drawing and make dimensional free hand sketches

WOODWORKING IN THE ARMED FORCES

Assault Engineer (Carpenter 2) Course Aim

The aim of the course is in six weeks to train a Carpenter 3 to the following standards:

- to produce clear drawings with dimensions of tasks he may be required to execute

- to cost, design and build simple timber buildings and constructions

- to supervise carpenters under his control

- to organise and control a carpenter's workshop, to include:
  - (i) the operation of machines, maintenance and safety regulations governing the use of machinery
  - (ii) the ordering, storing and control of the use of timber in his workshop
  - (iii) the ordering and control of fixatives, screws and tools in his workshop

Training Objectives

A Carpenter must be able to:

- calculate costs by use of formula

- apply trigonometry and geometry to his trade

- draw and work to a technical drawing

- operate and maintain all working machinery found in a carpenter's workshop

- be conversant with safety regulations pertaining to machinery

- store timber correctly

- understand insulation from both heat and sound

- build temporary and semi-permanent single storey timber buildings

In all his work the Carpenter & Joiner, in addition to using the basic hand tools, will also use portable machinery for the use in the field. He is trained to operate and maintain static woodworking machines in the workshop. These include the circular, dimension and cross-cut saws, overhand planers and thicknessers, mortice machines, spindle moulders, lathes, bandsaws as well as machines for sharpening and grinding.

He is trained in identifying and selecting soft and hardwoods, laminates and manufactured sheet products, ready made joinery, external sheet coverings, insulation materials, adhesives and preservatives, varnishes and French polishes and paints.

He is also called upon for occasional exhibition and presentation work, repairs of timberwork in all makes of trucks, buildings and boats. In a Royal Marine Commando Unit you will find a Corporal as Carpenter Shop Manager, and two marines.

THE ROYAL AEROSPACE
Jim Kingshot

The Royal Aerospace Establishment at Farnborough on the Surrey/Hampshire border is the birth place of British aviation. The first powered flight in the UK was made here. It was The Royal Aircraft Factory during the first world war and is now one of the largest research establishments in Europe. The RAE is probably best known to the general public as the venue of the SBAC Farnborough Air Show.

The Establishment has an extensive engineering and manufacturing capability, which offers about 80 apprentice places each year across the following trades: Fitter Mechanical, Fitter Mechanical Maintenance, Tool Maker, Electronic Craftsman, Avionics Radio/Radar Craftsman, Electrical Fitter, Avionics Electrical Instrument, Aircraft Airframe/Engine Fitter, Carpenter/Joiner, Sheetmetal Worker, Welder. These apprentices are not in the armed forces, but work closely with them.

Standards based training as introduced in 1984 follows the requirements of the various Industrial Training Boards, City & Guilds Institutes, The

Training Agency (previously known as the Manpower Services Commission) and the interests of the Ministry of Defence. The apprenticeship is framed around four phases of training, each phase taking about one year to complete, depending on the ability of the apprentice to reach the required standard. Each phase is broken down into segments of easily manageable learning with set standards of skill to be achieved before moving on to the next segment.

The four year apprenticeship is probably the finest craft training obtainable. The RAE apprentices are eagerly sort by industry, and it is surprising how many top executives have an RAE apprenticeship as a foundation stone.

Release to attend Technical College at least one day a week plays an important part in the training. Most carpentry & joinery apprentices achieve an Advanced Craft Certificate in Site Practice and Purpose Made Joinery, many gain a BTEC certificate. Apprentices who have shown outstanding abilities have been sent to university to gain a degree.

A synopsis of the Carpentry and Joinery Syllabus:

PHASE ONE
The use and care of hand tools, sharpening, indentification of timbers, timber conversion, selection and preparation, setting out, angle joints, lengthening joints, forming width joints, load bearing joints, fastenings, fixings, fittings, measurement and simple geometry, basic construction of: casements, sash windows, doors, frames and linings, floors, roofs, partitions. Computer literacy is also taught.

PHASE TWO
Construction of: doors, porches, porticos, windows, pivot hung sash, louvres, french windows, sky lights, dormers, lantern and borrowed lights, bay and oriel windows, stairs, internal fittings, finishing and polishing, powered hand tools, metric framing square, timber framed buildings, workshop geometry.

PHASE THREE
Segmental and circular headed doors, fire resisting doors, bulls eye windows, built in furniture, wall panelling, counters, screens and room dividers; wood cutting machinery: (hands on experience) circular saws, band re-saw, planing machines, mortising, tenoning, moulding, computer numerically controlled machines.

PHASE FOUR
Temporary timbering: arches, concrete form work, shoring, excavations, partitions; self-supporting, sound resisting, drawing office practices, (spent in the DO), land surveying, stressing, Health and Safety in Design.

Applying
Applications for apprenticeships should be made before February each year. These are sifted and those found suitable invited to take an aptitude test. Successful candidates are then interviewed and, if accepted, they are given a medical examination. Security clearance follows before joining the annual intake, usually in August.

Application forms and more details are obtainable from: The Industrial Personnel Department, Q101 Building, The Royal Aerospace Establishment, Farnborough, Hampshire GU14 6TD.

Although the number of companies mass producing furniture has diminished over the years (unlike the number of small workshops, which has mushroomed – *see Chapter 3*) there is still a good career to be had in the industry on the craft side, in design and in management.

There was once a great many companies in Britain making furniture, many of them growing up around High Wycombe, which became the heart of the furniture industry in this country.

Over the years some firms have been taken over by their competitors and some have gone out of business. Even so, there are several hundred businesses left, even if they are becoming concentrated into the hands of large and still expanding enterprises such as Parker Knoll, Ercol, and G Plan in High Wycombe, Stag in Nottingham, Rest Assured in Northamptonshire, Christie Tyler in South Wales, Gostin in Liverpool, and so on.

The furniture industry takes on around 500 youngsters a year. It also now recognises adult trainees as a category, although adults making a mid-life change of career, or who want to develop a hobby, or who have been made redundant, still only account for 2-3% of the annual intake.

Much of furniture production now is highly mechanised, although there are still firms using the old skills to various degrees. For example, Jaycee in Brighton (owned by Stag) is famous for the hand carving on some of its ranges.

Even companies with a high degree of mechanisation like their trainees to be skilled in various aspects of furniture making by hand, though, and run comprehensive training programmes. A person working a machine will produce better quality work if he can compare the result with what he could produce by hand.

High Wycombe is still at the heart of the furniture industry, which is why it has one of the most famous and best respected furniture colleges in the country, the courses having been developed in conjunction with the industry (see Buckinghamshire College in the listings).

Those joining a company will usually be given a work experience trial first to see which area they best fit into.

The amount of time spent at college by company trainees will vary depending on the colleges attended and the courses being taken. At Highbury, for example,

trainees attend a day a week with a two week block during the Easter term. At Buckinghamshire College, students will spend a week at college for every three at work for the first year, then a week at college for every four at work for the next two years.

Most trainees start by working towards City & Guild 555. Normally the first year is spent gaining a grounding in a variety of craft skills, although some students with the right educational background can miss out this first year and go straight on to Part Two.

In the second and third years of training students concentrate on their particular craft, still with a City & Guild qualification to be aimed for – such as 564 in Chair Making or 586 in Wood Machining.

The furniture industry's training, like most industries' these days, is modular, based on learning elements which build up into units. In the second year the preparatory modules are taken and in the third year the finals.

Companies and the various regional societies of the manufacturers which organise training on behalf of their members prefer trainees to have achieved a grade 'C' GCSE or above in mathematics, English and a craft subject. Applicants who have not been studying craft to exam level at school might have a hard time convincing a prospective employer that they are serious about wanting a craft job.

However, it is the people the industry looks at rather than just their qualifications and there is an acceptance that those who respond to craft subjects do not necessarily respond to academic subjects.

To gain an idea of which companies are looking for trainees you should contact the regional branches of the British Furniture Manufacturers Federation, listed in this book in the 'Helpful Organisations' chapter.

Even if your aim is eventually to set up your own workshop, training with a large company can be a useful way to begin. Although most modern factories use large machinery, trainees are still usually taught hand tool techniques. In any case, it would be an unusual commercial workshop which did not contain machinery, even if it is not quite to the size or sophistication of the computer controlled versions in some aspects of mass production. It might also be possible to learn some aspects of business management with a company.

If I were a carpenter, and I were a lady . . . I would be a rarity. But luckily less of a rarity these days than in the past.

More women are venturing into woodworking. On the work register compiled by the London agency called "Women and Manual Trades" (see Helpful Organisations chapter) more than 100 women are listed in the woodworking category. The increasing numbers are due to a variety of factors. One is the prevalence of power tools. In the past it took a fair amount of strength and physical stamina to carry out many of the steps required in woodworking. These days a few zips of the power tool take care of it. The tools have been a great leveller.

Another is the women's movement, which has encouraged women to step out of tight job categories and do whatever they enjoy doing. By the same token, the trend towards sexual equality has opened up woodworking courses to women – courses that they used to be automatically barred from.

Money is a reason, too, both on the expense and income side. A woman who hires a workman to do custom woodworking in her home is often astounded at how much the work costs, and may begin to think that if the work is this lucrative perhaps she should consider doing it herself.

Another cause is the snowball factor. The increasing numbers of women carpenters set examples for other women who are attracted to the field. I can remember one evening adult education class where I watched carpentry teacher Kate Payne, a woman with small, delicate hands, deftly marking a piece of wood with her sharp pencil. It made me wonder how men with their big chunky hands ever got into this profession.

Courses for Women

There are not many woodworking courses specifically for women, but the City & East London College (See Colleges listings) offers one called Women's Furniture Crafts. It is run by women and is only for women. It teaches skills to City & Guilds 555 standard Part 1.

The course is specifically for women who want to re-train or return to education after a break.

Many of the students have no previous experience of woodworking, or furniture making (skills apart from woodworking are included) but find the college offers a supportive educational environment.

The course tutor, Kate Payne, says: "The emergence of women in skilled manual trades is a direct result of courses like ours which open up opportunities for training in non-traditional areas.

"It has been very successful, with a 100% pass rate for five years running and 70% of last year's students went on to work or study in a directly related area.

"We have had several students go on to start their own furniture making business, designing, working freelance and working for established firms as trainees.

"Women say the course gives them the confidence to compete in the workplace and to approach employers.

"The college is in Shoreditch, the historical centre of the London furniture trade, so we are surrounded by crafts and suppliers of specialist materials, timber, tools, veneers and ironmongery. The area also has museums, libraries and at least one bookshop which caters primarily for woodworkers.

It is an inspiring place to be and we hope the course will bring new, talented workers into the trade there to re-vitalise the industry."

Unfortunately, getting into a carpentry course is much easier than actually finding a steady job when the training is over, especially if the training is not comprehensive.

My own experience seems to be typical of the level of difficulty women encounter, so I'll explain what has happened to me in my work as a kitchen fitter over the last two years.

I had done a bit of woodworking in my early 20s, mostly as a break from academic studies, and did not get involved in the field again until years later when I was considering replacing my kitchen.

The price of a new kitchen was so absurd that I considered building it myself. About this same time I heard about a Manpower Services Commission course in kitchen fitting at the Skills Training Agency in Deptford, and decided to sign up.

The course was supposed to teach basic carpentry, plus elementary plumbing, wiring, plastering and tiling. Our teacher had been drafted in to teach the course at the last minute. He was a good carpenter himself and a fair carpentry teacher,

but overall the course was hopeless. We students called it "teach yourself kitchen fitting" because there was so little useful guidance coming from the teacher.

I got the feeling that we students were being warehoused for the five months that the course lasted. When we left we certainly weren't skilled enough to get a decent job.

Even the tool box we had made as part of our training was unsuitable – it was very heavy once tools were packed in it, and the flimsy fasteners we had been given to put the handle on immediately started to pull through the wood after just a few days of use.

When I started looking for a kitchen fitting job I encountered both sexual discrimination (something I hadn't been confronted with in the course) and employer distrust of the government training background (quite justified, I'd have to admit).

Interestingly, some of the sex discrimination came from women. "You couldn't lift a double oven," one prissy woman told me when I walked into a kitchen shop looking for work.

Finally, after contacting about 30 potential employers, (some of whom, after hearing a woman's voice, asked if this was a joke) I was told by a rather up-market kitchen design company that they might have a kitchen fitting job for me. When I went for the interview they said they would consider me, but the job might not open up for a week or so.

Anxious to get a foot in the door, I offered to work in their kitchen making factory downstairs making cabinets until the fitting job became available.

The factory job was interesting, because I got to put the units together under factory conditions and because I got to deliver some of the units to the various sites and meet the fitting teams.

After a week in the factory I was told that the fitting job was no closer (I think the firm was quite happy to have me keep on working on the shop floor at a low wage) so I quit.

I then went back to one of the fitting teams, and, reminding them that I have made the cabinets they were fitting, asked for a job. They said yes.

The men on the team – a good-natured group of fellows – taught me a lot and I finally got good enough to do a kitchen on my own.

This was a rather frightening step to take, but I felt I had to do it if I ever wanted to earn good wages. Since I was getting requests for work through my "Women and Manual Trades" connections, I realized that I should take on the work myself and then just hire a subcontractor to do the parts I felt unsure of. I could see what he did, and do it myself the next time. I have done this for several jobs now, and it has worked very well.

Despite the difficulties, I do recommend woodworking for women. It's wonderful to build something that lasts, to transform an entire room, and, in the case of kitchen fitting, to make lights shine where you want them and make the water flow where you decide it should go.

> **"In a field like kitchen fitting, why should men design and install kitchens?"**

Learning these skills demistified many things. To understand what things are made of and how they're put together (like in a kitchen) has the effect of giving you X-ray vision. You feel much more in control of your environment. You're more in control of your life, too, because you don't have to wait around for high-priced repairmen to come and do simple repairs. You can handle them yourself.

And I think women are particularly well suited to woodworking. Many of them have superior spacial perception, better manual dexterity, and more patience for the job.

In a field like kitchen fitting, why should men design and install kitchens? A man's few seconds of thoughtlessness in the design process could condemn you to being stuck forever with an awkward corner base unit that you curse every time you try to extract a pot from it.

I think one of the best parts about being a woodworker is that what you make will be there for a long time. If I make a good dinner, people say "thank you", and there's nothing left but the memory of appetizing food. If I make a bookcase, it's different. I made a nicely proportioned one for friends about 18 years ago and now when I go back to visit them it's still there, filling the space it was made for. It's great to see it giving long term satisfaction.

LEWISHAM WOMENS WORKSPACE

Lewisham Womens Workspace is a woodwork workshop in Deptford, offering practical woodworking facilities to local Craftswomen. These are benches, hand tools and powered machinery for use by any female woodworker. It can cater for up to six women at any one time. Bench space is allocated on an hourly basis.

Creche facilities are available where up to 10 children are supervised by fully experienced staff. It is open for two, 2½ hourly sessions per day.

Lewisham Womens Workspace is co-operatively managed company, funded by the London Borough of Lewisham. It was set up in mid 1990 by a group of women woodworkers who, seeking to develop their own enterprises, saw the desperate need for a women's woodwork workshop where bench space, tools and equipment could be rented while children could be cared for and stimulated in a creche also run by the Co-operative.

The Workspace is currently in its developmental stage, but has the long term aim to encourage and develop access to careers in woodwork for all women of all ages, and to extend this further to the setting up of their own woodworking businesses.

Relevant vocational training will take place on the premises as well as marketing and financial management training.

Lewisham Womens Workspace offers an innovative approach to improving the skill levels of local women, at the same time furthering the development of small businesses.

If you are interested in woodworking, run your own small woodworking business, or are thinking of setting up your own enterprise why not contact Lewisham Womens Workshop to find out more, or telephone 081-461 4784 or 081-461 3151.

by Holly Smith

Construction is, in monetary terms, the UK's second largest industry. It is also becoming increasingly international with plenty of opportunities for qualified craftsmen to work elsewhere in Europe as training and building regulations become standardised. Europe represents 40% of the world's construction market – £300bn a year. That employs a lot of people.

There are two basic approaches to joining the building industry as a carpenter & joiner – the two are usually considered together although a carpenter normally works on site while a joiner stays in the workshop making the window frames and doors which the carpenter fits. Firstly, you can apply to a local (or national or international) construction company for a job. Or you can contact the Construction Industry Training Board (CITB) – see 'Helpful Organisations' in this book.

The construction industry still offers apprenticeships for craftsmen, although they have to a large extent been taken over by the Youth Training Scheme. It is the CITB which oversees apprenticeships, as well as Youth Training, or (if you are over 18) Employment Training schemes. YT and ET schemes are not necessarily run within companies, although it is possible to be on a YT scheme and be employed by a company at the same time.

With a YT scheme or apprenticeship you will be given on-the-job training plus time at college to learn more about the skills required – such as using hand and power tools and machines safely and accurately, qualities of timbers and finishes, etc. An ET scheme will be off the-job-for six months – but with practical experience included – and with a company for six months.

With the YTS the aim, after two years of training, is to gain a City & Guilds certificate and a skills test which will denote your level of competence. The certificate you receive will carry the NCVQ (National Council for Vocational Qualifications) stamp which should now be recognised throughout the EC. With Employment Training there is a skills test at the end of a year equivalent to the NCVQ test.

Firms which take on apprentices often recruit from YT schemes so school leavers lose nothing by registering with the CITB/YTS as an initial way into the industry. Indeed, it is often the easiest way in. On registration the trainee gives three choices of trade and the CITB tests the candidate's potential.

Entrants are expected to be able to read and write and possess some mathematical ability. Any skilled craftsman in the industry will need to be able to read drawings.

Once registered, the CITB will try to place the applicant with an approved firm. Many firms which take on YTS trainees will offer them an apprenticeship after a year or so and the time already served will be considered part of that apprenticeship.

Local authorities are still major recruiters of trainees in the construction industry. Most recruit directly into apprenticeships. Some take on YTS trainees and employ them after a year. As just one example, the London Borough of Hackney takes on 50 building trainees each year during August and September. The council, like most others, organises its own courses with local colleges. It tends to spread college attendance evenly throughout the training period whereas the CITB gives extended periods of college training before on-the-job training starts.

The CITB has its own main training centre at its headquarters in Bircham Newton (see 'Helpful Organisations' in this book). It is the largest training centre of its kind anywhere in the world and is considered to provide training of a high standard.

Since 1986 there has been almost a revolution in training in this industry. Why since 1986? Because that was when the National Council for Vocational Qualifications was set up and the Council has been a catalyst for training which has greatly improved the opportunities for trainees.

The new structure of qualifications has four levels – 1 is the foundation level and 4 is the higher level. At each level the National Vocational Qualifications test the trainee's skill, knowledge and understanding of his or her chosen trade and their ability to turn what they have learnt into a practical application.

The NCVQ does not train people, nor does it offer examinations. What it does is accredit qualifications offered by industry approved examining and testing bodies, such as City & Guilds and the CITB.

Going it alone

There are opportunities for carpenters & joiners to branch out on their own (see the 'Money' chapter about the realities of financing such a move). At the age of 26, Carl Whittaker did just that.

His enthusiasm for carpentry started when he was on an agricultural course. He saw the joinery shop at Lancing College, just outside Brighton. With a bit of haggling he moved over to the City & Guilds course in carpentry & joinery.

When he left college he worked for two firms in Brighton before moving to London where, he says, the work is far more interesting because people are prepared to pay for much more elaborate work than they are outside London. He says his average job in London would only crop up once or twice a year outside the capital. That was the sort of job he wanted – not just fitting new locks and banging up partitions on site.

While he was on a routine maintenance job for the firm he was working for in London he was asked if he did freelance work. He was asked the same question twice in a week. The jobs were making kitchen cupboards. The company he was with allowed him the use of their workshop in his spare time to carry out the work. From the first two jobs, five more came to him by recommendation and so it has gone on.

Within six weeks his private work had reached a point where he had to make a decision to cut it back or leave his job. He chose to start his own business.

The decision is not as automatic as it may sound. Suddenly there were no more pay packets, and no money was coming in until jobs were finished.

Sensibly, Whittaker visited an accountant and set up a separate bank account for his business, from which he pays himself. He also has a bank account for the tax man into which a third of the money he takes goes automatically.

He is not registered for VAT because neither are most of his customers. Although if he was registered he could claim back 15% on the materials he buys, he would also have to charge 15% more. So he stays under the turnover threshold at which registration becomes compulsory.

He does not intend that should last, though, and would like eventually to be running his own joinery company, employing other carpenters.

WHAT IS IN CARPENTRY AND JOINERY
J.C. Winters

Carpentry and joinery covers a broad range of activities from formwork to the creation of fine detail for stately home fixtures. The difference between the two subjects of carpentry and joinery is a little cloudy, which is why they are frequently grouped together. Generally, though, a carpenter fixes woodwork made by a joiner.

Carpentry is divided into two main areas: 'first fix' and 'second fix'. To define the two let us take the construction of a new house. The 'first fix' carpenter will be involved from an early stage erecting site huts, shuttering for foundations and formwork for any arched brickwork like door and window apertures.

As the walls progress upwards, bought-in joinery needs to be prepared and floor joists have to be built in. Once the walls are complete, the roof must be constructed. In most cases the roof will simply be a case of arranging ready-made roof trusses in position and fixing them. Alternatively, it may be an interesting design requiring a full knowledge of relevant calculations. The next jobs are inside the rapidly evolving house – building studwork walls and fixing ceilings, floors and door linings.

Once the building has been plastered, the 'second fixing' can begin. This includes hanging doors and fitting stairs, balusters, skirting boards, architraves, kitchen cupboards, built-in wardrobes, and so on. Greater care is necessary during these operations as all of the items are on view to the potential owner. The stairs, for instance, may be a focal point as you enter the house.

As with most trades these days, far less knowledge or skill is required due to bought-in

components, falling standards of workmanship and lower expectations of the customer.

In the case of commercial and public building, the first fix is mostly nailing together sheets of heavy, grubby shuttering ply for concrete pouring. The second fixing, however, may be more interesting as the internal fitments will be of better quality, more varied and often specially made to exacting requirements. Take a look at some of the work in shops, hotels, and other public buildings. Occasionally it is quite exceptional.

Having discussed carpentry, we now progress to joinery, which involves making the items the carpenter fixes on site. This includes doors, windows, kitchen and bedroom fitments, counters, bars, panelled work and anything you see inside made of wood.

To a large part, joinery has been taken over by massive, sophisticated machinery. In the mass-production of joinery the best work goes to the machine setters, which is a completely different subject. What is left is loading timber on one end of a machine and assembling the components that come off the other end. This can be soul destroy-ing work and is usually poorly paid. But do not despair. There are many small companies, particularly shopfitters, catering for the individual requirements of special customers. In such firms, far more handwork is involved as it is uneconomic to spend hours setting up large machines for small quantities and one-offs. There are, therefore, great opportunities for anyone starting a career in a small, versatile company, although you might find they specialise in one particular product, such as conservatories or kitchens.

Should you choose to enter a career in carpentry & joinery, a formal apprenticeship is probably the best way of learning the trade. This would involve attending college for one day a week to study for a City & Guilds examination. If you work hard enough to pass the 'craft level', you may be able to go on to 'advanced craft' and further. Having acquired your qualifications, any future employer will consider offering you work, safe in the knowledge that you have reached a competent level. Alternatively, you might enter the trade less formally, working alongside a skilled craftsman learning the trade directly from him. You won't get a certificate at the end but, if deserving, you will get a good reference to show a potential employer.

At the beginning of any form of apprenticeship the work might seem boring and meaningless. This is the time to absorb what is happening around you and take in the skills and methods that will be expected of you in the future. Above all, listen hard to instructions and carry them out to the very best of your ability. This way you will quickly inspire confidence and move on to more interesting tasks.

Depending which aspect of the carpentry & joinery trade you enter determines the variety of tools you will require; your foreman or boss will advise on this. A basic set might comprise the following: tape/rule, square, saw, chisels, mallet, drill and bits, hammer, screwdriver, plane, pincers, punch, bevel, oil stone and spirit level. One thing is certain, good tools cannot be purchased cheaply, so go to a reliable tool shop and enjoy the choice. You will get no joy from a set of three chisels for £6.99. When buying any hand tool try to find one that feels right for you. Pay attention to comfort and balance of the tool and look carefully at the quality and accuracy of manufacture. It will influence your work.

It is unlikely at this stage that power tools will be of any relevance, although they are worth a mention. As with hand tools, the same rules of choice apply with the addition of noting capacity and power output. Cordless power tools are now gaining popularity with the improvement of rechargeable batteries. They offer great freedom, especially on site where power supplies are often limited. However, they always seem to run out at a crucial moment. Do not be misled into thinking that greater accuracy is achieved with power tools – they only make the job less strenuous and quicker. Much skill is required in their efficient use. Safety must also be considered very seriously as a 225mm saw blade spinning round at nearly 100mph can be lethal, even in the most competent user's hands.

Having selected and purchased your tools, care and storage is important. Keep them clean and sharp and lightly oiled to prevent corrosion of metal parts. Do not let sharp edges knock against hard objects as a chip off the edge of a plane iron takes a long time to remove.

My own career started in 1972 with a small reputable shop fitting company in Hertfordshire. The work at first was a little boring but as time went on I was offered more interesting and challenging jobs. Having spent five years with this company, including four years of day release to college, I had gained a lot of experience and a fair amount of skill and knowledge. My hard work at college was rewarded by my passing with credit the City & Guilds Advanced Craft level in Carpentry & Joinery.

I then had a slight change of direction and worked in a prototype workshop making plastic components for fridge and freezer development. This was extremely interesting and taxing, working to fine

tolerances from precise engineering drawings.

Two years later, in 1980, I got married and moved to a run-down cottage in Norfolk. My wife, Caron, worked full-time and I spent three years renovating our home including making all new windows and doors completely by hand. It was during this period that I realised how limited both my tool kit and knowledge was. The tool problem was solved with birthday presents, trips to a secondhand tool stall and ingenuity. Additional knowledge came from library books, woodwork magazines and trial and error.

The cottage renovation could have been completed in a shorter time had it not been for the birth of my son after one year. Caron returned to work and I combined the renovation work with being Mum.

In 1983 the cottage was virtually complete and I inherited a useful sum of money which I invested in a small combination machine. Caron was expecting our second child and we decided this would be the ideal chance to start self-employment. We would have the financial cushion of Caron's maternity allowance and her job would be kept open for six months for her to return to if everything failed. Our 'living room' had always been the workshop while renovating the cottage and it was from this base that I became a self-employed joiner, offering high quality custom-made joinery and cabinets.

I did not advertise, but relied on word of mouth. This proved effective and the demand was overwhelming. We had explained to our extremely understanding neighbours that we would move to proper premises if the business proved successful. This being the case, we started looking and were fortunate enough to find a lovely property complete with workshops and planning permission for business use in the centre of a picturesque village.

We moved in February 1985 and settled in fairly quickly. But with larger workshops came bigger bills and so, to ease the burden of overheads, I employed a talented, yet inexperienced friend to learn the trade. This has all worked out fairly well, although there have been some long hours worked and sleepless nights spent worrying about customers who don't like paying their bills.

Finally, I must mention the raw material – wood. There are numerous different species, all with their own characteristics and uses. The most common of these are the pines, firs and spruces used mainly for construction purposes and a majority of furniture. With luck, you will experience the joy of working the various hardwoods and less common softwood, each one having its own distinctive working properties, smell and texture. For every metre of solid wood you use, the chances are you will use a square metre of man-made board. Again, these have their various characteristics ranging from crude and rough chipboard to the considerable strength of plywood.

British-made dinghies, motor cruisers, ocean-going yachts and power boats can be seen all over the world as a testament to the country's continuation of its maritime tradition.

Many of the boats may be glass reinforced plastics these days, but there is still a great deal of woodwork both in their fittings and in their construction – a boat has to be built up from its backbone (or keel) and even a GRP boat starts from a mould created from a traditional wooden design with planks bent over ribs to create the sweep from bow to stern. In any case, wooden hulled boats are still popular.

While the big shipyards have disappeared, many smaller companies have thrived, building boats for the leisure industry.

There are well established training routes through Skillbuild and City & Guilds for those who want to join the industry. They provide proper, systematic education in the crafts involved in boat building.

A good first point of contact to enter the industry is to visit a boat builder or contact the British Marine Industries Federation at Vale Road, Oatlands Park, Weybridge, Surrey KT13 9NS (Tel: 0932 854511).

School leavers can enrol on Youth Training Schemes within the industry or there are college courses available (see the chapter listing courses in this book). For those prepared to work hard on intensive courses (which cost £4,000 or so) the BMIF recommends two private training centres (see the chapter listing independent colleges) which award their own diplomas as well as expecting students to sit City & Guilds examinations within the one year course.

There is a great diversity of jobs within boatbuilding. The boat itself starts life as a drawing designed by the architect. The loftsman then translates and enlarges the design into full scale drawings. Sometimes these are marked out on a floor with the smaller pieces being drawn onto pieces of wood. It has to be done exactly because each piece relates to another – the hull and deck shapes, bulkheads and a good deal of the interior joinery for the boat.

Cutting planks to make the shape requires a lot of skill and experience. You have to know how to choose a good length without knots and blemishes; you have to know about the various types of wood and how to plane and pare, bend and shape.

Boatbuilders also have to know about what happens when wood meets salt or fresh water and how it will react in the various climatic conditions the world has to offer. It matters what fixings are

used, too. Some metals react quickly with salt water and screws can just fall out.

Wooden boats are constructed in different ways – clinker, carvel, cold-moulded, lapstrake. Each method of bending and fixing the planks still has to result in a watertight hull.

Each technique is an art in itself and experienced boatbuilders who know about all of them are at the top of the industry.

Certainly it is much easier to make GRP boats and to learn how to make them. Most boats these days are GRP (glass reinforced plastic) because it is the cheapest way of production, but there is still a lot of wood on a GRP boat.

Pictures: W. G. P. Davies, Marine Builders' Training Trust.

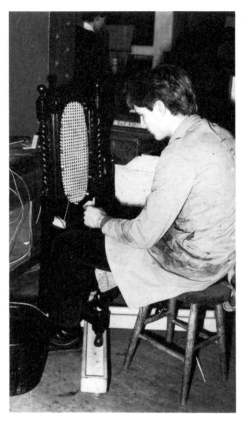

Because wood is used in a wide variety of applications and has been for thousands of years there is always likely to be a demand for people who know how to restore what has been made in the material. But restoration is not the sort of work likely to be undertaken by people without some existing knowledge of a woodworking skill.

Old woodwork which has survived up to this point and which somebody wants restored is likely to be valuable. If the work is poor the option of getting a new piece made is not likely to appeal to the person who wanted the restoration work done.

Restoration of woodwork is required in most fields – furniture, buildings, musical instruments, boats, carvings, and so on.

In each case distinct skills are required and they often involve a knowledge which goes beyond wood. For example, in building work a knowledge of other building materials might well be useful; in furniture restoration an understanding of covering materials and seat weaving could be handy; and in repairing wooden statues there may be gilding, painting or other finishes which also have to be repaired.

The lists of colleges in this book indicate some of the training courses available in this field.

Here, Ted Doulton of the Rural Development Commission, looks at the courses on furniture restoration run by the Commission.

LEARNING TO RESTORE FURNITURE

The Rural Industries Bureau began training people in furniture restoration in 1956 when Stan Learoyd started to work for them. At this time instruction in furniture making was already well established in the RIB under the guidance of consultant the late Edward Barnsley, one of Britain's great furniture designer-makers. Many drawings in the Rural Development Commission's current furniture catalogue are attributed to him.

Soon after the war, a Furniture Restoration Department was set up to restore furniture in the possession of the National Trust, Historic Buildings and private individuals. Its formation gave rise to complaints from existing restorers that the RIB was taking work away from them. Some of them unfortunately did not have the expertise to carry out such work. The RIB Restoration Department was established to provide training in response to these complaints. It would seem from the records that there was a steady flow of furniture in need of restoration through the Wimbledon workshops and the work done was also used for instructional purposes. It would also appear that the number of students and courses increased steadily. The courses were not running all the time, but visits were continually made to houses to prepare estimates and to find restorers who were capable of undertaking the work. As a result, many craftsmen who would benefit from learning additional skills were found.

In my opinion, you should be proficient in one of the woodworking skills before becoming a furniture restorer. Most, if not all, the good furniture restorers I know have been either cabinet makers or furniture makers. Incidentally, the difference between these two was explained to me many years ago: cabinet makers make everything except chairs; furniture makers make chairs as well.

The courses for which I am responsible are primarily for tradesmen or craftsmen and women who have had at least three years experience in the trade or formal training in a recognised college. There are, of course, some people who start up in business in furniture making or furniture restoration without formal training and, providing they fall within our terms of reference, we are quite prepared to help them.

There is no hard and fast rule about the order in which people should attend our courses, but woodworkers who wish to extend into restoration should attend the four day No 1 Preparation Course. This course, which lasts from lunchtime Monday to lunchtime Friday, deals mainly with the things that should not be done to antique furniture, such as stripping off a polished surface, which can immediately devalue a piece of furniture by up to one third. It also looks at what materials should and should not be used for different periods. For example, American oak should not be used to repair a piece of furniture made of European oak.

How to remove screws and nails which should not be there in the first place without doing too much damage is a subject in itself.

Another topic always covered in the course is the use – or misuse – of animal glue. When I see animal glue being used in workshops or colleges I understand why people think modern glues are better. But this is not so. For interior work, providing it is at the correct temperature and of the right consistency and the joint fits properly, animal glue works extremely well.

After attending the No 1 Preparation Course, the restorer can choose to attend other courses according to his needs.

Carving is a four day course concerned mainly with how to sharpen and use tools, how to set out using tools rather than, as many books suggest, cardboard templates. In the time it takes to make a cardboard template for egg and tongue moulding, at least 6in of mould can be carved – and time is money.

As much restoration work involves replacing pieces which are broken or missing, holding work for restoration presents many problems. For example, it is relatively easy to carve a new leg, but to repair a leg that is fixed to a chair presents a further problem.

Furniture makers find the carving course useful because it extends their range of skills. It means that if they are asked to make chairs with carved legs they get the reward and satisfaction of doing all the work themselves, although if there is a full-time carver in the area it may still be more cost effective to put the work out.

The gilding course is also four days. This goes back to basics and demonstrates the whole process: the preparation of surfaces to be gilded, the mixing of gesso, laying the gold, burnishing, toning and distressing. This is important because unless you understand how gilding is done in the first place, it is impossible to restore it properly. Therefore, until people have understood the basics of gilding, they do not receive instruction in the techniques of restoration.

There are two reasons why people have gilded furniture in their homes – to show their wealth and to reflect the light. Many gilded mirrors are fitted with candle holders. Unfortunately, in the Victorian period, these were often coated with black or dark lacquer and recently some have been ''repaired'' with the so-called gold paint from spray cans. A lot of gilt work has been devalued in this way. It is difficult and time consuming to remove these added coats without affecting the original surface.

Woodturning is a two day course mainly concerned with sharpening techniques and the correct use of tools. There are a number of good books on woodturning but one thing they cannot do is demonstrate how to use the skew chisel and gouge, which are among the most difficult of tasks.

After the No 1 Preparation Course, the course on veneering, colouring and polishing is the most popular. In a few years' time, some timbers already rare may only be available in veneer form. That will greatly increase the demand for craftsmen with veneering skills. Fortunately, veneering does not require a lot of equipment and once you have the know-how it is fairly easy to do.

Many people think veneering is inferior to solid timber. In fact, if properly done, the opposite is true.

Methods of cleaning up by hand are performed by students and surfaces are prepared ready for colouring and, finally, polishing. The course can be split into a two day veneering or a two day polishing course or taken as a complete four day course. Other courses can be arranged to suit individual needs. However, it is important to remember that to become a proficient restorer takes a long time. After 43 years which started with the restoration of bomb damage furniture and wooden helicopter blades in the RAF, I realise that what I know is only a small proportion of what there is to know.

The Anselm Fraser school of antique furniture restoration.

Below is listed alphabetically addresses and telephone numbers of all Schools, Colleges and Training Centres that hold courses within the woodworking trade.

Aberdare College of Further Education	Cwmdare Road, Aberdare, Mid-Glamorgan CF44 8ST	Tel: 0685 873405
Aberdeen Technical College	Gallowgate, Aberdeen, Grampian AB9 1DN	Tel: 0224 640366
Accrington & Rossendale College	Sandy Lane, Accrington, Lancashire BB5 2AW	Tel: 0254 393521
Angus Technical College	Keptie Road, Arbroath, Angus DD11 3EA	Tel: 0241 72056
Anniesland College	Hatfield Drive, Glasgow G12 0YE	Tel: 041-357 3969
Antrim Technical College	Fountain Street, Antrim, Northern Ireland BT41 4AL	Tel: 08494 63916
Armagh College of Further Education	Lonsdale Street, Lisanally Lane, Armagh, Northern Ireland	Tel: 0861 522205
Arnold & Carlton College of Further Education	Digby Avenue, Mapperley, Nottingham, Nottinghamshire NG3 6DR	Tel: 0602 876503
Astra Training Services Ltd	Bristol Skillcentre, Gill Avenue, Fishponds, Bristol, Avon BS16 2QL	Tel: 0272 653241
Astra Training Services Ltd	Milton Keynes Skillcentre, Chesney Wold, Bleak Hall, Milton Keynes, Buckinghamshire MK6 1LX	Tel: 0908 670001
Astra Training Services Ltd	Slough Skillcentre, Walpole Road, Chippenham, Slough, Buckinghamshire SL1 6AU	Tel: 0628 605222
Astra Training Services Ltd	Peterborough Skillcentre, Saville Road, Westwood, Peterborough, Cambridgeshire PE3 6TQ	Tel: 0733 267242
Astra Training Services Ltd	Runcorn Skillcentre, Castle Rise, Runcorn, Cheshire WA7 5XR	Tel: 09285 65921
Astra Training Services Ltd	Billingham-on-Tees Skillcentre, Industrial Estate, Leeholme Road, Billingham-on-Tees, Cleveland TS23 3TE	Tel: 0642 560811
Astra Training Services Ltd	Wrexham Skillcentre, Bersham Road, Wrexham, Clwyd LL13 7HU	Tel: 0978 355555

SCHOOLS, COLLEGES & TRAINING CENTRES

Astra Training Services Ltd	Redruth Skillcentre, Wilson Way, Pool Industrial Estate, Redruth, Cornwall TS15 3SD	Tel: 0209 213231
Astra Training Services Ltd	Langley Moore Skillcentre, Littleburn Trading Estate, Langley Moore, Co Durham DH7 8HG	Tel: 091 3780601
Astra Training Services Ltd	Plymouth Skillcentre, Newnham Industrial Estate, Stronde Road, Plympton St Mary, Plymouth, Devon PL7 4BS	Tel: 0752 335921
Astra Training Services Ltd	Barking Skillcentre, 25 Thames Road, Barking, Essex IG11 0HR	Tel: 081-591 2662
Astra Training Services Ltd	Basildon Skillcentre, Bentalls, Cranes Farm Road, Basildon, Essex SS14 3BT	Tel: 0268 533225
Astra Training Services Ltd	Port Talbot Skillcentre, Cramic Way, Port Talbot, West Glamorgan SA13 1RY	Tel: 0639 871177
Astra Training Services Ltd	Gloucester Skillcentre, 117 Bristol Road, Gloucester, Gloucestershire GL1 5SP	Tel: 0452 27721
Astra Training Services Ltd	Gwent Skillcentre, Corporation Road, Newport, Gwent NP9 0YT	Tel: 0633 271160
Astra Training Services Ltd	Southampton Skillcentre, West Bay Road, Southampton, Hampshire SO9 3SH	Tel: 0703 228281
Astra Training Services Ltd	Scunthorpe Skillcentre, 7c Colin Road, Scunthorpe, South Humberside DN16 1TT	Tel: 0724 872238
Astra Training Services Ltd	Medway Skillcentre, Courteney Road, Gillingham, Kent ME8 0RY	Tel: 0634 360404
Astra Training Services Ltd	Accrington Skillcentre, Chamberlain Road, Accrington, Lancashire HU8 8HL	Tel: 0482 20738
Astra Training Services Ltd	Preston Skillcentre, 180 Longridge Road, Preston, Lancashire PR2 5AP	Tel: 0772 652021
Astra Training Services Ltd	Rochdale Skillcentre, Chichester Street, Rochdale, Lancashire OL16 2A6	Tel: 0706 341514

Astra Training Services Ltd	Wigan Skillcentre, Swan Lane, Hindley Green, Wigan, Lancashire WN2 4HD	Tel: 0942 56123
Astra Training Services Ltd	Leicester Skillcentre, Humberstone Lane, Leicester, Leicestershire LE4 7JW	Tel: 0533 769101
Astra Training Services Ltd	Trafford Park Skillcentre, Guinness Road, Trafford Park, Manchester M17 1SD	Tel: 061-872 6042
Astra Training Services Ltd	Enfield Skillcentre, Lockfield Avenue, Enfield, Middlesex EN3 7PX	Tel: 081-805 1365
Astra Training Services Ltd	Norwich Skillcentre, Mile Cross Road, Norwich, Norfolk NR2 4LR	Tel: 0603 429181
Astra Training Services Ltd	Nottingham Skillcentre, Lilac Grove, Beeston, Nottingham, Nottinghamshire NG9 1QY	Tel: 0602 221112
Astra Training Services Ltd	Lancing - West Sussex Skillcentre, Churchill Industrial Estate, Chartwell Road, Lancing, West Sussex BN15 8UB	Tel: 0903 764331
Astra Training Services Ltd	Tyneside Skillcentre, Green Lane, Felling, Gateshead, Tyne and Wear NE10 0LA	Tel: 091-469 4314
Astra Training Services Ltd	Handsworth Skillcentre, Middlemore Road, Handsworth, Birmingham, West Midlands B21 0BT	Tel: 021-554 5222
Astra Training Services Ltd	Coventry Skillcentre, Binns Close, Torrington Avenue, Coventry, West Midlands CV4 9TB	Tel: 0203 474544
Astra Training Services Ltd	Wolverhampton Skillcentre, Craddock Street, Whitmore Reans, Wolverhampton, West Midlands WV6 QJ	Tel: 0902 27173
Astra Training Services Ltd	Swindon Skillcentre, Faraday Road, Dorcan, Swindon, Wiltshire SN3 5HB	Tel: 0793 641671
Astra Training Centre Ltd	Sheffield Skillcentre, Richmond Park Road, Sheffield, South Yorkshire S13 8HT	Tel: 0742 446471

SCHOOLS, COLLEGES & TRAINING CENTRES

Astra Training Services Ltd	Bradford Skillcentre, Common Road, Low Moor, Bradford, West Yorkshire BD2 0SF	Tel: 0274 600911
Astra Training Services Ltd	Leeds Skillcentre, Parkside Lane, Leeds, West Yorkshire LS11 5SZ	Tel: 0532 704661
Athlone Regional Technical College	Dublin Road, Athlone, Co Westmeath, Eire	Tel: 0902 72647
Autotech Marine Training Ltd	Dominion Road, Wallisdown, Bournemouth, Dorset BH11 8LH	Tel: 0202 570341
Aylesbury College	Oxford Road, Aylesbury, Buckinghamshire HP21 8PD	Tel: 0296 34111
Ayr College	Dam Park, Ayr KA8 0EU	Tel: 0292 265184
Ballymena Technical College	Farm Lodge Avenue, Ballymena, County Antrim, Northern Ireland BT43 7DJ	Tel: 0266 652871
Ballynahinch College	Church Road, Ballynahinch, County Down, Northern Ireland BT24 8LP	Tel: 023 856 2369
Banbridge College of Further Education	Castlewellan Road, Banbridge, County Down, Northern Ireland BT32 4AY	Tel: 08206 62289
Banff & Buchan College of Further Education	Argyll Road, Fraserburgh, Aberdeenshire AB4 5RF	Tel: 03465 5777
Barking College of Technology	Dagenham Road, Romford, Essex RM7 OXU	Tel: 0708 766841
Barmulloch College	Rye Road, Glasgow G21 3JY	Tel: 041-558 9071
Barnsley College of Technology	Church Street, Barnsley, South Yorkshire S70 2AX	Tel: 0226 730191
Barrow College of Further Education	Howard Street, Barrow in Furness, Cumbria LA14 1NB	Tel: 0229 825017
Barry College of Further Education	Colcot Road, Barry, South Glamorgan CF6 8YJ	Tel: 0446 733251
Basford Hall College of Further Education	Stockhill Lane, Nottingham, Nottinghamshire NG6 0NB	Tel: 0602 704541
Basingstoke College of Technology	Worting Road, Basingstoke, Hampshire RG21 1TN	Tel: 0256 54141
BCS College of Building	24 Main Street, Bulwell, Nottingham, Nottinghamshire NG6 8QL	Tel: 0602 274921

Bedford College of Higher Education	Cauldwell Street, Bedford, Bedfordshire MK42 9AH	Tel: 0234 45151
Belfast College of Technology	College Square East, Belfast, Northern Ireland BT1 6DJ	Tel: 0232 327244
Bilston Community College	Westfield Road, Bilston, Wolverhampton, West Midlands WV14 6ER	Tel: 0902 42871
Birmingham Polytechnic	Perry Barr, Birmingham, West Midlands B42 2SU	Tel: 021-331 5000
Bishop Auckland Technical College	Woodhouse Lane, Bishop Auckland, Co. Durham DL14 6JZ	Tel: 0388 603052
BIYTE	14 Frederick Place, Bristol, Avon BS8 1AS	Tel: 0272 737281/ 736323
Blackburn College	Feilden Street, Blackburn, Lancashire BB2 1LH	Tel: 0254 55144
Blackpool & The Fylde College	Palatine Road, Blackpool, Lancashire FY2 0HB	Tel: 0253 52352
Bolton Metropolitan College	Manchester Road, Bolton, Lancashire BL2 1ER	Tel: 0204 31411
Borders College of Further Education	Thorniedean, Melrose Road, Galashiels TD1 2AF	Tel: 0896 57755
Boston College of Further Education	Rowley Road, Boston, Lincolnshire PE21 6JF	Tel: 0205 365701
Bournemouth & Poole College of Further Education	North Road, Poole, Dorset BH14 0LS	Tel: 0202 747600
Bradford & Ilkley Community College	Great Horton Road, Bradford, West Yorkshire BD7 1AY	Tel: 0274 753080
Braintree College of Further Education	Church Lane, Braintree, Essex CM7 5SN	Tel: 0376 21711
Bridgend College of Technology	Cowbridge Road, Bridgend, Mid-Glamorgan CF31 3DF	Tel: 0656 55588
Bridgwater College	Bath Road, Bridgwater, Somerset TA6 4PZ	Tel: 0278 455464
Brighton College of Technology	Pelham Street, Brighton, East Sussex BN1 4FA	Tel: 0273 667788
Bristol Polytechnic	Faculty of Art and Design, Clanage Road, Bower Ashton, Bristol, Avon BS3 2JU	Tel: 0272 660222
Brooklyn Technical College (Great Barr)	Aldridge Road, Great Barr, Birmingham, West Midlands B44 8NE	Tel: 021-360 3543

SCHOOLS, COLLEGES & TRAINING CENTRES

Brunel Technical College	Ashley Down, Bristol, Avon BS7 9BU	Tel: 0272 241241
Buckinghamshire College of Higher Education	Queen Alexandra Road, High Wycombe, Buckinghamshire HP11 2JZ	Tel: 0494 22141
Builders Training Association Ltd	Hunts Lane, Stratford, London E15	Tel: 081-519 8216
Builders Training Association Ltd	Kirkby Training Centre, South Boundary Road, Knowsley Industrial Park, Merseyside L33 7SF	Tel: 051-548 7587
Building Crafts Training School	153 Great Titchfield Street, London W1P 7FR	Tel: 071-636 0480
Burnley College	Shorey Bank, Ormerod Road, Burnley, Lancashire BB11 2RX	Tel: 0282 36111
Burton Upon Trent Technical College	Lichfield Street, Burton Upon Trent, Staffordshire DE14 3RL	Tel: 0283 45401
Cambridge Regional College	Newmarket Road, Cambridge, Cambridgeshire CB5 8EG	Tel: 0223 357545
Cambuslang College	Hamilton Road, Cambuslang, Glasgow G72 7NY	Tel: 041-641 6600
Canterbury College	New Dover Road, Canterbury, Kent CT1 3AJ	Tel: 0227 66081
Cardonald College of Further Education	690 Mosspark Drive, Glasgow G52 3AY	Tel: 041-883 6151/ 1119
Carlisle College	Victoria Place, Carlisle, Cumbria CA1 1HS	Tel: 0228 24464
Carmarthenshire College of Technology & Art	Ammanford Campus, Tir-y-dail, Ammanford, Dyfed SA18 3TA	Tel: 0269 591978
Carshalton College of Further Education	Nightingale Road, Carshalton, Surrey SM5 2EJ	Tel: 081-647 0021
Castlereagh College of Further Education	Montgomery Road, Belfast, Northern Ireland BT6 9JD	Tel: 0232 797144
Central Manchester College	Lower Hardman Street, Manchester, Gt Manchester M3 3ER	Tel: 061-831 7791
Ceredigion College of Further Education	Llanbadarn Campus, Llanbadarn Fawr, Dyfed SY23 2BP	Tel: 0970 4511
Chelmsford College of Further Education	Upper Moulsham Street, Chelmsford, Essex CM2 0JQ	Tel: 0245 265611
Chesterfield College of Technology & Arts	Infirmary Road, Chesterfield, Derbyshire S41 7NG	Tel: 0246 31212

Chichester College of Technology	Westgate Fields, Chichester, West Sussex PO19 1SB	Tel: 0243 786321
Chippenham Technical College	Cocklebury Road, Chippenham, Wiltshire SN15 3QD	Tel: 0249 444501
Cilestel Training Services	The Old Vicarage, School Lane, Heckingham, Norwich, Norfolk NR14 6QP	Tel: 0508 46289
City College	Abercrombie Campus, Clarence Street, Liverpool, Merseyside L1 4DB	Tel: 051-708 0423
City & East London College	Rochelle Street, Arnold Circus, London E2 7ES	Tel: 071-739 7123/ Fax: 071-588 9024
City & Guilds of London Art School	124 Kennington Park Road, London SE11 4DJ	Tel: 071-735 2306/ 5210
City of Bath Technical College	Avon Street, Bath, Avon BA1 1UP	Tel: 0225 312191
City of London Polytechnic	41-47 Commercial Road, London E1 1LA	Tel: 071-247 1953
Clackmannan College of Further Education	Branshill Road, Alloa, Clackmannanshire FK10 3BT	Tel: 0259 215121
Cleveland Technical College	Corporation Road, Redcar, Cleveland TS10 1EZ	Tel: 0642 473132
Clydebank College	Kilbowie Road, Clydebank, Dunbartonshire G81 2AA	Tel: 041-952 7771
Coalville Technical College	Bridge Road, Coalville, Leicester, Leicestershire LE6 2QR	Tel: 0530 36136
Colchester Institute	Sheepen Road, Colchester, Essex CO3 3LL	Tel: 0206 570271
Coleg Powys	Coleg Howell Harris, Penlan, Brecon, Powys LD3 9SR	Tel: 0874 5252
Coleraine Technical College	Union Street, Coleraine, Northern Ireland BT52 1QA	Tel: 0265 54717/8
Connemara West Centre	Letterfrack, Co Galway, Ireland	Tel: 095-41047/ 41044/ Fax: 095-41112
Cork Technical College	Rossa Avenue, Bishopstown, Cork, Eire	Tel: 010 353 21 545222
Cornwall College of Further & Higher Education	Redruth, Cornwall TR15 3RD	Tel: 0209 712911

Cornwall College	School of Yacht and Boat Building, Falmouth Marine Centre, Killigrew Street, Falmouth, Cornwall TR11 3QS	Tel: 0326 313326
Coventry Technical College	Butts, Coventry, West Midlands CV1 3GD	Tel: 0203 57221
Crawley College	College Road, Crawley, West Sussex RH10 1NR	Tel: 0293 612686
Croydon College	Fairfield, Croydon, Surrey CR9 1DX	Tel: 081-686 5700
Darlington College of Technology	Cleveland Avenue, Darlington, Co. Durham DL3 7BB	Tel: 0325 467651
Derby Tertiary College	Wilmorton, Derby, Derbyshire DE2 8UG	Tel: 0332 757570
Derwentside Tertiary College	Park Road, Consett, Co. Durham DH8 5EE	Tel: 0207 502906
Dewsbury College	Halifax Road, Dewsbury, West Yorkshire WF13 2AS	Tel: 0924 465916
Doncaster College	Construction & Minerals Engineering Division, School of Construction, Ellers Road, Bessacarr, Doncaster, South Yorkshire DN4 7BA	Tel: 0302 539446
Down College of Further Education	Downpatrick, County Down, Northern Ireland BT30 6ND	Tel: 0396 615815
Dublin College of Technology	Bolton Street, Dublin, Eire	Tel: 0001 727177
Dudley College of Technology	The Broadway, Dudley, West Midlands DY1 4AS	Tel: 0384 455433/ 53585
Dumfries & Galloway College of Technology	Heathhall, Dumfries DG1 3QZ	Tel: 0387 61261/ Fax: 0387 50006
Dun Laoghaire Community College	Cumberland Street, Dun Laoghaire, Co Dublin, Ireland	Tel: 001 809676
Dundalk Regional Technical College	Dublin Road, Dundalk, Eire	Tel: 010 353 42 34785
Dundee College of Further Education	Old Glamis Road, Dundee DD3 8LE	Tel: 0382 819021
Dungannon Further Education College	Circular Road, Dungannon, County Tyrone, Northern Ireland BT71 6BQ	Tel: 086 87 22323
Eastbourne College of Art & Technology	St Anne's Road, Eastbourne, East Sussex BN21 2HS	Tel: 0323 644711

East Devon College of Further Education	Bolham Road, Tiverton, Devon EX16 6SH	Tel: 0884 254247
East Hertfordshire College	Turnford, Broxbourne, Hertfordshire EN10 6AF	Tel: 0992 466451
Eastleigh College of Further Education	Chestnut Avenue, Eastleigh, Hampshire SO5 5HT	Tel: 0703 614444
East Surrey College	Gatton Point, Redhill, Surrey RH1 2JX	Tel: 0737 72611
East Yorkshire College of Further Education	St Mary's Walk, Bridlington, North Humberside YO16 5JW	Tel: 0262 672676
Ebbw Vale College of Further Education	Ebbw Vale, Gwent NP3 6LE	Tel: 0495 302083
Erith College of Technology	Tower Road, Belvedere, Kent DA17 6JA	Tel: 032 24 42331
Exeter College	Hele Road, Exeter, Devon EX4 4JS	Tel: 0392 53514
Falkirk College of Technology	Grangemouth Road, Falkirk, Central Region FK2 9AD	Tel: 0324 24981
Fermanagh College of Further Education	Fairview Avenue, Enniskillen, County Fermanagh, Northern Ireland BT74 6AE	Tel: 0365 322431
Fife College of Technology	St Brycedale Avenue, Kirkcaldy, Fife KY1 1EX	Tel: 0592 268591/7
Galway Regional Technical College	Dublin Road, Galway, Eire	Tel: 010 353 91 53161
Gateshead Tertiary College	Durham Road, Gateshead, Tyne and Wear NE9 5BN	Tel: 091-477 70524
Glasgow College of Building & Printing	60 North Hanover Street, Glasgow G1 2BP	Tel: 041-332 9969
Gloucestershire College of Art & Technology	Brunswick Campus, Brunswick Road, Gloucester, Gloucestershire GL1 1HU	Tel: 0452 426500
Grantham College of Further Education	Stonebridge Road, Grantham, Lincolnshire NG31 9AP	Tel: 0476 63141
Gt. Yarmouth College of Further Education	Southtown, Great Yarmouth, Norfolk NR31 0ED	Tel: 0493 655261
Grimsby College of Technology & Art	Nuns Corner, Grimsby, South Humberside DN34 5BQ	Tel: 0472 79292
Guernsey College of Further Education	Route des Coutanchez, St Peter Port, Guernsey	Tel: 0481 727121
Guildford College of Technology	Stoke Park, Guildford, Surrey GU1 1EZ	Tel: 0483 31251
Gwynedd Technical College	Bangor, Gwynedd LL57 2TP	Tel: 0248 370125

SCHOOLS, COLLEGES & TRAINING CENTRES

Hackney College	Keltan House, 89-115 Mare Street, London E8 4RG	Tel: 081-985 8484
Hall Green College	Cole Bank Road, Birmingham, West Midlands B28 8ES	Tel: 021-778 2311
Halton College of **Further Education**	Kingsway, Widnes, Cheshire WA8 7QQ	Tel: 051-423 1391
Hammersmith & West London **College**	40 Lime Grove, London W12	Tel: 081-743 3321
Harlow College	College Gate, The High, Harlow, Essex CM20 1LT	Tel: 0279 441288
Harrogate College of Art **& Technology**	Hornbeam Park, Hookstone Road, Harrogate, North Yorkshire HG2 8QT	Tel: 0423 879466
Hartlepool College of **Further Education**	Stockton Street, Hartlepool, Cleveland TS25 7NT	Tel: 0429 275453
Hastings College of Art **& Technology**	Archery Road, St Leonards on Sea, East Sussex TN38 0HX	Tel: 0424 423847
Hendon College of **Further Education**	Cornermead, Grahame Park Way, Grahame Park, London NW9 5KA	Tel: 081-200 8300
Herefordshire Technical College	Folly Lane, Hereford HR1 1LS	Tel: 0432 352235
Hertfordshire Centre for **Building Studies**	St Peter's Road, St Albans, Hertfordshire AL1 3RX	Tel: 0727 47074
Highbury College of Technology	Dovercourt Road, Cosham, Portsmouth, Hampshire PO6 2SA	Tel: 0705 383131
Highlands College	PO Box 142, St Saviour, Jersey	Tel: 0534 71800
Hinckley College of **Further Education**	London Road, Hinckley, Leicestershire LE10 1HQ	Tel: 0455 251222
Hopwood Hall Tertiary College	St Mary's Gate, Rochdale, Lancashire OL12 6RY	Tel: 0706 345346
Huddersfield Technical College	New North Road, Huddersfield, West Yorkshire HD1 5NN	Tel: 0484 36521
Hugh Baird College of Technology	Balliol Road, Bootle, Merseyside L20 7EW	Tel: 051-922 6704
Hull College of Further Education	Queen's Gardens, Hull, North Humberside HU1 3DG	Tel: 0482 29943
Huntingdonshire College	California Road, Huntingdon, Cambridgeshire PE18 7BL	Tel: 0480 52346

Inverness College of Further & Higher Education	3 Longman Road, Inverness IV1 1SA	Tel: 0463 236681
Isle College	Ramnoth Road, Wisbech, Cambridgeshire PE13 2JE	Tel: 0945 582561
Isle of Man College of Further Education	Homefield Road, Douglas, Isle of Man	Tel: 0624 23113
Isle of Wight College of Arts & Technology	Medina Way, Newport, Isle of Wight PO30 5TA	Tel: 0983 526631
Isle of Wight Industrial Group Training Scheme	6 Dodnor Lane, Dodnor Industrial Estate, Newport, Isle of Wight PO30 5XA	Tel: 0983 525583
Jacob Kramer College	Vernon Street, Leeds, West Yorkshire LS2 8PH	Tel: 0532 439931
James Watt College	Finnart Street, Greenock, Renfrewshire PA16 8HF	Tel: 0475 24433
Jewel & Esk Valley College	Newbattle Road, Dalkeith, Mid-Lothian EH22 3AE	031-663 1951
Keighley College	Cavendish Street, Keighley, West Yorkshire BD21 3DF	Tel: 0274 758555
Kendal College of Further Education	Milnthorpe Road, Kendal, Cumbria LA9 5AY	Tel: 0539 724313
Kent Training Centre Ltd	Honeywood Road, Whitfield, Dover, Kent CT16 3EH	Tel: 0304 825628
Kidderminster College of Further Education	Hoo Road, Kidderminster, Worcestershire DY10 1LX	Tel: 0562 820811
Kilkeel Technical College	Greencastle Street, Kilkeel, Newry, County Down, Northern Ireland BT34 4BH	Tel: 069 37 62582
Kingston Polytechnic	Penrhyn Road, Kingston upon Thames, Surrey KT1 2EE	Tel: 081-549 1366
Kirkwall Further Education Centre	Kirkwall Grammar School, Kirkwall, Orkney KW15 1JG	Tel: 0856 2102
Knowsley Community Centre	Cherryfield Drive, Kirkby, Merseyside L32 8SF	Tel: 051-443 4324
Lancaster & Morecambe College	Morecambe Road, Lancaster, Lancashire LA1 2TY	Tel: 0524 66215/ Fax: 0524 843078
Langley College	Station Road, Langley, Slough, Berkshire SL3 8BY	Tel: 0753 49222
Langside College	50 Prospecthill Road, Glasgow G42 9LB	Tel: 041-649 4991

SCHOOLS, COLLEGES & TRAINING CENTRES

Larne College of Further Education	32-34 Pound Street, Larne, County Antrim, Northern Ireland BT40 1SQ	Tel: 0574 72268
Lauder Technical College	Halbeath, Dunfermline, Fife KY11 5DY	Tel: 0383 726201
Leeds College of Building	North Street, Leeds, West Yorkshire LS2 7QT	Tel: 0532 430765
Leeds Polytechnic	Calverley Street, Leeds, West Yorkshire LS1 3HE	Tel: 0532 832600
Leek College of Further Education & School of Art	Stockwell Street, Leek, Staffordshire ST13 6DP	Tel: 0538 382506/ 384115
Leicester Polytechnic	PO Box 143, Leicester, Leicestershire LE1 9BH	Tel: 0533 551551
Leigh College	Wilkinson Street, Leigh, Lancashire WN7 4AH	Tel: 0942 608811
Lewes Tertiary College	Mountfield Road, Lewes, East Sussex BN7 2XH	Tel: 0273 483188
Lewisham College	Worsley Bridge Road, Lower Sydenham, London SE26 5BD	Tel: 081-650 8227
Lews Castle College	Stornoway, Isle of Lewis PA86 0XR	Tel: 0851 3311
Limavady Technical College	Limavady, County Londonderry, Northern Ireland BT49 0EX	Tel: 050 47 62334
Lisburn College of Further Education	Castle Street, Lisburn, County Antrim, Northern Ireland BT27 4SU	Tel: 084 6677225
Little Surrenden Workshops	Ashford Road, Bethersden, Nr Ashford, Kent TN26 3BG	Tel: 023 382 589
Loughborough College	Radmoor, Loughborough, Leicestershire LE11 3BT	Tel: 0509 215831
Lowestoft College	St Peter's Street, Lowestoft, Suffolk NR32 2NB	Tel: 0502 583521
Lurgan College of Further Education	Kitchen Hill, Lurgan, County Armagh, Northern Ireland BT66 6AZ	Tel: 076 22 6135
Luton College of Higher Education	Park Square, Luton, Bedfordshire LU1 3JU	Tel: 0582 34111
Magherafelt College of Further Education	22 Moneymore Road, Magherafelt, County Londonderry, Northern Ireland BT45 6AE	Tel: 0648 32462

Manchester Polytechnic	All Saints, Manchester, Gt Manchester M15 6BH	Tel: 061-228 6171
Marine & Commercial Training	Marine Training House, Harbour Road, Oulton Broad, Lowestoft, Suffolk NR32 3LZ	Tel: 0502 569663
Marine Training & Development	International Boatbuilding Centre, Harbour Road, Oulton Broad, Lowestoft, Suffolk NR32 3LZ	Tel: 0502 569663
Marine Builders Training Trust	Hazel Road, Woolston, Southampton, Hampshire SO2 7GB	Tel: 0703 446824
Meirionnydd College	Dolgellau, Gwynedd LL40 2YF	Tel: 0341 422827
Melton Mowbray College of Further Education	Asfordby Road, Melton Mowbray, Leicestershire LE13 0HJ	Tel: 0664 67431
Merthyr Tydfil Technical College	Ynysfach, Merthyr Tydfil, Mid-Glamorgan CF48 1AR	Tel: 0685 723663
Merton College	Morden Park, London Road, Morden, Surrey SM4 5QX	Tel: 081-640 3001
Mid-Cheshire College of Further Education	Hartford Campus, Northwich, Cheshire CW8 1LJ	Tel: 0606 75281/ 74344/74842
Mid-Cornwall College	Palace Road, St Austell, Cornwall PL25 4BW	Tel: 0726 67911
Middlesex Polytechnic	Trent Park, Cockfosters Road, Barnet, Hertfordshire EN4 0PT	Tel: 081-368 1299
Mid-Kent College of Higher & Further Education	Horsted, Maidstone Road, Chatham, Kent ME5 9UQ	Tel: 0634 44470
Mid-Warwickshire College of Further Education	Warwick New Road, Leamington Spa, Warwickshire CV32 5JE	Tel: 0926 311711
Montgomery College of Further Education	Llanidloes Road, Newtown, Powys SY16 1BE	Tel: 0686 622722
Moray College of Further Education	Hay Street, Elgin, Morayshire IV30 2NN	Tel: 0343 543425
Motherwell College	Dalzell Drive, Motherwell, Lanarkshire ML1 2DD	Tel: 0698 59641/7
NACRO	Hutchinson Street, Stockton-on-Tees, Cleveland	Tel: 0642 615554
Neath College	Dwr Y Felin Road, Neath, West Glamorgan SA10 7RF	Tel: 0639 634271
Nene College	Moulton Park, Northampton, Northamptonshire NN2 7AL	Tel: 0604 715000

Newark Technical College	Chauntry Park, Newark, Nottinghamshire NG24 1BP	Tel: 0636 705921
Newbury College of Further Education	Oxford Road, Newbury, Berkshire RG13 1PQ	Tel: 0635 42824
Newcastle College	Maple Terrace, Newcastle upon Tyne, Tyne & Wear NE4 7SA	Tel: 091-273 8866
Newcastle College of Further Education	Donard Street, Newcastle, County Down, Northern Ireland BT33 0AP	Tel: 039 67 22451
New College	Framwellgate Moor, Durham, Co. Durham DH1 5ES	Tel: 091 386 2421
Newham Community College	High Street South, London E6 4ER	Tel: 081-472 1480
Newport College of Further Education	Nash Road, Newport, Gwent NP6 2BR	Tel: 0633 274861
Newry Technical College	Patrick Street, Newry, County Down, Northern Ireland BT35 8DN	Tel: 0693 61071
New Technical College	Coleraine Road, Ballymoney, County Antrim, Northern Ireland BT53 6BT	Tel: 02656 62258/ 62339
Newtownabbey Technical College	Shore Road, Newtownabbey, County Antrim, Northern Ireland BT37 9RS	Tel: 0232 864331
Norfolk College of Arts & Technology	Tennyson Avenue, King's Lynn, Norfolk PE30 2QW	Tel: 0553 761144
Northbrook College of Design & Technology	Broadwater Road, Worthing, West Sussex BN14 8HJ	Tel: 0903 31445
North Cheshire College	Fearnhead, Warrington, Cheshire WA2 0DB	Tel: 0925 814343
North Devon College	Old Sticklepath Hill, Barnstaple, Devon EX31 2BQ	Tel: 0271 45291
North Down and Ards College of Further Education	Castle Park Road, Bangor, County Down, Northern Ireland BT20 4TF	Tel: 0247 271254/5
North East Derbyshire College of Further Education	Rectory Road, Clowne, Chesterfield, Derbyshire S43 4BQ	Tel: 0246 810332
North East London College	Park Road, Bonds Green, London N11 2QF	Tel: 081-888 7123
North East Surrey College of Technology	Reigate Road, Ewell, Surrey KT17 3DS	Tel: 081-394 1731

North East Wales Institute of Higher Education	Deeside, Connah's Quay, Clwyd CH5 4BR	Tel: 0244 817531
North Hertfordshire College	Cambridge Road, Hitchin, Hertfordshire SG4 0JD	Tel: 0462 422882
North Lincolnshire College	Gainsborough Centre, Morton Terrace, Gainsborough DN21 2SU	Tel: 0427 617471
North Lincolnshire College	Lincoln Site, Cathedral Street, Lincoln, Lincolnshire LN2 5HQ	Tel: 0522 510530
North Lindsey College	Kingsway, Scunthorpe, South Humberside DN17 1AJ	Tel: 0724 281111
North Nottinghamshire College of Further Education	Carlton Road, Worksop, Nottinghamshire S81 7HP	Tel: 0909 473561
North Oxfordshire Technical College & School of Art	Broughton Road, Banbury, Oxfordshire OX16 9QA	Tel: 0295 252221
North Tyneside College of Further Education	Embleton Avenue, Wallsend, Tyne and Wear NE28 9NJ	Tel: 091 262 4081
Northumberland College of Art & Technology	College Road, Ashington, Northumberland NE26 9RG	Tel: 0670 813248
North Warwickshire College of Technology & Art	Hinckley Road, Nuneaton, Warwickshire CV11 6BH	Tel: 0203 349321
North West College of Technology	Strand Road, Londonderry, Northern Ireland BT48 7BY	Tel: 0504 266711
North West Kent College of Technology	Miskin Road, Dartford, Kent DA1 2LU	Tel: 0322 225471
Norwich City College of Further & Higher Education	Ipswich Road, Norwich, Norfolk NR2 2LJ	Tel: 0603 660011
Oldham College of Technology	Rochdale Road, Oldham, Lancashire OL9 6AA	Tel: 061-624 5214
Omagh College of Further Education	Omagh, County Tyrone, Northern Ireland BT79 7AH	Tel: 0662 45433
Oswestry College	College Road, Oswestry, Shropshire SY11 2SA	Tel: 0691 653067
OTJ Training	198 Prescot Road, Aughton, Lancashire L39 5AG	Tel: 0695 421646
Oxford College of Further Education	Oxpens Road, Oxford, Oxfordshire OX1 1SA	Tel: 0865 245871
Parkwood College	Shirecliffe Road, Sheffield, South Yorkshire S5 8XZ	Tel: 0742 768301
Pembrokeshire Technical College	Merlins Bridge, Haverfordwest, Dyfed	Tel: 0437 765247

SCHOOLS, COLLEGES & TRAINING CENTRES

Percival Whitley College of Further Education	Francis Street, Halifax, West Yorkshire HX1 3UZ	Tel: 0422 358221
Perth College of Further Education	Brahan Estate, Creiff Road, Perth PH1 2NX	Tel: 0738 21171
Peterborough Regional College	Park Crescent, Peterborough, Cambridgeshire PE1 4DZ	Tel: 0733 67366
Plymouth College of Further Education	King's Road, Plymouth, Devon PL1 5QG	Tel: 0752 264786
Plymouth Community Boatyard	3 Richmond Walk, Plymouth, Devon PL1 4LL	Tel: 0752 509738
Pontypool College	Blaendare Road, Pontypool, Gwent NP4 5YE	Tel: 049 55 55141
Pontypridd Technical College	Ynys Terrace, Rhydyfelin, Pontypridd, Mid-Glamorgan CF37 5RN	Tel: 0443 400121
Portadown College of Further Education	26-44 Lurgan Road, Portadown, Craigavon, County Armagh, Northern Ireland BT63 5BL	Tel: 0762 337111
Ravensbourne College of Design & Communication	Walden Road, Chislehurst, Kent BR7 5SN	Tel: 081-468 7071
Reading College of Technology	Crescent Road, Reading, Berkshire RG1 5RQ	Tel: 0734 583501
Reid Kerr College	Renfrew Road, Paisley, Renfrewshire PA3 4DR	Tel: 041-889 4225
Rhondda College of Further Education	Llwynypia, Tonypandy, Rhondda, Mid-Glamorgan CF40 2TQ	Tel: 0443 432187
Richmond upon Thames College	Egerton Road, Twickenham, Middlesex TW2 7SJ	Tel: 081-892 6656
Rother Valley College of Further Education	Doe Quarry Lane, Dinnington, Sheffield, South Yorkshire S31 7NH	Tel: 0909 550550
Rotherham College of Art & Technology	Eastwood Lane, Rotherham, South Yorkshire S65 1EG	Tel: 0709 362111
Royal Academy of Dramatic Art	62-64 Gower Street, London WC1E 6ED	Tel: 071-636 7076
Royal Forest of Dean College	Cinderford, Gloucestershire GL14 2JY	Tel: 0594 22191/ 33416
Royal National College for Visually Handicapped	College Road, Hereford, Herefordshire HR1 1EB	Tel: 0432 265725
Royal National Institute for the Blind Colleges	224 Great Portland Street, London W1N 6AA	Tel: 071-388 1266

Rycotewood College	Priest End, Thame, Oxfordshire OX9 2AF	Tel: 084-421 2501
St. Helens College	Water Street, St Helens, Merseyside WA10 1PZ	Tel: 0744 33766
St. Loye's College	Fairfield House, Topsham Road, Exeter, Devon EX2 6EP	Tel: 0392 55428
Salford College of Further Education	The Crescent Campus, Windsor Building, Withington Street, Salford, Lancashire M6 5BG	Tel: 061-745 8520
Salisbury College of Technology	Southampton Road, Salisbury, Wiltshire SP1 2LW	Tel: 0722 23711
Sandwell College of Further & Higher Education	Woden Road South, Wednesbury, West Midlands WS10 0PE	Tel: 021-556 6000
Scarborough Technical College	Lady Edith's Drive, Scarborough, North Yorkshire YO12 5RN	Tel: 0723 372105
Selby Tertiary College	Abbot's Road, Selby, North Yorkshire YO8 8AT	Tel: 0757 702606
Shetland College of Further Education	Gressy Loan, Lerwick, Shetland ZE1 0BB	Tel: 0595 5514
Shrewsbury College of Art & Technology	London Road, Shrewsbury, Shropshire SY2 6PR	Tel: 0743 231544
Somerset College of Arts & Technology	Wellington Road, Taunton, Somerset TA1 5AX	Tel: 0823 83403
Somerset Training Centre	58 Salmon Parade, Bridgwater, Somerset TA6 5JT	Tel: 0278 428494
Southall College of Technology	Beaconsfield Road, Southall, Middlesex UB1 1DP	Tel: 081-574 3448
Southampton College of Higher Education	East Park Terrace, Southampton, Hampshire SO9 4WW	Tel: 0703 229381
Southampton Technical College	St Mary Street, Southampton, Hampshire SO9 4WX	Tel: 0703 635222
South Bristol College	Technology Division, Marksbury Centre, Bedminster, Bristol, Avon BS3 5JL	Tel: 0272 661105
South Cheshire College	Dane Bank Avenue, Crewe, Cheshire CW2 8AB	Tel: 0270 69133
South Devon College of Arts & Technology	Newton Road, Torquay, Devon TQ2 5BY	Tel: 0803 213242/ 217512
South East Derbyshire College	Field Road, Ilkeston, Derbyshire DE7 5RS	Tel: 0602 324212
Southend College of Technology	Carnarvon Road, Southend on Sea, Essex SS2 6LS	Tel: 0702 432205

SCHOOLS, COLLEGES & TRAINING CENTRES

South Fields College of **Further Education**	Aylestone Road, Leicester, Leicestershire LE2 7LW	Tel: 0533 541818
South Glamorgan Institute of **Higher Education**	Western Avenue, Llandaff, Cardiff, South Glamorgan CF5 2YB	Tel: 0222 551111
South Kent College of Technology	The Grange, Shorncliffe Road, Folkestone, Kent CT20 2NA	Tel: 0303 850061
South Mersey College	Riversdale Road, Liverpool, Merseyside L19 3QR	Tel: 051-427 1227
Southport College of Art **& Technology**	Mornington Road, Southport, Merseyside PR9 0TT	Tel: 0704 542411
South Tyneside College	St George's Avenue, South Shields, Tyne and Wear NE34 6ET	Tel: 091-456 0403
Stafford College	Earl Street, Stafford, Staffordshire ST16 2QR	Tel: 0785 223800
Stockport College of Further **& Higher Education**	Wellington Road South, Stockport, Cheshire SK1 3UQ	Tel: 061-480 7331
Stoke-on-Trent College	Stoke Road, Shelton, Stoke-on-Trent, Staffordshire ST4 2DG	Tel: 0782 208208
Stourbridge College of Technology **& Art**	Hagley Road, Stourbridge, West Midlands DY8 1LY	Tel: 038 43 78531
Stroud College	Stratford Road, Stroud, Gloucestershire GL5 4AH	Tel: 0453 763424
Suffolk College of Higher **& Further Education**	Rope Walk, Ipswich, Suffolk IP4 1LT	Tel: 0473 55885
Swindon College	Regent Circus Swindon, Wiltshire SN1 1PT	Tel: 0793 491591
Tameside College of Technology	Beaufort Road, Ashton under Lyne, Lancashire OL6 6NX	Tel: 061-330 6911
Telford College of Art **& Technology**	Haybridge Road, Wellington, Telford, Shropshire TF1 2NP	Tel: 0952 612505
Telford College of **Further Education**	Crewe Toll, Edinburgh EH4 2NZ	Tel: 031-332 2491
Thanet Technical College	Ramsgate Road, Broadstairs, Kent CT10 1PN	Tel: 0843 65111
Thomas Court Centre	26 Handbury Lane, Dublin, Ireland	Tel: 0001 531 772
Thurrock Technical College	Woodview, Grays, Essex RM16 4YR	Tel: 0375 391199
Thurso Technical College	Ormlie Road, Thurso, Caithness KW14 7EE	Tel: 0847 66161

TICC Skillcentres Ltd	Cumbria Skillcentre, Glasson Industrial Estate, Maryport, Cumbria CA15 8NY	Tel: 0900 812771
TICC Skillcentres Ltd	East Lancs Skillcentre, Eagle Street, Accrington, Lancashire BB5 1NS	Tel: 0254 395521
TICC Skillcentre Ltd	White House Road, Ipswich, Suffolk IP1 5NX	Tel: 0473 47464
Tile Hill College	Tile Hill Lane, Tile Hill, Coventry, West Midlands CV4 9SU	Tel: 0203 694200
Tottenham College of Technology	High Road, Tottenham, London N15 4RU	Tel: 081-802 3111
Tralee Regional Technical College	Clash, Tralee, County Kerry, Eire	Tel: 010 353 66 22319
Trent Polytechnic	Burton Street, Nottingham, Nottinghamshire NG1 4BU	Tel: 0602 418418
Tresham College	St Mary's Road, Kettering, Northamptonshire NN15 7BS	Tel: 0536 85353
Trowbridge College	College Road, Trowbridge, Wiltshire BA14 0ES	Tel: 0225 766241
Vauxhall College of Building & Further Education	Belmore Street, London SW8 2JY	Tel: 071-498 1234
Wakefield District College	Margaret Street, Wakefield, West Yorkshire WF1 2DH	Tel: 0924 370501
Walsall College of Technology	St Pauls Street, Walsall, West Midlands WS1 1XN	Tel: 0922 720824
Waltham Forest College	Forest Road, London E17 4JB	Tel: 081-527 2311
Waterford Regional Technical College	Cork Road, Waterford, Eire	Tel: 010 353 51 75934
Wearside College of Further Education	Sea View Road West, Grangetown, Sunderland, Tyne and Wear SR2 9LH	Tel: 091 5670794
West Cheshire College	Handbridge Centre, Eaton Road, Handbridge, Chester, Cheshire CH4 7ER	Tel: 0244 677677
West Cumbria College	Park Lane, Workington, Cumbria CA14 2RW	Tel: 0900 64331
West Dean College	West Dean, Chichester, West Sussex PO18 0QZ	Tel: 0243 63 301
West Glamorgan Institute of Higher Education	Mount Pleasant, Swansea, West Glamorgan SA1 6ED	Tel: 0792 469004

SCHOOLS, COLLEGES & TRAINING CENTRES

West Kent College of Further Education	Brook Street, Tonbridge, Kent TN9 2PW	Tel: 0732 358101
West Lothian College of Further Education	Marjoribanks Street, Bathgate, West Lothian EH48 1QJ	Tel: 0506 634300
West Nottinghamshire College of Further Education	Derby Road, Mansfield, Nottinghamshire NG18 5BH	Tel: 0623 27191
Weston Super Mare College of Further Education	Knightstone Road, Weston Super Mare, Avon BS23 2AL	Tel: 0934 621301
West Suffolk College of Further Education	Out Risbygate, Bury St Edmunds, Suffolk IP33 3RL	Tel: 0284 701301
Weymouth College	Cranford Avenue, Weymouth, Dorset DT4 7LQ	Tel: 030 57 761100
Wigan College of Technology	Parsons Walk, Wigan, Lancashire WN1 1RR	Tel: 0942 494911
Willesden College of Technology	Denzil Road, London NW10 2XD	Tel: 081-451 3411
Wimpey Craft Training Centre	Stockwood Road, Brislington, Bristol, Avon BS4 5LT	Tel: 0272 725280
Wimpey Craft Training Centre	High Street, Westend, Southampton, Hampshire SO3 3JJ	Tel: 0703 475361
Wirral Metropolitan College	Borough Road, Birkenhead, Wirral L42 9QD	Tel: 051-653 5555
Wolverhampton Polytechnic	Molineux Street, Wolverhampton, West Midlands WV1 1SB	Tel: 0902 313000
Worcester Technical College	Deansway, Worcester, Hereford and Worcester WR1 2JF	Tel: 0905 723383
W R Tuson College	St Vincent's Road, Fulwood, Preston, Lancashire PR2 4UR	Tel: 0772 53558
Yeovil College	Ilchester Road, Yeovil, Somerset BA21 3BA	Tel: 0935 23921
York College of Arts & Technology	Dringhouses, York, North Yorkshire YO2 1UA	Tel: 0904 704141
Ystrad Mynach College of Further Education	Twyn Road, Ystrad Mynach, Hengoed, Mid-Glamorgan CF8 7XR	Tel: 0443 816888

A County listing of educational establishments and training centres showing briefly courses held.

AVON

Astra Training Services Ltd (Bristol Skillcentre)
Carpentry and Joinery

BIYTE
Boatbuilding

Bristol Polytechnic
Three Dimensional Design (Wood/Metal/Plastics)

Brunel Technical College
Carpentry and Joinery
Furniture Making
Machine Woodworking

City of Bath Technical College
Carpentry and Joinery

South Bristol College
Boatbuilding

Weston Super Mare College of Further Education
Carpentry and Joinery

Wimpey Craft Training Centre
Carpentry and Joinery

BEDFORDSHIRE

Bedford College of Higher Education
Carpentry and Joinery
Machine Woodworking Safety

Luton College of Higher Education
Carpentry and Joinery
Shopfitting
Machine Woodworking

BERKSHIRE

Langley College
Carpentry and Joinery
French Polishing
Finishing

Newbury College of Further Education
Carpentry and Joinery

Reading College of Technology
Carpentry and Joinery
Machine Woodworking

BUCKINGHAMSHIRE

Astra Training Services Ltd (Milton Keynes Skillcentre)
Carpentry and Joinery

Astra Training Services Ltd (Slough Skillcentre)
Carpentry and Joinery

Aylesbury College
Carpentry and Joinery

Buckinghamshire College of Higher Education
Carpentry and Joinery
Furniture/Cabinet Making
Machine Woodworking

CAMBRIDGESHIRE

Astra Training Services Ltd (Peterborough Skillcentre)
Carpentry and Joinery

Cambridge Regional College
Carpentry and Joinery
Furniture Making
Musical Instruments
Finishing
Restoration

Huntingdonshire College
Carpentry and Joinery
Machine Woodworking

Isle College
Carpentry and Joinery
Furniture Making

Peterborough Regional College
Carpentry and Joinery

CHESHIRE

Astra Training Services Ltd (Runcorn Skillcentre)
Carpentry and Joinery

Halton College of Further Education
Carpentry and Joinery
Machine Woodworking

Mid-Cheshire College of Further Education
Carpentry and Joinery
Machine Woodworking

North Cheshire College
Carpentry and Joinery

South Cheshire College
Carpentry and Joinery

Stockport College of Further & Higher Education
Carpentry and Joinery

West Cheshire College
Carpentry and Joinery
Furniture Restoration

CLEVELAND

Astra Training Services Ltd (Billingham-on-Tees Skillcentre)
Carpentry and Joinery

Cleveland Technical College
Carpentry and Joinery
Machine Woodworking

Hartlepool College of Further Education
Carpentry and Joinery
Wood Machining

NACRO
Boatbuilding

CORNWALL
Astra Training Services Ltd (Redruth Skillcentre)
Carpentry and Joinery

Cornwall College of Further & Higher Education
Carpentry and Joinery

Cornwall College (Falmouth Marine Centre)
Furniture Making
Boat Building

Mid-Cornwall College
Carpentry and Joinery

CO DURHAM
Astra Training Services Ltd (Langley Moore Skillcentre)
Carpentry and Joinery

Bishop Auckland Technical College
Carpentry and Joinery

Darlington College of Technology
Carpentry and Joinery
Furniture Making
Machine Woodworking

Derwentside Tertiary College
Carpentry and Joinery

New College
Carpentry and Joinery

CUMBRIA
Barrow College of Further Education
Carpentry and Joinery

Carlisle College
Carpentry and Joinery
Wood Machining

Kendal College of Further Education
Carpentry and Joinery

TICC Skillcentres Ltd (Cumbria Skillcentre)
Carpentry and Joinery

West Cumbria College
Carpentry and Joinery

DERBYSHIRE
Chesterfield College of Technology & Arts
Carpentry and Joinery

Derby Tertiary College
Carpentry and Joinery

North East Derbyshire College of Further Education
Carpentry and Joinery

South East Derbyshire College
Carpentry and Joinery

DEVON
Astra Training Services Ltd (Plymouth Skillcentre)
Carpentry and Joinery

East Devon College of Further Education
Carpentry and Joinery

Exeter College
Carpentry and Joinery
Cabinet Making
Finishing
Wood Machining

North Devon College
Carpentry and Joinery
Machine Woodworking

Plymouth College of Further Education
Carpentry and Joinery
Machine Woodworking

Plymouth Community Boatyard
Boatbuilding

St. Loye's College
Carpentry and Joinery

South Devon College of Arts & Technology
Carpentry and Joinery
Shopfitting
French Polishing

DORSET
Autotech Marine Training Ltd.
Boatbuilding

Bournemouth & Poole College of Further Education
Carpentry and Joinery
Boat Building
Shopfitting
Furniture/Cabinet Making
French Polishing
Wood Machining
Fitted Furniture Installation

Weymouth College
Carpentry and Joinery

ESSEX
Astra Training Services Ltd (Barking Skillcentre)
Carpentry and Joinery

Astra Training Services Ltd (Basildon Skillcentre)
Carpentry and Joinery

Barking College of Technology
Carpentry and Joinery
Machine Woodworking

Braintree College of Further Education
Carpentry and Joinery

Chelmsford College of Further Education
Carpentry and Joinery

Colchester Institute
Carpentry and Joinery
Machine Woodworking

Harlow College
Carpentry and Joinery
Furniture Making

Southend College of Technology
Carpentry and Joinery
Shopfitting
Furniture
French Polishing
Finishing
Restoration

Thurrock Technical College
Carpentry and Joinery (+DIY)
Machine Woodworking
Furniture Restoration (DIY)

GLOUCESTERSHIRE

Astra Training Services Ltd (Gloucester Skillcentre)
Carpentry and Joinery

Gloucestershire College of Art & Technology
Carpentry and Joinery
Furniture Making
Machine Woodworking

Royal Forest of Dean College
Carpentry and Joinery

Stroud College
Carpentry and Joinery

GREATER MANCHESTER

Astra Training Services Ltd (Trafford Park Skillcentre)
Carpentry and Joinery

Central Manchester College
Carpentry and Joinery
Furniture Making
Machine Woodworking

Manchester Polytechnic
Three Dimensional Design (Wood/Metal/Ceramics)

HAMPSHIRE

Astra Training Services Ltd (Southampton Skillcentre)
Carpentry and Joinery
Machine Woodworking

Basingstoke College of Technology
Carpentry and Joinery

Eastleigh College of Further Education
Carpentry and Joinery

Highbury College of Technology
Carpentry and Joinery
Furniture Making
Machine Woodworking

Marine Builders Training Trust
Carpentry and Joinery
Boat Building
Furniture/Cabinet Making
Upholstery

Southampton College of Higher Education
Boatbuilding

Southampton Technical College
Carpentry and Joinery
Boat Building
Machine Woodworking
Wood Turning

Wimpey Craft Training Centre
Carpentry and Joinery

HEREFORDSHIRE

Herefordshire Technical College
Carpentry and Joinery
Furniture/Cabinet Making
French Polishing
Finishing
Restoration
Wood Carving
Wood Turning
Machine Woodworking

Royal National College for Visually Handicapped
Musical Instruments

HERTFORDSHIRE

East Hertfordshire College
Carpentry and Joinery

Hertfordshire Centre for Building Studies
Carpentry and Joinery
Furniture Making
Machine Woodworking

Middlesex Polytechnic
Three-Dimensional Design (Furniture and Related Products)

North Hertfordshire College
Carpentry and Joinery

HUMBERSIDE (SOUTH)

Astra Training Services Ltd (Scunthorpe Skillcentre)
Carpentry and Joinery

Grimsby College of Technology & Arts
Carpentry and Joinery

North Lindsey College
Carpentry and Joinery

HUMBERSIDE (NORTH)

East Yorkshire College of Further Education
Carpentry and Joinery
Machine Woodworking
Furniture Making

Hull College of Further Education
Carpentry and Joinery
Furniture/Cabinet Making
Machine Woodworking
Shop Fitting
French Polishing
Finishing (Wood and Metal)
Restoration
Wood Turning
Marquetry
Upholstery

ISLE OF MAN

Isle of Man College of Further Education
Carpentry and Joinery

ISLE OF WIGHT

Isle of Wight College of Arts & Technology
Carpentry and Joinery
Boat Building

Isle of Wight Industrial Group Training Scheme
Boatbuilding

KENT

Astra Training Services Ltd (Medway Skillcentre)
Carpentry and Joinery

Canterbury College of Technology
Carpentry and Joinery

Erith College of Technology
Carpentry and Joinery
Machine Woodworking

Kent Training Centre Ltd (Dover)
Carpentry and Joinery

Little Surrenden Workshops
Furniture Making
Restoration

Mid-Kent College of Higher & Further Education
Carpentry and Joinery
Furniture Making
Machine Woodworking
Wood Turning

North West Kent College of Technology
Carpentry and Joinery

Ravensbourne College of Design & Communication
Furniture Making

South Kent College of Technology
Carpentry and Joinery
Machine Woodworking
Furniture Making

Thanet Technical College
Carpentry and Joinery
Furniture Restoration
Wood Carving
Wood Machining

West Kent College of Further Education
Carpentry and Joinery
Furniture Making

LANCASHIRE

Accrington & Rossendale College
Carpentry and Joinery
Finishing
Restoration
Wood Turning

Astra Training Services Ltd (Accrington Skillcentre)
Carpentry and Joinery

Astra Training Services Ltd (Preston Skillcentre)
Carpentry and Joinery

Astra Training Services Ltd (Rochdale Skillcentre)
Carpentry and Joinery

Astra Training Services Ltd (Wigan Skillcentre)
Carpentry and Joinery
Machine Woodworking

Blackburn College
Carpentry and Joinery
Machine Woodworking

Blackpool & The Fylde College
Carpentry and Joinery

Bolton Metropolitan College
Carpentry and Joinery
Machine Woodworking

Burnley College
Carpentry and Joinery
Furniture Making

Hopwood Hall Tertiary College
Carpentry and Joinery

Lancaster & Morecambe College
Carpentry and Joinery

Leigh College
Carpentry and Joinery

Oldham College of Technology
Carpentry and Joinery
Furniture Making
Machine Woodworking

OTJ Training
Furniture Making

Salford College of Further Education
Carpentry and Joinery
Shopfitting

Tameside College of Technology
Carpentry and Joinery

TICC Skillcentres Ltd (East Lancs Skillcentre)
Carpentry and Joinery

Wigan College of Technology
Carpentry and Joinery

W R Tuson College
Carpentry and Joinery

LEICESTERSHIRE

Astra Training Services Ltd (Leicester Skillcentre)
Carpentry and Joinery

Coalville Technical College
Carpentry and Joinery

Hinckley College of Further Education
Carpentry and Joinery

Leicester Polytechnic
Three Dimensional Design (Furniture Related Products)

Loughborough College
Carpentry and Joinery
Furniture Making

Melton Mowbray College of Further Education
Carpentry and Joinery

South Fields College of Further Education
Carpentry and Joinery
Furniture Making
Machine Woodworking
Shopfitting

LINCOLNSHIRE

Boston College of Further Education
Carpentry and Joinery

Grantham College of Further Education
Carpentry and Joinery
Boat Building
Shopfitting
Furniture/Cabinet Making
Wood Carving
Machine Woodworking

North Lincolnshire College
Carpentry and Joinery
Machine Woodworking

LONDON

Builders Training Association Ltd
Carpentry and Joinery

Building Crafts Training School
Shopfitting
Wood Turning

City & East London College
Women only Workshop
Furniture Making (Women only)
Woodwork

City & Guilds London Art School
Carving and Gilding

City of London Polytechnic
Furniture Making

Hackney College
Carpentry and Joinery
Shop Fitting

Hammersmith & West London College
Carpentry and Joinery
Shopfitting
Wood Machining

Hendon College of Further Education
Carpentry and Joinery

Lewisham College
Carpentry and Joinery

Newham Community College
Carpentry and Joinery

North East London College
Carpentry and Joinery

Royal Academy of Dramatic Art
Stage Carpentry

Royal National Institute for the Blind Colleges
Picture Framing

Tottenham College of Technology
Carpentry and Joinery
Shopfitting
Furniture/Cabinet Making

Vauxhall College of Building & Further Education
Carpentry and Joinery
Machine Woodworking

Waltham Forest College
Carpentry and Joinery
Machine Woodworking

Willesden College of Technology
Carpentry and Joinery
Machine Woodworking

MERSEYSIDE

Builders Training Association Ltd (Kirkby Training Centre)
Carpentry and Joinery

City College
Furniture Making
Machine Woodworking

Hugh Baird College of Technology
Carpentry and Joinery

Knowsley Community College
Carpentry and Joinery

St. Helens College
Carpentry and Joinery
Furniture/Cabinet Making
Furniture Restoration
French Polishing
Wood Carving
Wood Turning

South Mersey College
Carpentry and Joinery

Southport College of Art & Technology
Carpentry and Joinery

Wirral Metropolitan College
Carpentry and Joinery
Boat Building

MIDDLESEX

Astra Training Services Ltd (Enfield Skillcentre)
Carpentry and Joinery

Richmond upon Thames College
Carpentry and Joinery

Southall College of Technology
Carpentry and Joinery

NORFOLK

Astra Training Services Ltd (Norwich Skillcentre)
Carpentry and Joinery

Cilestel Training Services
Boatbuilding

Gt. Yarmouth College of Further Education
Carpentry and Joinery

Norfolk College of Arts & Technology
Carpentry and Joinery
Machine Woodworking

Norwich City College of Further & Higher Education
Carpentry and Joinery
Furniture/Cabinet Making
Machine Woodworking

NORTHAMPTONSHIRE

Nene College
Carpentry and Joinery
Machine Woodworking

Tresham College
Carpentry and Joinery

NORTHUMBERLAND

Northumberland College of Art & Technology
Carpentry and Joinery

NOTTINGHAMSHIRE

Astra Training Services Ltd (Nottingham Skillcentre)
Carpentry and Joinery
Machine Woodworking

Arnold & Carlton College of Further Education
Carpentry and Joinery
Boat Building
Furniture Making

Basford Hall College of Further Education
Carpentry and Joinery
Furniture Making
Restoration
Timber Industry

BCS College of Building
Carpentry and Joinery

Newark Technical College
Carpentry and Joinery

North Nottinghamshire College of Further Education
Carpentry and Joinery

Trent Polytechnic
Furniture Design

West Nottinghamshire College of Further Education
Carpentry and Joinery

OXFORDSHIRE

North Oxfordshire Technical College & School of Art
Carpentry and Joinery

Oxford College of Further Education
Carpentry and Joinery
Machine Woodworking

Rycotewood College
Furniture/Cabinet Making
French Polishing
Finishing
Restoration
Wood Carving
Wood Turning

SHROPSHIRE

Oswestry College
Carpentry and Joinery
Wood Carving

Shrewsbury College of Art & Technology
Carpentry and Joinery
Furniture Making

Telford College of Art & Technology
Carpentry and Joinery

SOMERSET

Bridgwater College
Carpentry and Joinery
Furniture Making
Machine Woodworking
Toy Making
Pattern and Modelmaking

Somerset College of Arts & Technology
Carpentry and Joinery
Restoration
Wood Carving
Machine Woodworking

Somerset Training Centre
Carpentry and Joinery

Yeovil College
Carpentry and Joinery
Furniture Making

STAFFORDSHIRE

Burton Upon Trent Technical College
Carpentry and Joinery
Machine Woodworking

Leek College of Further Education & School of Art
Carpentry and Joinery
Wood Carving
Wood Turning

Stafford College
Carpentry and Joinery

Stoke-on-Trent College
Carpentry and Joinery
Shopfitting
Finishing - Staining and Graining
Wood Turning
Wood Machining

SUFFOLK

Lowestoft College
Carpentry and Joinery
Boat Building

Marine & Commercial Training
Boatbuilding

Marine Training & Development
Boatbuilding

Suffolk College of Higher & Further Education
Carpentry and Joinery
Furniture/Cabinet Making
Machine Woodworking

TICC Skillcentre Ltd
Carpentry and Joinery

West Suffolk College of Further Education
Carpentry and Joinery

SURREY

Carshalton College of Further Education
Carpentry and Joinery

Croydon College
Carpentry and Joinery
Machine Woodworking

East Surrey College
Carpentry and Joinery

Guildford College of Technology
Carpentry and Joinery

Kingston Polytechnic
Three Dimensional Design (Furniture Related Products)

Merton College
Musical Instruments

North East Surrey College of Technology
Carpentry and Joinery

SUSSEX (EAST)

Brighton College of Technology
Carpentry and Joinery
Furniture Making

Eastbourne College of Art & Technology
Carpentry and Joinery

Hastings College of Art & Technology
Carpentry and Joinery
Furniture Making

Lewes Tertiary College
Carpentry and Joinery
Shopfitting

SUSSEX (WEST)

Astra Training Services Ltd (Lancing -
West Sussex Skillcentre)
Carpentry and Joinery
Wood Machining

Chichester College of Technology
Carpentry and Joinery

Crawley College
Carpentry and Joinery
Shopfitting
Furniture/Cabinet Making
Machine Woodworking
Timber Technology

Northbrook College of Design & Technology
Carpentry and Joinery

West Dean College
Antique Furniture Restoration
Early Musical Instrument Making

TYNE AND WEAR

Astra Training Services Ltd (Tyneside Skillcentre)
Carpentry and Joinery

Gateshead Tertiary College
Carpentry and Joinery
Wood Turning
DIY Woodwork
Woodwork (for Students with special needs)

Newcastle College
Carpentry and Joinery
Furniture Making

North Tyneside College of Further Education
Carpentry and Joinery

South Tyneside College
Carpentry and Joinery
Boat Building

Wearside College of Further Education
Carpentry and Joinery
Shopfitting

WARWICKSHIRE

Mid-Warwickshire College of Further Education
Carpentry and Joinery
Furniture/Cabinet Making

North Warwickshire College of Technology & Art
Carpentry and Joinery

WEST MIDLANDS

Astra Training Services Ltd (Coventry Skillcentre)
Carpentry and Joinery

Astra Training Services Ltd (Handsworth
Skillcentre)
Carpentry and Joinery

Astra Training Services Ltd (Wolverhampton
Skillcentre)
Carpentry and Joinery

Bilston Community College
Carpentry and Joinery
Machine Woodworking

Birmingham Polytechnic
Cabinet Making and Upholstery
Three Dimensional Design (Furniture Related
Products)

Brooklyn Technical College (Great Barr)
Carpentry and Joinery
Machine Woodworking
Shopfitting

Coventry Technical College
Carpentry and Joinery
Machine Woodworking

Dudley College of Technology
Carpentry and Joinery

Hall Green College
Carpentry and Joinery

Sandwell College of Further & Higher Education
Carpentry and Joinery
Shopfitting
Furniture/Cabinet Making
French Polishing
Finishing
Restoration
Wood Turning

Stourbridge College of Technology & Art
Carpentry and Joinery

Tile Hill College
Boatbuilding

Walsall College of Technology
Carpentry and Joinery

Wolverhampton Polytechnic
Three Dimensional Design (Wood Metal Plastics)

WILTSHIRE

Astra Training Services Ltd (Swindon Skillcentre)
Carpentry and Joinery

Chippenham Technical College
Carpentry and Joinery
Furniture
Finishing
Restoration
Wood Turning

Salisbury College of Technology
Carpentry and Joinery
Machine Woodworking

Swindon College
Carpentry and Joinery
Wood Turning
Machine Woodworking

Trowbridge College
Carpentry and Joinery
Furniture Making

WORCESTERSHIRE

Kidderminster College of Further Education
Carpentry and Joinery
Boat Building

Worcester Technical College
Carpentry and Joinery
Machine Woodworking

YORKSHIRE (NORTH)

Harrogate College of Art & Technology
Carpentry and Joinery

Scarborough Technical College
Carpentry and Joinery

Selby Tertiary College
Carpentry and Joinery

York College of Arts & Technology
Carpentry and Joinery
Furniture Restoration

YORKSHIRE (SOUTH)

Astra Training Centre Ltd (Sheffield Skillcentre)
Carpentry and Joinery

Barnsley College of Technology
Carpentry and Joinery
Machine Woodworking

Doncaster College
Carpentry and Joinery
Shopfitting
Machine Woodworking

Parkwood College
Carpentry and Joinery
Furniture/Cabinet Making
French Polishing
Finishing
Machine Woodworking

Rother Valley College of Further Education
Carpentry and Joinery
Furniture Making

Rotherham College of Art & Technology
Carpentry and Joinery

YORKSHIRE (WEST)

Astra Training Services Ltd (Bradford Skillcentre)
Carpentry and Joinery

Astra Training Services Ltd (Leeds Skillcentre)
Carpentry and Joinery
Machine Woodworking

Bradford & Ilkley Community College
Carpentry and Joinery

Dewsbury College
Carpentry and Joinery

Huddersfield Technical College
Carpentry and Joinery
Furniture Making
Machine Woodworking

Jacob Kramer College
Furniture Making

Keighley College
Carpentry and Joinery
Machine Woodworking

Leeds College of Building
Carpentry and Joinery
Machine Woodworking
Shopfitting

Leeds Polytechnic
Three Dimensional Design (Furniture and Related Products)

Percival Whitley College of Further Education
Carpentry and Joinery
Machine Woodworking

Wakefield District College
Carpentry and Joinery

NORTHERN IRELAND

BELFAST

Belfast College of Technology
Carpentry and Joinery
Machine Woodworking

COLERAINE

Coleraine Technical College
Carpentry and Joinery

CO ANTRIM

Antrim Technical College
Carpentry and Joinery

Ballymena Technical College
Carpentry and Joinery
Machine Woodworking

Larne College of Further Education
Carpentry and Joinery

Lisburn College of Further Education
Carpentry and Joinery
French Polishing
Restoration
Wood Carving
Wood Turning

New Technical College
Carpentry and Joinery

Newtownabbey Technical College
Carpentry and Joinery

CO ARMARGH

Armagh College of Further Education
Carpentry and Joinery

Lurgan College of Further Education
Carpentry and Joinery
Furniture/Cabinet Making
Wood Carving
Wood Turning

Portadown College of Further Education
Carpentry and Joinery

Castlereagh College of Further Education
Carpentry and Joinery

CO DOWN

Ballynahinch College
Carpentry and Joinery
Machine Woodworking

Banbridge College of Further Education
Carpentry and Joinery

Down College of Further Education
Carpentry and Joinery
Machine Woodworking

Kilkeel Technical College
Carpentry and Joinery

Newcastle College of Further Education
Carpentry and Joinery

Newry Technical College
Carpentry and Joinery

North Down & Ards College of Further Education
Carpentry and Joinery

CO FERMANAGH

Fermanagh College of Further Education
Carpentry and Joinery

CO LONDONDERRY

Limavady Technical College
Carpentry and Joinery

Magherafelt College of Further Education
Carpentry and Joinery

North West College of Technology
Carpentry and Joinery
Machine Woodworking

CO TYRONE

Dungannon Further Education College
Carpentry and Joinery

Omagh College of Further Education
Carpentry and Joinery

SOUTHERN IRELAND

CORK

Cork Technical College
Carpentry and Joinery

DUBLIN

Dun Laoghaire Community College
Furniture Making

Dublin College of Technology
Carpentry and Joinery
Wood Machining
Furniture Making

Thomas Court Centre
Furniture Making

CO GALWAY

Connemara West Centre
Furniture/Cabinet Making

Galway Regional Technical College
Carpentry and Joinery
Furniture Making

CO KERRY

Tralee Regional Technical College
Carpentry and Joinery

CO KILDARE

Army Apprentice School
Carpentry and Joinery

CO LOUTH

Dundalk Regional Technical College
Carpentry and Joinery

CO WESTMEATH

Athlone Regional Technical College
Carpentry and Joinery

WATERFORD
Waterford Regional Technical College
Carpentry and Joinery

SCOTLAND
BORDERS
Borders College of Further Education
Carpentry and Joinery

CENTRAL
Clackmannan College of Further Education
Carpentry and Joinery

DUMFRIES & GALLOWAY
Dumfries & Galloway College of Technology
Carpentry and Joinery

Falkirk College of Technology
Carpentry and Joinery

FIFE
Fife College of Technology
Carpentry and Joinery
Shopfitting
Furniture/Cabinet Making
French Polishing
Finishing
Restoration
Wood Turning
Design

Lauder Technical College
Carpentry and Joinery

GRAMPIAN
Aberdeen Technical College
Carpentry and Joinery
Machine Woodworking

Banff & Buchan College of Further Education
Carpentry and Joinery

Moray College of Further Education
Carpentry and Joinery
Furniture/Cabinet Making
Musical Instruments
French Polishing
Finishing
Restoration

HIGHLAND
Inverness College of Further & Higher Education
Carpentry and Joinery

Thurso Technical College
Carpentry and Joinery

LOTHIAN
Jewel & Esk Valley College
Carpentry and Joinery

Telford College of Further Education
Carpentry and Joinery
Furniture/Upholstery

West Lothian College of Further Education
Carpentry and Joinery

STRATHCLYDE
Anniesland College
Carpentry and Joinery
Boat Building

Ayr College
Carpentry and Joinery

Barmulloch College
Carpentry and Joinery

Cambuslang College
Carpentry and Joinery

Cardonald College of Further Education
Carpentry and Joinery

Clydebank College
Carpentry and Joinery

Glasgow College of Building & Printing
Carpentry and Joinery
Shopfitting
Furniture/Cabinet Making
French Polishing
Finishing
Restoration

James Watt College
Carpentry and Joinery
Boat Building

Langside College
Carpentry and Joinery

Motherwell College
Carpentry and Joinery

Reid Kerr College
Carpentry and Joinery

TAYSIDE
Angus Technical College
Carpentry and Joinery

Dundee College of Further Education
Carpentry and Joinery
Wood Machining

Perth College of Further Education
Carpentry and Joinery

ORKNEY
Kirkwall Further Education Centre
Carpentry and Joinery

OUTER HEBRIDES
Lews Castle College
Carpentry and Joinery

SHETLAND
Shetland College of Further Education
Carpentry and Joinery

WALES
CLWYD
Astra Training Services Ltd (Wrexham Skillcentre)
Carpentry and Joinery

North East Wales Institute of Higher Education
Carpentry and Joinery
Machine Woodworking

DYFED
Carmarthenshire College of Technology & Art
Carpentry and Joinery

Ceredigion College of Further Education
Carpentry and Joinery

Pembrokeshire College
Carpentry and Joinery

GLAMORGAN (MID)
Aberdare College of Further Education
Carpentry and Joinery

Bridgend College of Technology
Carpentry and Joinery
Furniture/Cabinet Making

Merthyr Tydfil Technical College
Carpentry and Joinery
Furniture Making
Wood Turning

Pontypridd Technical College
Carpentry and Joinery

Rhondda College of Further Education
Carpentry and Joinery

Ystrad Mynach College of Further Education
Carpentry and Joinery
Machine Woodworking

GLAMORGAN (SOUTH)
Barry College of Further Education
Carpentry and Joinery
Shopfitting
Wood Turning

South Glamorgan Institute of Higher Education
Carpentry and Joinery
Machine Woodworking

GLAMORGAN (WEST)
Astra Training Services Ltd (Port Talbot Skillcentre)
Carpentry and Joinery

Neath College
Carpentry and Joinery
Machine Woodworking

West Glamorgan Institute of Higher Education
Carpentry and Joinery
Machine Woodworking

GWENT
Astra Training Services Ltd (Gwent Skillcentre)
Carpentry and Joinery

Ebbw Vale College of Further Education
Carpentry and Joinery

Newport College of Further Education
Carpentry and Joinery
Machine Woodworking
Shopfitting

Pontypool College
Carpentry and Joinery
Machine Woodworking

GWYNEDD
Gwynedd Technical College
Carpentry and Joinery

Meirionnydd College
Carpentry and Joinery

POWYS
Coleg Powys
Carpentry and Joinery

Montgomery College of Further Education
Carpentry and Joinery

GUERNSEY
Guernsey College of Further Education
Carpentry and Joinery
Boat Building

JERSEY
Highlands College
Carpentry and Joinery
Machine Woodworking

DIRECTORY OF COURSES

In this chapter are listed, in alphabetical order under the subjects covered, the names and addresses of State schools, colleges and Training Centres offering further education courses in the various branches of woodworking.

The courses covered are listed below together with the pages on which they appear. Where the majority of courses lead to a City and Guilds certificate, the relevant syllabuses are given in chapter 5.

CARPENTRY AND JOINERY

City and Guilds of London Institute Certificates:
585 Carpentry and Joinery Craft Certificate
585 Carpentry and Joinery Advanced Craft, Site Practice
585 Carpentry and Joinery Advanced Craft, Formwork
585 Carpentry and Joinery Advanced Craft, Purpose Made Joinery
585 Carpentry and Joinery Advanced Craft, Maintenance Work
585 Carpentry and Joinery Advanced Craft, (Subjects not specified)
6111 Basic Carpentry and Joinery Skills Test
CITB 'Off the Job' Carpentry and Joinery

Aberdare College of Further Education
Cwmdare Road, Aberdare,
Mid-Glamorgan CF44 8ST
(Tel: 0685 873405)

C&G 585 Carpentry and Joinery Craft — Day Release

Aberdeen Technical College
Gallowgate, Aberdeen,
Grampian AB9 1DN
(Tel: 0224 640366)

C&G 585 Advanced Craft, Site Practice — Day Release
C&G 585 Advanced Craft, Purpose Made Joinery — Day Release

Accrington & Rossendale College
Sandy Lane, Accrington,
Lancashire BB5 2AW
(Tel: 0254 393521)

C&G 585 Carpentry and Joinery Craft — Block Release/ Day Release
C&G 585 Advanced Craft, Purpose Made Joinery — Day Release

Angus Technical College
Keptie Road, Arbroath,
Angus DD11 3EA
(Tel: 0241 72056)

C&G 585 Advanced Craft, Purpose Made Joinery — Day Release
C&G 585 Advanced Craft, Site Practice — Day Release

Anniesland College
Hatfield Drive, Glasgow
G12 0YE
(Tel: 041-357 3969)

C&G 585 Advanced Craft, Site Practice — Day Release
C&G 585 Advanced Craft, Formwork — Day Release
C&G 585 Advanced Craft, Purpose Made Joinery — Day Release
C&G 585 Advanced Craft, Maintenance Work — Day Release

Antrim Technical College
Fountain Street, Antrim,
Northern Ireland BT41 4AL
(Tel: 08494 63916)

C&G 585 Carpentry and Joinery Craft — Day Release
C&G 585 Advanced Craft, Site Practice — Evening
C&G 585 Advanced Craft, Formwork — Evening
C&G 585 Advanced Craft, Purpose Made Joinery — Evening

CARPENTRY AND JOINERY

Armagh College of Further Education
Lonsdale Street, Lisanally Lane,
Armagh, Northern Ireland
(Tel: 0861 522205)

C&G 585 Carpentry and Joinery Craft — Full Time/ Day Release
C&G 585 Advanced Craft, Site Practice — Day Release
C&G 585 Advanced Craft, Purpose Made Joinery — Day Release/ Evening

Astra Training Services Ltd
Bristol Skillcentre,
Gill Avenue, Fishponds, Bristol,
Avon BS16 2QL
(Tel: 0272 653241)

C&G 585 Carpentry and Joinery Craft — Day Time

Astra Training Services Ltd
Milton Keynes Skillcentre,
Chesney Wold, Bleak Hall,
Milton Keynes,
Buckinghamshire MK6 1LX
(Tel: 0908 670001)

C&G 585 Carpentry and Joinery Craft — Day Time

Astra Training Services Ltd
Slough Skillcentre,
Walpole Road, Chippenham,
Slough, Buckinghamshire
SL1 6AU
(Tel: 0628 605222)

C&G 585 Carpentry and Joinery Craft — Day Time

Astra Training Services Ltd
Peterborough Skillcentre,
Saville Road, Westwood,
Peterborough, Cambridgeshire
PE3 6TQ
(Tel: 0733 267242)

C&G 585 Carpentry and Joinery Craft — Full Time

Astra Training Services Ltd
Runcorn Skillcentre,
Castle Rise, Runcorn,
Cheshire WA7 5XR
(Tel: 09285 65921)

C&G 585 Carpentry and Joinery Craft — Full Time

Astra Training Services Ltd
Billingham-on-Tees Skillcentre,
Industrial Estate, Leeholme Road,
Billingham-on-Tees, Cleveland
TS23 3TE
(Tel: 0642 560811)

C&G 585 Carpentry and Joinery Craft — Day Time

Astra Training Services Ltd
Wrexham Skillcentre,
Bersham Road, Wrexham,
Clwyd LL13 7HU
(Tel: 0978 355555)

C&G 585 Carpentry and Joinery Craft — Day Time

Astra Training Services Ltd
Redruth Skillcentre, Wilson Way,
Pool Industrial Estate, Redruth,
Cornwall TR15 3SD
(Tel: 0209 213231)

C&G 585 Carpentry and Joinery
Craft

- Day Time

Astra Training Services Ltd
Langley Moore Skillcentre,
Littleburn Trading Estate,
Langley Moore,
Co Durham DH7 8HG
(Tel: 091 3780601)

C&G 585 Carpentry and Joinery
Craft

- Day Time

Astra Training Services Ltd
Plymouth Skillcentre,
Newnham Industrial Estate,
Stronde Road, Plympton St Mary,
Plymouth, Devon PL7 4BS
(Tel: 0752 335921)

C&G 585 Carpentry and Joinery
Craft

- Day Time

Astra Training Services Ltd
Barking Skillcentre,
25 Thames Road, Barking,
Essex IG11 0HR
(Tel: 081-591 2662)

C&G 585 Carpentry and Joinery
Craft

- Day Time

Astra Training Services Ltd
Basildon Skillcentre,
Bentalls, Cranes Farm Road,
Basildon, Essex SS14 3BT
(Tel: 0268 533225)

C&G 585 Carpentry and Joinery
Craft

- Day Time

Astra Training Services Ltd
Port Talbot Skillcentre,
Cramic Way, Port Talbot,
West Glamorgan
SA13 1RY
(Tel: 0639 871177)

C&G 585 Carpentry and Joinery
Craft

- Full Time

Astra Training Services Ltd
Gloucester Skillcentre,
117 Bristol Road, Gloucester,
Gloucestershire GL1 5SP
(Tel: 0452 27721)

C&G 585 Carpentry and Joinery
Craft

- Day Time

Astra Training Services Ltd
Gwent Skillcentre,
Corporation Road, Newport,
Gwent NP9 0YT
(Tel: 0633 271160)

C&G 585 Carpentry and Joinery
Craft

- Day Time

CARPENTRY AND JOINERY

Astra Training Services Ltd Southampton Skillcentre, West Bay Road, Southampton, Hampshire SO9 3SH (Tel: 0703 228281)	C&G 585 Carpentry and Joinery Craft	- Day Time
Astra Training Services Ltd Scunthorpe Skillcentre, 7c Colin Road, Scunthorpe, South Humberside DN16 1TT (Tel: 0724 872238)	C&G 585 Carpentry and Joinery Craft	- Full Time
Astra Training Services Ltd Medway Skillcentre, Courteney Road, Gillingham, Kent ME8 0RY (Tel: 0634 360404)	C&G 585 Carpentry and Joinery Craft CITB 'Off the Job' Carpentry and Joinery	- Day Time - Full Time
Astra Training Services Ltd Accrington Skillcentre, Chamberlain Road, Accrington, Lancashire HU8 8HL (Tel: 0482 20738)	C&G 585 Carpentry and Joinery Craft	- Day Time
Astra Training Services Ltd Preston Skillcentre, 180 Longridge Road, Preston, Lancashire PR2 5AP (Tel: 0772 652021)	C&G 585 Carpentry and Joinery Craft	- Day Time
Astra Training Services Ltd Rochdale Skillcentre, Chichester Street, Rochdale, Lancashire OL16 2A6 (Tel: 0706 341514)	C&G 585 Carpentry and Joinery Craft	- Day Time
Astra Training Services Ltd Wigan Skillcentre, Swan Lane, Hindley Green, Wigan, Lancashire WN2 4HD (Tel: 0942 56123)	C&G 585 Carpentry and Joinery Craft	- Day Time
Astra Training Services Ltd Leicester Skillcentre, Humberstone Lane, Leicester, Leicestershire LE4 7JW (Tel: 0533 769101)	C&G 585 Carpentry and Joinery Craft	- Day Time
Astra Training Services Ltd Trafford Park Skillcentre, Guinness Road, Trafford Park, Manchester M17 1SD (Tel: 061-872 6042)	C&G 585 Carpentry and Joinery Craft	- Day Time

Astra Training Services Ltd
Enfield Skillcentre,
Lockfield Avenue, Enfield,
Middlesex EN3 7PX
(Tel: 081 805 1365)

C&G 585 Carpentry and Joinery
Craft

\- Day Time

Astra Training Services Ltd
Norwich Skillcentre,
Mile Cross Road,
Norwich, Norfolk NR2 4LR
(Tel: 0603 429181)

C&G 585 Carpentry and Joinery
Craft

\- Day Time

Astra Training Services Ltd
Nottingham Skillcentre,
Lilac Grove, Beeston, Nottingham,
Nottinghamshire NG9 1QY
(Tel: 0602 221112)

C&G 585 Carpentry and Joinery
Craft

\- Full Time

Astra Training Services Ltd
Lancing – West Sussex Skillcentre,
Churchill Industrial Estate,
Chartwell Road, Lancing,
West Sussex BN15 8UB
(Tel: 0903 764331)

C&G 585 Carpentry and Joinery
Craft

\- Day Time

Astra Training Services Ltd
Tyneside Skillcentre,
Green Lane, Felling, Gateshead,
Tyne and Wear NE10 0LA
(Tel: 091-469 4314)

C&G 585 Carpentry and Joinery
Craft

\- Day Time

Astra Training Services Ltd
Handsworth Skillcentre,
Middlemore Road, Handsworth,
Birmingham, West Midlands
B21 0BT
(Tel: 021-554 5222)

C&G 585 Carpentry and Joinery
Craft

\- Day Time

Astra Training Services
Coventry Skillcentre,
Binns Close, Torrington Avenue,
Coventry,
West Midlands CV4 9TB
(Tel: 0203 474544)

C&G 585 Carpentry and Joinery
Craft

\- Day Time

Astra Training Services Ltd
Wolverhampton Skillcentre,
Craddock Street, Whitmore Reans,
Wolverhampton, West Midlands
WV6 QJ
(Tel: 0902 27173)

C&G 585 Carpentry and Joinery
Craft

\- Day Time

DIRECTORY OF COURSES

CARPENTRY AND JOINERY

Astra Training Services Ltd Swindon Skillcentre, Faraday Road, Dorcan, Swindon, Wiltshire SN3 5HB (Tel: 0793 641671)	C&G 585 Carpentry and Joinery Craft	- Day Time
Astra Training Services Ltd Sheffield Skillcentre, Richmond Park Road, Sheffield, South Yorkshire S13 8HT (Tel: 0742 446471)	C&G 585 Carpentry and Joinery Craft	- Day Time
Astra Training Services Ltd Bradford Skillcentre, Common Road, Low Moor, Bradford, West Yorkshire BD12 0SF (Tel: 0274 600911)	C&G 585 Carpentry and Joinery Craft	- Full Time
Astra Training Services Ltd Leeds Skillcentre, Parkside Lane, Leeds, West Yorkshire LS11 5SZ (Tel: 0532 704661)	C&G 585 Carpentry and Joinery Craft	- Day Time
Athlone Regional Technical College Dublin Road, Athlone, Co Westmeath, Eire (Tel: 0902 72647)	C&G 585 Carpentry and Joinery Craft C&G 585 Advanced Craft, (Subjects not specified)	- Day Release - Day Release
Aylesbury College Oxford Road, Aylesbury, Buckinghamshire HP21 8PD (Tel: 0296 34111)	C&G 585 Carpentry and Joinery Craft	- Day Release/ Block Release
Ayr College Dam Park, Ayr KA8 0EU (Tel: 0292 265184)	C&G 585 Advanced Craft, Purpose Made Joinery	- Block Release
Ballymena Technical College Farm Lodge Avenue, Ballymena, County Antrim, Northern Ireland BT43 7DJ (Tel: 0266 652871)	C&G 585 Carpentry and Joinery Craft C&G 585 Advanced Craft, Site Practice	- Day Release/ Evening - Day Release/ Evening
Ballynahinch College Church Road, Ballynahinch, County Down, Northern Ireland BT24 8LP (Tel: 023 856 2369)	C&G 585 Carpentry and Joinery Craft C&G 585 Advanced Craft, Purpose Made Joinery	- Day Release/ Evening - Day Release/ Evening

CARPENTRY AND JOINERY

Banbridge College of Further Education
Castlewellan Road, Banbridge,
County Down, Northern Ireland
BT32 4AY
(Tel: 08206 62289)

C&G 585 Carpentry and Joinery Craft	- Day Release/ Evening
C&G 585 Advanced Craft, Purpose Made Joinery	- Day Release/ Evening

Banff & Buchan College of Further Education
Argyll Road, Fraserburgh,
Aberdeenshire AB4 5RF
(Tel: 03465 5777)

C&G 585 Advanced Craft, Purpose Made Joinery	- Day Release

Barking College of Technology
Dagenham Road, Romford,
Essex RM7 OXU
(Tel: 0708 766841)

C&G 585 Carpentry and Joinery Craft	- Day Release
C&G 585 Advanced Craft, Site Practice	- Day Release
C&G 585 Advanced Craft, Purpose Made Joinery	- Day Release

Barnsley College of Technology
Church Street, Barnsley,
South Yorkshire S70 2AX
(Tel: 0226 730191)

C&G 585 Carpentry and Joinery Craft	- Day Release
C&G 585 Advanced Craft, Site Practice	- Day Release
C&G 585 Advanced Craft, Purpose Made Joinery	- Day Release

Barrow College of Further Education
Howard Street, Barrow in Furness,
Cumbria LA14 1NB
(Tel: 0229 825017)

C&G 585 Carpentry and Joinery Craft	- Day Release
C&G 585 Advanced Craft, Purpose Made Joinery	- Day Release
CITB 'Off the Job' Carpentry and Joinery	- Full Time

Barry College of Further Education
Colcot Road, Barry,
South Glamorgan CF6 8YJ
(Tel: 0446 733251)

C&G 585 Carpentry and Joinery Craft	- Day Release
C&G 585 Advanced Craft, Purpose Made Joinery	- Day Release

Basford Hall College of Further Education
Stockhill Lane, Nottingham,
Nottinghamshire NG6 0NB
(Tel: 0602 704541)

C&G 585 Carpentry and Joinery Craft	- Day Release
C&G 585 Advanced Craft, Site Practice	- Day Release
C&G 585 Advanced Craft, Formwork	- Day Release
C&G 585 Advanced Craft, Purpose Made Joinery	- Day Release
C&G 585 Advanced Craft, Maintenance Work	- Day Release

CARPENTRY AND JOINERY

Basingstoke College of Technology
Worting Road, Basingstoke,
Hampshire RG21 1TN
(Tel: 0256 54141)

C&G 585 Carpentry and Joinery Craft — Block Release/ Day Release
C&G 585 Advanced Craft, Site Practice — Day Release

BCS College of Building
24 Main Street, Bulwell,
Nottingham, Nottinghamshire
NG6 8QL
(Tel: 0602 274921)

C&G 585 Carpentry and Joinery Craft — Day Time/ Evening

Bedford College of Higher Education
Cauldwell Street, Bedford,
Bedfordshire MK42 9AH
(Tel: 0234 45151)

C&G 585 Carpentry and Joinery Craft — Day Release
C&G 585 Advanced Craft, Site Practice — Day Release
C&G 585 Advanced Craft, Purpose Made Joinery — Day Release

Belfast College of Technology
College Square East, Belfast,
Northern Ireland BT1 6DJ
(Tel: 0232 327244)

C&G 585 Carpentry and Joinery Craft — Day Release
C&G 585 Advanced Craft, Site Practice — Day Release

Bilston Community College
Westfield Road, Bilston,
Wolverhampton, West Midlands,
WV14 6ER
(Tel: 0902 42871)

C&G 585 Carpentry and Joinery Craft — Day Release
C&G 585 Advanced Craft, Site Practice — Day Release
C&G 585 Advanced Craft, Purpose Made Joinery — Day Release

Bishop Auckland Technical College
Woodhouse Lane,
Bishop Auckland,
Co Durham DL14 6JZ
(Tel: 0388 603052)

C&G 585 Carpentry and Joinery Craft — Day Release
C&G 585 Advanced Craft, Site Practice — Day Release
C&G 585 Advanced Craft, Purpose Made Joinery — Day Release
YTS Carpentry and Joinery — Full Time

Blackburn College
Feilden Street, Blackburn,
Lancashire BB2 1LH
(Tel: 0254 55144)

C&G 585 Carpentry and Joinery Craft — Day Release
C&G 585 Advanced Craft, Purpose Made Joinery — Day Release

Blackpool & The Fylde College
Palatine Road, Blackpool,
Lancashire FY2 0HB
(Tel: 0253 52352)

C&G 585 Carpentry and Joinery Craft — Block Release/ Day Release
C&G 585 Advanced Craft, Purpose Made Joinery — Day Release

Bolton Metropolitan College
Manchester Road, Bolton,
Lancashire BL2 1ER
(Tel: 0204 31411)

C&G 585 Carpentry and Joinery Craft — Block Release/ Day Release
C&G 585 Advanced Craft, Site Practice — Block Release/ Day Release
C&G 585 Advanced Craft, Purpose Made Joinery — Day Release

CARPENTRY AND JOINERY

Borders College of Further Education Thorniedean, Melrose Road, Galashiels TD1 2AF (Tel: 0896 57755)	C&G 585 Carpentry and Joinery Craft	- Day Release
	C&G 585 Advanced Craft, (Subjects not specified)	- Day Release
Boston College of Further Education Rowley Road, Boston, Lincolnshire PE21 6JF (Tel: 0205 365701)	C&G 585 Carpentry and Joinery Craft	- Day Release
	C&G 585 Advanced Craft, Site Practice	- Day Release
Bournemouth & Poole College of Further Education North Road, Poole, Dorset BH14 0LS (Tel: 0202 747600)	C&G 585 Carpentry and Joinery Craft	- Block Release/ Day Release
	C&G 585 Advanced Craft, Site Practice	- Day Release/ Evening
	C&G 585 Advanced Craft, Purpose Made Joinery	- Day Release/ Evening
Bradford & Ilkley Community College Great Horton Road, Bradford, West Yorkshire BD7 1AY (Tel: 0274 753080)	C&G 585 Carpentry and Joinery Craft	- Day Release
	C&G 585 Advanced Craft, Site Practice	- Day Release
	C&G 585 Advanced Craft, Purpose Made Joinery	- Day Release
	CITB 'Off the Job' Carpentry and Joinery Craft	- Block Release
Braintree College of Further Education Church Lane, Braintree, Essex CM7 5SN (Tel: 0376 21711)	C&G 585 Carpentry and Joinery Craft	- Day Release/ Evening
Bridgend College of Technology Cowbridge Road, Bridgend, Mid-Glamorgan CF31 3DF (Tel: 0656 55588)	C&G 585 Carpentry and Joinery Craft	- Day Release
	C&G 585 Advanced Craft, Purpose Made Joinery	- Day Release
Bridgwater College Bath Road, Bridgwater, Somerset TA6 4PZ (Tel: 0278 455464)	C&G 585 Carpentry and Joinery Craft	- Day Release
	C&G 585 Advanced Craft, Site Practice	- Day Release
Brighton College of Technology Pelham Street, Brighton, East Sussex BN1 4FA (Tel: 0273 667788)	C&G 585 Carpentry and Joinery Craft	- Block Release
	C&G 585 Advanced Craft, Purpose Made Joinery	- Block Release
Brooklyn Technical College (Great Barr) Aldridge Road, Great Barr, Birmingham, West Midlands B44 8NE (Tel: 021-360 3543)	C&G 585 Carpentry and Joinery Craft	- Block Release/ Day Release
	C&G 585 Advanced Craft, Site Practice	- Day Release
	C&G 585 Advanced Craft, Purpose Made Joinery	- Day Release

CARPENTRY AND JOINERY

Brunel Technical College
Ashley Down, Bristol,
Avon BS7 9BU
(Tel: 0272 241241)

C&G 585 Carpentry and Joinery Craft — Full Time/ Block Release/ Day Release
C&G 585 Advanced Craft, Site Practice — Block Release/ Day Release
C&G 585 Advanced Craft, Purpose Made Joinery — Block Release/ Day Release

Buckinghamshire College of Higher Education
Queen Alexandra Road,
High Wycombe,
Buckinghamshire HP11 2JZ
(Tel: 0494 22141)

C&G 585 Carpentry and Joinery Craft — Day Release/ Evening
C&G 585 Advanced Craft, Site Practice — Day Release
C&G 585 Advanced Craft, Purpose Made Joinery — Day Release

Builders Training Association Ltd
Hunts Lane, Stratford,
London E15
(Tel: 081-519 8216)

C&G 585 Carpentry and Joinery Craft — Block Release

Builders Training Association Ltd
Kirkby Training Centre,
South Boundary Road,
Knowsley Industrial Park,
Merseyside L33 7SF
(Tel: 051-548 7587)

C&G 585 Carpentry and Joinery Craft — Day Time

Burnley College
Shorey Bank, Ormerod Road,
Burnley, Lancashire BB11 2RX
(Tel: 0282 36111)

C&G 585 Carpentry and Joinery Craft — Day Release
C&G 585 Advanced Craft, Purpose Made Joinery — Day Release/ Evening

Burton Upon Trent Technical College
Lichfield Street,
Burton Upon Trent,
Staffordshire DE14 3RL
(Tel: 0283 45401)

C&G 585 Carpentry and Joinery Craft — Block Release/ Day Release
C&G 585 Advanced Craft, Site Practice — Day Release
C&G 585 Advanced Craft, Purpose Made Joinery — Day Release

Cambridge Regional College
Newmarket Road, Cambridge,
Cambridgeshire CB5 8EG
(Tel: 0223 357545)

C&G 585 Carpentry and Joinery Craft — Day Release/ Evening
C&G 585 Advanced Craft, Purpose Made Joinery — Day Release
C&G 585 Advanced Craft, Joinery Site Practice — Day Release
CITB 'Off the Job' Carpentry and Joinery Craft — Block Release

Cambuslang College
Hamilton Road, Cambuslang,
Glasgow G72 7NY
(Tel: 041-641 6600)

C&G 585 Advanced Craft, Site Practice — Block Release/ Day Release/ Evening

CARPENTRY AND JOINERY

Canterbury College
New Dover Road, Canterbury,
Kent CT1 3AJ
(Tel: 0227 66081)

| C&G 585 Carpentry and Joinery Craft | - Day Release/ Block Release |
| C&G 585 Advanced Craft, Purpose Made Joinery | - Day Release |

Carlisle College
Victoria Place,
Carlisle, Cumbria CA1 1HS
(Tel: 0228 24464)

C&G 585 Carpentry and Joinery Craft	- Day Release
C&G 585 Advanced Craft, Site Practice	- Day Release
C&G 585 Advanced Craft, Purpose Made Joinery	- Day Release
CITB 'Off the Job' Carpentry and Joinery	- Day Release

Carmarthenshire College of Technology & Art
Ammanford Campus, Tir-y-dail,
Ammanford, Dyfed SA18 3TA
(Tel: 0269 591978)

| C&G 585 Carpentry and Joinery Craft | - Day Release |
| C&G 585 Advanced Craft, Site Practice | - Block Release |

Carshalton College of Further Education
Nightingale Road, Carshalton,
Surrey SM5 2EJ
(Tel: 081-647 0021)

| C&G 585 Carpentry and Joinery Craft | - Day Release |

Castlereagh College of Further Education
Montgomery Road, Belfast,
Northern Ireland BT6 9JD
(Tel: 0232 797144)

C&G 585 Carpentry and Joinery Craft	- Day Release
C&G 585 Advanced Craft, Site Practice	- Day Release
C&G 585 Advanced Craft, Purpose Made Joinery	- Day Release

Central Manchester College
Lower Hardman Street,
Manchester, Gt Manchester
M3 3ER
(Tel: 061-831 7791)

| C&G 585 Carpentry and Joinery Craft | - Block Release/ Day Release |
| C&G 585 Advanced Craft, Site Practice | - Day Release |

Ceredigion College of Further Education
Llanbadarn Campus,
Llanbadarn Fawr,
Dyfed SY23 2BP
(Tel: 0970 4511)

| C&G 585 Advanced Craft, Site Practice | - Block Release |

Chelmsford College of Further Education
Upper Moulsham Street,
Chelmsford, Essex CM2 0JQ
(Tel: 0245 265611)

C&G 585 Carpentry and Joinery Craft	- Day Release
C&G 585 Advanced Craft, (Subjects not specified)	- Day Release
CITB 'Off the Job' Carpentry and Joinery	- Block Release/ Full Time

CARPENTRY AND JOINERY

Chesterfield College of Technology & Arts
Infirmary Road, Chesterfield,
Derbyshire S41 7NG
(Tel: 0246 31212)

C&G 585 Carpentry and Joinery Craft	- Block Release/ Day Release
C&G 585 Advanced Craft, Site Practice	- Day Release
C&G 585 Advanced Craft, Purpose Made Joinery	- Day Release
CITB 'Off the Job' Carpentry and Joinery	- Block Release

Chichester College of Technology
Westgate Fields, Chichester,
West Sussex PO19 1SB
(Tel: 0243 786321)

C&G 585 Carpentry and Joinery Craft	- Block Release/ Day Release
C&G 585 Advanced Craft, Purpose Made Joinery	- Day Release
C&G 585 Advanced Craft, (Subjects not specified)	- Day Release

City of Bath Technical College
Avon Street, Bath,
Avon BA1 1UP
(Tel: 0225 312191)

C&G 585 Carpentry and Joinery Craft	- Full Time/ Block Release/ Day Release
C&G 585 Advanced Craft, Purpose Made Joinery	- Day Release

Cleveland Technical College
Corporation Road, Redcar,
Cleveland TS10 1EZ
(Tel: 0642 473132)

C&G 585 Carpentry and Joinery Craft	- Block Release/ Day Release
C&G 585 Advanced Craft, Site Practice	- Block Release/ Day Release
C&G 585 Advanced Craft, Formwork	- Block Release/ Day Release
C&G 585 Advanced Craft, Purpose Made Joinery	- Block Release/ Day Release
C&G 585 Advanced Craft, Maintenance Work	- Block Release/ Day Release

Clydebank College
Kilbowie Road, Clydebank,
Dunbartonshire G81 2AA
(Tel: 041-952 7771)

C&G 585 Advanced Craft, Site Practice	- Block Release

Coalville Technical College
Bridge Road, Coalville, Leicester,
Leicestershire LE6 2QR
(Tel: 0530 36136)

C&G 585 Carpentry and Joinery Craft	- Evening (Adults only)
C&G 585 Advanced Craft, Maintenance Work	- Evening (Adults only)

Colchester Institute
Sheepen Road, Colchester,
Essex CO3 3LL
(Tel: 0206 570271)

C&G 585 Carpentry and Joinery Craft	- Day Release
C&G 585 Advanced Craft, Site Practice	- Day Release
C&G 585 Advanced Craft, Purpose Made Joinery	- Day Release

CARPENTRY AND JOINERY

Coleg Powys Coleg Howell Harris, Penlan, Brecon, Powys LD3 9SR (Tel: 0874 5252)	C&G 585 Carpentry and Joinery Craft	- Block Release
	C&G 585 Advanced Craft, Site Practice	- Day Release
	C&G 585 Advanced Craft, Formwork	- Day Release
	C&G 585 Advanced Craft, Purpose Made Joinery	- Day Release
	C&G 585 Advanced Craft, Maintenance Work	- Day Release
Coleraine Technical College Union Street, Coleraine, Northern Ireland BT52 1QA (Tel: 0265 54717/8)	C&G 585 Carpentry and Joinery Craft	- Day Release
	C&G 585 Advanced Craft, Site Practice	- Block Release
	C&G 585 Advanced Craft, Formwork	- Day Release
	C&G 585 Advanced Craft, Purpose Made Joinery	- Day Release
	C&G 585 Advanced Craft, Maintenance Work	- Day Release
Cork Technical College Rossa Avenue, Bishopstown, Cork, Eire (Tel: 010 353 21 545222)	C&G 585 Carpentry and Joinery Craft	- Day Release
	C&G 585 Advanced Craft, (Subjects not specified)	- Day Release
Cornwall College of Further & **Higher Education** Redruth, Cornwall TR15 3RD (Tel: 0209 712911)	C&G 585 Carpentry and Joinery Craft	- Block Release
	C&G 585 Advanced Craft, Site Practice	- Block Release/ Day Release
	C&G 585 Advanced Craft, Purpose Made Joinery	- Block Release/ Day Release
Coventry Technical College Butts, Coventry, West Midlands CV1 3GD (Tel: 0203 57221)	C&G 585 Carpentry and Joinery Craft	- Day Release
	C&G 585 Advanced Craft, Site Practice	- Day Release
	C&G 585 Advanced Craft, Purpose Made Joinery	- Day Release
Crawley College College Road, Crawley, West Sussex RH10 1NR (Tel: 0293 612686)	C&G 585 Carpentry and Joinery Craft	- Day Release/ Block Release/ Evening
	C&G 585 Advanced Craft, Maintenance Work	- Block Release
Croydon College Fairfield, Croydon, Surrey CR9 1DX (Tel: 081-686 5700)	C&G 585 Carpentry and Joinery Craft	- Day Release/ Evening
	C&G 585 Advanced Craft, Purpose Made Joinery	- Day Release

CARPENTRY AND JOINERY

Darlington College of Technology
Cleveland Avenue, Darlington,
County Durham DL3 7BB
(Tel: 0325 467651)

C&G 585 Carpentry and Joinery Craft — Block Release/ Day Release
C&G 585 Advanced Craft, Site Practice — Day Release/ Evening
C&G 585 Advanced Craft, Purpose Made Joinery — Day Release/ Evening

Derby Tertiary College
Wilmorton, Derby,
Derbyshire DE2 8UG
(Tel: 0332 757570)

C&G 585 Carpentry and Joinery Craft — Block Release/ Day Release

Derwentside Tertiary College
Park Road, Consett,
Co Durham DH8 5EE
(Tel: 0207 502906)

C&G 585 Carpentry and Joinery Craft — Day Release

Dewsbury College
Halifax Road, Dewsbury,
West Yorkshire WF13 2AS
(Tel: 0924 465916)

C&G 585 Carpentry and Joinery Craft — Day Release
C&G 585 Advanced Craft, Purpose Made Joinery — Day Release

Doncaster College
Construction & Minerals
Engineering Division, School of
Construction, Ellers Road,
Bessacarr, Doncaster DN4 7BA
(Tel: 0302 539446)

C&G 585 Carpentry and Joinery Craft — Block Release/ Day Release
C&G 585 Advanced Craft, Site Practice — Block Release/ Day Release
C&G 585 Advanced Craft, Purpose Made Joinery — Block Release/ Day Release

Down College of Further Education
Downpatrick, County Down,
Northern Ireland BT30 6ND
(Tel: 0396 615815)

C&G 585 Carpentry and Joinery Craft — Day Release/ Evening
C&G 585 Advanced Craft, Site Practice — Block Release

Dublin College of Technology
Bolton Street, Dublin, Eire
(Tel: 0001 727177)

C&G 585 Carpentry and Joinery Craft — Day Release
C&G 585 Advanced Craft, (Subjects not specified) — Day Release

Dudley College of Technology
The Broadway, Dudley,
West Midlands DY1 4AS
(Tel: 0384 455433/53585)

C&G 585 Carpentry and Joinery Craft — Day Release/ Evening
C&G 585 Advanced Craft, Site Practice — Day Release/ Evening
C&G 585 Advanced Craft, Purpose Made Joinery — Day Release/ Evening

Dumfries & Galloway College of Technology
Heathhall, Dumfries DG1 3QZ
(Tel: 0387 61261/
Fax: 0387 50006)

C&G 585 Advanced Craft, Site Practice — Day Release/ Evening
CITB YTS Carpentry and Joinery — Block Release

Dundalk Regional Technical College
Dublin Road, Dundalk, Eire
(Tel: 010 353 42 34785)

C&G 585 Carpentry and Joinery Craft — Day Release
C&G 585 Advanced Craft, (Subjects not specified) — Day Release

Dundee College of Further Education	C&G 585 Advanced Craft, (Subjects not specified)	- Day Release
Old Glamis Road, Dundee DD3 8LE (Tel: 0382 819021)	CITB 'Off the Job' Carpentry and Joinery	- Day Release
Dungannon Further Education College	C&G 585 Carpentry and Joinery Craft	- Apprentice Training/ Day Release
Circular Road, Dungannon, County Tyrone, Northern Ireland BT71 6BQ (Tel: 086 87 22323)	C&G 585 Advanced Craft, Site Practice	- Day Release
Eastbourne College of Art & Technology	C&G 585 Carpentry and Joinery Craft	- Block Release/ Day Release/ Evening
St Anne's Road, Eastbourne, East Sussex BN21 2HS (Tel: 0323 644711)	C&G 585 Advanced Craft, Purpose Made Joinery	- Day Release/ Evening
East Devon College of Further Education	C&G 585 Carpentry and Joinery Craft	- Day Release
Bolham Road, Tiverton, Devon EX16 6SH (Tel: 0884 254247)	C&G 585 Advanced Craft, Site Practice	- Day Release
	C&G 585 Advanced Craft, Formwork	- Day Release
	C&G 585 Advanced Craft, Purpose Made Joinery	- Day Release
	C&G 585 Advanced Craft, Maintenance Work	- Day Release
	CITB 'Off the Job' Carpentry and Joinery	- Block Release
East Hertfordshire College	C&G 595 Carpentry and Joinery Craft	- Day Release
Turnford, Broxbourne, Hertfordshire EN10 6AF (Tel: 0992 466451)	Non-vocational Carpentry and Joinery	- Evening
Eastleigh College of Further Education	C&G 585 Carpentry and Joinery Craft	- Full Time/ Block Release
Chestnut Avenue, Eastleigh, Hampshire SO5 5HT (Tel: 0703 614444)	C&G 585 Advanced Craft, Site Practice	- Day Release
	C&G 585 Advanced Craft, Purpose Made Joinery	- Day Release
East Surrey College	C&G 585 Carpentry and Joinery Craft	- Block Release/ Day Release/ Evening
Gatton Point, Redhill, Surrey RH1 2JX (Tel: 0737 72611)	C&G 585 Advanced Craft, Site Practice	- Day Release
	C&G 585 Advanced Craft, Purpose Made Joinery	- Day Release
East Yorkshire College of Further Education	C&G 585 Carpentry and Joinery Craft	- Day Release
St Mary's Walk, Bridlington, North Humberside YO16 5JW (Tel: 0262 672676)	C&G 585 Advanced Craft, Site Practice	- Evening

CARPENTRY AND JOINERY

Erith College of Technology
Tower Road, Belvedere,
Kent DA17 6JA
(Tel: 032 24 42331)

C&G 585 Carpentry and Joinery Craft — Block Release/ Day Release/ Evening

C&G 585 Advanced Craft, Site Practice — Block Release/ Day Release/ Evening

C&G 585 Advanced Craft, Formwork — Block Release/ Day Release/ Evening

C&G 585 Advanced Craft, Purpose Made Joinery — Block Release/ Day Release/ Evening

Exeter College
Hele Road, Exeter,
Devon EX4 4JS
(Tel: 0392 53514)

C&G 585 Carpentry and Joinery Craft — Block Release

C&G 585 Advanced Craft, Purpose Made Joinery — Day Release

Falkirk College of Technology
Grangemouth Road, Falkirk,
Central Region FK2 9AD
(Tel: 0324 24981)

C&G 585 Advanced Craft, Site Practice — Day Release

C&G 585 Advanced Craft, Purpose Made Joinery — Day Release

Fermanagh College of Further Education
Fairview Avenue, Enniskillen,
County Fermanagh,
Northern Ireland BT74 6AE
(Tel: 0365 322431)

C&G 585 Carpentry and Joinery Craft — Day Release

C&G 585 Advanced Craft, Site Practice — Day Release

Fife College of Technology
St Brycedale Avenue, Kirkcaldy,
Fife KY1 1EX
(Tel: 0592 268591/7)

C&G 585 Advanced Craft, Site Practice — Block Release

C&G 585 Advanced Craft, Purpose Made Joinery — Block Release/ Day Release

Galway Regional Technical College
Dublin Road, Galway, Eire
(Tel: 010 353 91 53161)

C&G 585 Carpentry and Joinery Craft — Day Release

C&G 585 Advanced Craft, (Subjects not specified) — Day Release

Gateshead Tertiary College
Durham Road, Gateshead,
Tyne and Wear NE9 5BN
(Tel: 091 477 70524)

C&G 585 Carpentry and Joinery Craft — Day Release

C&G 585 Advanced Crafts, (Subjects not specified) — Day Release

Glasgow College of Building & Printing
60 North Hanover Street,
Glasgow G1 2BP
(Tel: 041-332 9969)

C&G 585 Advanced Craft, Site Practice — Block Release/ Day Release/ Evening

C&G 585 Advanced Craft, Purpose Made Joinery — Block Release/ Day Release/ Evening

Gloucestershire College of Art & Technology
Brunswick Campus,
Brunswick Road, Gloucester,
Gloucestershire GL1 1HU
(Tel: 0452 426500)

C&G 585 Carpentry and Joinery Craft — Day Release

C&G 585 Advanced Craft, Site Practice — Day Release

C&G 585 Advanced Craft, Purpose Made Joinery — Day Release

Grantham College of Further Education
Stonebridge Road, Grantham,
Lincolnshire NG31 9AP
(Tel: 0476 63141)

C&G 585 Carpentry and Joinery Craft — Day Release
C&G 585 Advanced Craft, Site Practice — Day Release
C&G 585 Advanced Craft, Purpose Made Joinery — Day Release

Gt. Yarmouth College of Further Education
Southtown, Great Yarmouth,
Norfolk NR31 0ED
(Tel: 0493 655261)

C&G 585 Carpentry and Joinery Craft — Block Release
C&G 585 Advanced Craft, (Subjects not specified) — Day Release

Grimsby College of Technology and Art
Nuns Corner, Grimsby,
South Humberside DN34 5BQ
(Tel: 0472 79292)

C&G 585 Carpentry and Joinery Craft — Day Release/ Block Release
C&G 585 Advanced Craft, Site Practice — Day Release
C&G 585 Advanced Craft, Purpose Made Joinery — Day Release

Guernsey College of Further Education
Route des Coutanchez,
St Peter Port, Guernsey
(Tel: 0481 727121)

C&G 585 Carpentry and Joinery Craft — Day Release
C&G 585 Advanced Craft, Site Practice — Day Release
C&G 585 Advanced Craft, Purpose Made Joinery — Day Release

Guildford College of Technology
Stoke Park, Guildford,
Surrey GU1 1EZ
(Tel: 0483 31251)

C&G 585 Carpentry and Joinery Craft — Day Release
C&G 585 Advanced Craft, Site Practice — Day Release
C&G 585 Advanced Craft, Purpose Made Joinery — Day Release

Gwynedd Technical College
Bangor, Gwynedd LL57 2TP
(Tel: 0248 370125)

C&G 585 Carpentry and Joinery Craft — Day Release
C&G 585 Advanced Craft, Site Practice — Block Release
C&G 585 Advanced Craft, Purpose Made Joinery — Day Release

Hackney College
Keltan House, 89-115 Mare Street,
London E8 4RG
(Tel: 081-985 8484)

C&G 585 Carpentry and Joinery Craft — Full Time/ Block Release/ Day Release/ Evening
C&G 585 Advanced Craft, Site Practice — Day Release/ Evening
C&G 585 Advanced Craft, Formwork — Day Release/ Evening
C&G 585 Advanced Craft, Purpose Made Joinery — Day Release/ Evening
C&G 585 Advanced Craft, Maintenance Work — Day Release

CARPENTRY AND JOINERY

Hall Green College
Cole Bank Road, Birmingham,
West Midlands B28 8ES
(Tel: 021-778 2311)

C&G 585 Carpentry and Joinery Craft	- Block Release/ Day Release
C&G 585 Advanced Craft, Site Practice	- Day Release
C&G 585 Advanced Craft, Purpose Made Joinery	- Day Release
C&G 585 Advanced Craft, Maintenance Work	- Day Release

Halton College of Further Education
Kingsway, Widnes,
Cheshire WA8 7QQ
(Tel: 051-423 1391)

| C&G 585 Carpentry and Joinery Craft | - Day Release |
| C&G 585 Advanced Craft, Purpose Made Joinery | - Day Release |

Hammersmith & West London College
40 Lime Grove, London W12
(Tel: 081 743 3321)

C&G 585 Carpentry and Joinery Craft	- Day Release
C&G 585 Advanced Craft, Site Practice	- Day Release
C&G 585 Advanced Craft, Purpose Made Joinery	- Day Release
C&G 585 Advanced Craft, Formwork	- Day Release
C&G 585 Advanced Craft, Maintenance	- Day Release
YTS 'Off the Job' Carpentry and Joinery Craft	- Full Time/ Block Release

Harlow College
College Gate, The High, Harlow,
Essex CM20 1LT
(Tel: 0279 441288)

| C&G 585 Carpentry and Joinery Craft | - Day Release |
| C&G 585 Advanced Craft, Site Practice | - Day Release |

Harrogate College of Art & Technology
Hornbeam Park, Hookstone Road,
Harrogate, North Yorkshire
HG2 8QT
(Tel: 0423 879466)

C&G 585 Carpentry and Joinery Craft	- Day Release
C&G 585 Advanced Craft, Purpose Made Joinery	- Day Release
CITB/YTS 'Off the Job' Carpentry and Joinery	- Block Release

Hartlepool College of Further Education
Stockton Street, Hartlepool,
Cleveland TS25 7NT
(Tel: 0429 275453)

| C&G 585 Carpentry and Joinery Craft | - Day Release/ Evening |
| C&G 585 Advanced Craft, Site Practice | - Block Release/ Day Release |

Hastings College of Art & Technology
Archery Road,
St Leonards on Sea,
East Sussex TN38 0HX
(Tel: 0424 423847)

C&G 585 Carpentry and Joinery Craft	- Full Time/ Day Release
C&G 585 Advanced Craft, Site Practice	- Day Release
C&G 585 Advanced Craft, Formwork	- Day Release
C&G 585 Advanced Craft, Purpose Made Joinery	- Day Release
C&G 585 Advanced Craft, Maintenance Work	- Day Release

CARPENTRY AND JOINERY

Hendon College of Further Education Cornermead, Grahame Park Way, Grahame Park, London NW9 5KA (Tel: 081-200 8300)	C&G 585 Carpentry and Joinery Craft	- Day Release
Herefordshire Technical College Folly Lane, Hereford HR1 1LS (Tel: 0432 352235)	C&G 585 Carpentry and Joinery Craft C&G 585 Advanced Craft, (Subject not specified)	- Day Release/ Evening - Day Release
Hertfordshire Centre for Building Studies St Peter's Road, St Albans, Hertfordshire AL1 3RX (Tel: 0727 47074)	C&G 585 Carpentry and Joinery Craft C&G 585 Advanced Craft, Site Practice C&G 585 Advanced Craft, Formwork C&G 585 Advanced Craft, Purpose Made Joinery	- Block Release/ Evening - Block Release - Block Release - Block Release
Highbury College of Technology Dovercourt Road, Cosham, Portsmouth, Hampshire PO6 2SA (Tel: 0705 383131)	C&G 585 Carpentry and Joinery Craft C&G 585 Advanced Craft, Site Practice C&G 585 Advanced Craft, Purpose Made Joinery	- Block Release - Block Release - Block Release
Highlands College PO Box 142, St Saviour, Jersey (Tel: 0534 71800)	C&G 585 Advanced Craft, Purpose Made Joinery	- Day Release
Hinckley College of Further Education London Road, Hinckley, Leicestershire LE10 1HQ (Tel: 0455 251222)	C&G 585 Carpentry and Joinery Craft C&G 585 Advanced Craft, Site Practice C&G 585 Advanced Craft, Purpose Made Joinery	- Day Release - Day Release - Day Release
Hopwood Hall Tertiary College St Mary's Gate, Rochdale, Lancashire OL12 6RY (Tel: 0706 345346)	C&G 585 Carpentry and Joinery Craft C&G 585 Advanced Craft, Purpose Made Joinery CITB 'Off the Job' Carpentry and Joinery	- Day Release - Day Release - Block Release
Huddersfield Technical College New North Road, Huddersfield, West Yorkshire HD1 5NN (Tel: 0484 36521)	C&G 585 Advanced Craft, Site Practice C&G 585 Advanced Craft, Formwork C&G 585 Advanced Craft, Purpose Made Joinery C&G 585 Advanced Craft, Maintenance Work	- Block Release/ Day Release/ Evening - Block Release/ Day Release/ Evening - Block Release/ Day Release/ Evening - Block Release/ Day Release

CARPENTRY AND JOINERY

Hugh Baird College of Technology
Balliol Road, Bootle,
Merseyside L20 7EW
(Tel: 051-922 6704)

C&G 585 Carpentry and Joinery Craft — Block Release/ Day Release
C&G 585 Advanced Craft, Purpose Made Joinery — Day Release

Hull College of Further Education
Queen's Gardens, Hull,
North Humberside HU1 3DG
(Tel: 0482 29943)

C&G 585 Carpentry and Joinery Craft — Block Release/ Day Release/ Evening
C&G 585 Advanced Craft, Purpose Made Joinery — Day Release/ Evenings

Huntingdonshire College
California Road, Huntingdon,
Cambridgeshire PE18 7BL
(Tel: 0480 52346)

C&G 585 Carpentry and Joinery Craft — Day Release
C&G 585 Advanced Craft, Site Practice — Day Release
C&G 585 Advanced Craft, Purpose Made Joinery — Day Release
C&G 585 Advanced Craft, Maintenance Work — Day Release
C&G 585 Carpentry and Joinery Craft for the Mature Student — Evening

Inverness College of Further & Higher Education
3 Longman Road, Inverness
IV1 1SA
(Tel: 0463 236681)

C&G 585 Carpentry and Joinery Craft — Block Release
C&G 585 Advanced Craft, Purpose Made Joinery — Block Release

Isle College
Ramnoth Road, Wisbech,
Cambridgeshire PE13 2JE
(Tel: 0945 582561)

C&G 585 Carpentry and Joinery Craft — Day Release
C&G 585 Advanced Craft, Purpose Made Joinery — Day Release

Isle of Man College of Further Education
Homefield Road, Douglas,
Isle of Man
(Tel: 0624 23113)

C&G 585 Carpentry and Joinery Craft — Day Release
C&G 585 Advanced Craft, Purpose Made Joinery — Day Release

Isle of Wight College of Arts & Technology
Medina Way, Newport,
Isle of Wight PO30 5TA
(Tel: 0983 526631)

C&G 585 Carpentry and Joinery Craft — Full Time/ Block Release
C&G 585 Advanced Craft, Site Practice — Day Release

James Watt College
Finnart Street, Greenock,
Renfrewshire PA16 8HF
(Tel: 0475 24433)

C&G 585 Advanced Craft, Site Practice — Day Release
C&G 585 Advanced Craft, Purpose Made Joinery — Day Release

Jewel & Esk Valley College Newbattle Road, Dalkeith, Mid-Lothian EH22 3AE (Tel: 031-663 1951)	C&G 585 Advanced Craft, Site Practice	- Block Release
	C&G 585 Advanced Craft, Maintenance Work	- Block Release
	CITB 'Off the Job' Carpentry and Joinery	- Full Time
	Apprentice Training - Carpentry and Joinery	- Block Release

Keighley College
Cavendish Street, Keighley,
West Yorkshire BD21 3DF
(Tel: 0274 758555)
	C&G 585 Carpentry and Joinery
	  Craft
		- Block Release/
		  Day Release

	C&G 585 Advanced Craft, (Subjects not specified)	- Day Release
Kendal College of Further Education Milnthorpe Road, Kendal, Cumbria LA9 5AY (Tel: 0539 724313)	C&G 585 Advanced Craft, Purpose Made Joinery	- Day Release
	C&G 585 Advanced Craft, (Subjects not specified)	- Day Release
Kent Training Centre Ltd Honeywood Road, Whitfield, Dover, Kent CT16 3EH (Tel: 0304 825628)	C&G 585 Carpentry and Joinery Craft	- Day Time
Kidderminster College of Further Education Hoo Road, Kidderminster, Worcestershire DY10 1LX (Tel: 0562 820811)	C&G 585 Carpentry and Joinery Craft	- Day Release
Kilkeel Technical College Greencastle Street, Kilkeel, Newry, County Down, Northern Ireland BT34 4BH (Tel: 069 37 62582)	C&G 585 Carpentry and Joinery Craft	- Evening
Knowsley Community College Cherryfield Drive, Kirkby, Merseyside L32 8SF (Tel: 051-443 4324)	C&G 585 Carpentry and Joinery Craft	- Day Release
	C&G 585 Advanced Craft, Purpose Made Joinery	- Day Release
Lancaster & Morecambe College Morecambe Road, Lancaster, Lancashire LA1 2TY (Tel: 0524 66215/ Fax: 0524 843078)	C&G 585 Carpentry and Joinery Craft	- Day Release
	C&G 585 Advanced Craft, Purpose Made Joinery	- Day Release

Langley College
Station Road, Langley, Slough,
Berkshire SL3 8BY
(Tel: 0753 49222)
	C&G 585 Carpentry and Joinery
	  Craft
		- Block Release/
		  Day Release

	C&G 585 Advanced Craft, Site Practice	- Day Release
	C&G 585 Advanced Craft, Purpose Made Joinery	- Day Release

CARPENTRY AND JOINERY

Larne College of Further Education
32-34 Pound Street, Larne,
County Antrim,
Northern Ireland
BT40 1SQ
(Tel: 0574 72268)
	C&G 585 Carpentry and Joinery
	  Craft
	C&G 585 Advanced Craft,
	  Purpose Made Joinery
		- Day Release
		
		- Day Release

Lauder Technical College
Halbeath, Dunfermline,
Fife KY11 5DY
(Tel: 0383 726201)
	C&G 585 Carpentry and Joinery
	  Craft
	C&G 585 Advanced Craft,
	  Site Practice
		- Day Release
		
		- Day Release/
		  Evening

Leeds College of Building
North Street, Leeds,
West Yorkshire LS2 7QT
(Tel: 0532 430765)
	C&G 585 Carpentry and Joinery
	  Craft
	C&G 585 Advanced Craft,
	  Site Practice
	C&G 585 Advanced Craft,
	  Purpose Made Joinery
		- Block Release/
		  Day Release
		- Block Release/
		  Day Release
		- Block Release/
		  Day Release

Leek College of Further Education & School of Art
Stockwell Street, Leek,
Staffordshire ST13 6DP
(Tel: 0538 382506/384115)
	C&G 585 Carpentry and Joinery
	  Craft
	C&G 585 Advanced Craft,
	  Purpose Made Joinery
		- Day Release
		
		- Day Release

Leigh College
Wilkinson Street, Leigh,
Lancashire WN7 4AH
(Tel: 0942 608811)
	C&G 585 Carpentry and Joinery
	  Craft
	C&G 585 Advanced Craft,
	  (Subjects not specified)
		- Full Time/
		  Day Release
		- Day Release

Lewes Tertiary College
Mountfield Road, Lewes,
East Sussex BN7 2XH
(Tel: 0273 483188)
	C&C 585 Carpentry and Joinery
	  Craft
	C&G 585 Advanced Craft,
	  (Subjects not Specified)
		- Day Release
		
		- Block Release

Lewisham College
Worsley Bridge Road,
Lower Sydenham,
London SE26 5BD
(Tel: 081-650 8227)
	C&G 585 Carpentry and Joinery
	  Craft
	C&G 585 Advanced Craft,
	  Site Practice
	C&G 585 Advanced Craft,
	  Purpose Made Joinery
		- Block Release/
		  Day Release
		- Block Release/
		  Day Release
		- Block Release

Lews Castle College Stornoway, Isle of Lewis PA86 0XR (Tel: 0851 3311)	C&G 585 Advanced Craft, Site Practice	- Block Release

Limavady Technical College
Limavady, County Londonderry,
Northern Ireland BT49 0EX
(Tel: 050 47 62334)
	C&G 585 Carpentry and Joinery
	  Craft
	C&G 585 Advanced Craft,
	  Site Practice
		- Day Release
		
		- Block Release

CARPENTRY AND JOINERY

Lisburn College of Further Education
Castle Street, Lisburn,
County Antrim,
Northern Ireland
BT27 4SU
(Tel: 084 6677225)

C&G 585 Carpentry and Joinery Craft — Day Release
C&G 585 Advanced Craft, Site Practice — Block Release/ Evening

Loughborough College
Radmoor, Loughborough,
Leicestershire LE11 3BT
(Tel: 0509 215831)

C&G 585 Carpentry and Joinery Craft — Day Release
C&G 585 Advanced Craft, Purpose Made Joinery — Day Release

Lowestoft College
St Peter's Street, Lowestoft,
Suffolk NR32 2NB
(Tel: 0502 583521)

C&G 585 Carpentry and Joinery Craft — Block Release
C&G 585 Advanced Craft, Site Practice — Day Release
C&G 585 Advanced Craft, Purpose Made Joinery — Day Release

Lurgan College of Further Education
Kitchen Hill, Lurgan,
County Armagh,
Northern Ireland
BT66 6AZ
(Tel: 076 22 6135)

C&G 585 Carpentry and Joinery Craft — Day Release

Luton College of Higher Education
Park Square, Luton,
Bedfordshire LU1 3JU
(Tel: 0582 34111)

C&G 585 Carpentry and Joinery Craft — Block Release/ Day Release
C&G 585 Advanced Craft, Site Practice — Day Release
C&G 585 Advanced Craft, Purpose Made Joinery — Block Release/ Day Release

Magherafelt College of Further Education
22 Moneymore Road,
Magherafelt,
County Londonderry,
Northern Ireland BT45 6AE
(Tel: 0648 32462)

C&G 585 Carpentry and Joinery Craft — Day Release
C&G 585 Advanced Craft, Purpose Made Joinery — Day Release

Meirionnydd College
Dolgellau, Gwynedd LL40 2YF
(Tel: 0341 422827)

C&G 585 Advanced Craft, Purpose Made Joinery — Day Release

Melton Mowbray College of Further Education
Asfordby Road, Melton Mowbray,
Leicestershire LE13 0HJ
(Tel: 0664 67431)

C&G 585 Carpentry and Joinery Craft — Day Release

CARPENTRY AND JOINERY

Merthyr Tydfil Technical College
Ynysfach, Merthyr Tydfil,
Mid-Glamorgan CF48 1AR
(Tel: 0685 723663)

C&G 585 Carpentry and Joinery Craft — Block Release/ Day Release
C&G 585 Advanced Craft, Site Practice — Block Release/ Day Release
C&G 585 Advanced Craft, Purpose Made Joinery — Block Release/ Day Release

Mid-Cheshire College of Further Education
Hartford Campus, Northwich,
Cheshire CW8 1LJ
(Tel: 0606 75281/74344/74842)

C&G 585 Carpentry and Joinery Craft — Day Release
C&G 585 Advanced Craft, Purpose Made Joinery — Day Release

Mid-Cornwall College
Palace Road, St Austell,
Cornwall PL25 4BW
(Tel: 0726 67911)

C&G 585 Carpentry and Joinery Craft — Day Release
C&G 585 Advanced Craft, Site Practice — Day Release
C&G 585 Advanced Craft, Purpose Made Joinery — Day Release

Mid-Kent College of Higher & Further Education
Horsted, Maidstone Road,
Chatham, Kent ME5 9UQ
(Tel: 0634 44470)

C&G 585 Carpentry and Joinery Craft — Day Release
C&G 585 Advanced Craft, Site Practice — Day Release
C&G 585 Advanced Craft, Purpose Made Joinery — Day Release

Mid-Warwickshire College of Further Education
Warwick New Road,
Leamington Spa,
Warwickshire CV32 5JE
(Tel: 0926 311711)

C&G 585 Carpentry and Joinery Craft — Day Release
C&G 585 Advanced Craft, Site Practice — Day Release
C&G 585 Advanced Craft, Purpose Made Joinery — Day Release

Montgomery College of Further Education
Llanidloes Road, Newtown,
Powys SY16 1BE
(Tel: 0686 622722)

C&G 585 Carpentry and Joinery Craft — Block Release/ Day Release
C&G 585 Advanced Craft, Purpose Made Joinery — Day Release

Moray College of Further Education
Hay Street, Elgin,
Morayshire IV30 2NN
(Tel: 0343 543425)

C&G 585 Advanced Craft, Purpose Made Joinery — Day Release

Neath College
Dwr Y Felin Road,
Neath,
West Glamorgan SA10 7RF
(Tel: 0639 634271)

C&G 585 Carpentry and Joinery Craft — Day Release/ Block Release
C&G 585 Advanced Craft, Site Practice — Day Release
C&G 585 Advanced Craft, Purpose Made Joinery — Day Release

Nene College
Moulton Park, Northampton,
Northamptonshire NN2 7AL
(Tel: 0604 715000)

C&G 585 Carpentry and Joinery Craft — Block Release/ Day Release
C&G 585 Advanced Craft, Purpose Made Joinery — Block Release/ Day Release

Newark Technical College Chauntry Park, Newark, Nottinghamshire NG24 1BP (Tel: 0636 705921)	C&G 585 Carpentry and Joinery Craft C&G 585 Advanced Craft, Purpose Made Joinery	- Full Time/ Day Release - Day Release
Newbury College of Further Education Oxford Road, Newbury, Berkshire RG13 1PQ (Tel: 0635 42824)	C&G 585 Carpentry and Joinery Craft C&G 585 Advanced Craft, (Subjects not specified) CITB 'Off the Job' Carpentry and Joinery	- Block Release - Block Release - Evening
Newcastle College Maple Terrace, Newcastle upon Tyne, Tyne & Wear NE4 7SA (Tel: 091-273 8866)	C&G 585 Carpentry and Joinery Craft C&G 585 Advanced Craft, Site Practice	- Block Release/ Day Release - Block Release/ Day Release
Newcastle College of Further Education Donard Street, Newcastle, County Down, Northern Ireland BT33 0AP (Tel: 039 67 22451)	C&G 585 Carpentry and Joinery Craft C&G 585 Advanced Craft, Site Practice	- Day Release - Block Release/ Evening
New College Framwellgate Moor, Durham, Co. Durham DH1 5ES (Tel: 091 386 2421)	C&G 585 Carpentry and Joinery Craft C&G 585 Advanced Craft, Site Practice C&G 585 Advanced Craft, Formwork	- Day Release - Day Release/ Evening - Day Release/ Evening
Newham Community College High Street South, London E6 4ER (Tel: 081-472 1480)	C&G 585 Carpentry and Joinery Craft C&G 585 Advanced Craft (Subjects not specified)	- Day Release/ Evening - Part Time Day/ Evenings
Newport College of Further Education Nash Road, Newport, Gwent NP6 2BR (Tel: 0633 274861)	C&G 585 Carpentry and Joinery Craft C&G 585 Advanced Craft, Site Practice C&G 585 Advanced Craft, Formwork C&G 585 Advanced Craft, Purpose Made Joinery	- Block Release/ Day Release - Block Release - Day Release - Day Release
Newry Technical College Patrick Street, Newry, County Down, Northern Ireland BT35 8DN (Tel: 0693 61071)	C&G 585 Carpentry and Joinery Craft C&G 585 Advanced Craft, (Subjects not specified)	- Day Release - Day Release

CARPENTRY AND JOINERY

New Technical College
Coleraine Road, Ballymoney,
County Antrim, Northern Ireland
BT53 6BT
(Tel: 02656 62258/62339)

C&G 585 Carpentry and Joinery
Craft

- Day Release

Newtownabbey Technical College
Shore Road, Newtownabbey,
County Antrim, Northern Ireland
BT37 9RS
(Tel: 0232 864331)

C&G 585 Carpentry and Joinery
Craft

- Day Release

C&G 585 Advanced Craft,
Site Practice

- Block Release/
Evening

C&G 585 Advanced Craft,
Formwork

- Day Release/
Evening

C&G 585 Advanced Craft,
Purpose Made Joinery

- Day Release/
Evening

C&G 585 Advanced Craft,
Maintenance Work

- Day Release

Norfolk College of Arts & Technology
Tennyson Avenue, King's Lynn,
Norfolk PE30 2QW
(Tel: 0553 761144)

C&G 585 Carpentry and Joinery
Craft

- Block Release/
Day Release

C&G 585 Advanced Craft,
Site Practice

- Block Release/
Day Release

Northbrook College of Design & Technology
Broadwater Road, Worthing,
West Sussex BN14 8HJ
(Tel: 0903 31445)

C&G 585 Carpentry and Joinery
Craft

- Day Release

C&G 585 Advanced Craft,
Site Practice

- Day Release

C&G 585 Advanced Craft,
Purpose Made Joinery

- Day Release

North Cheshire College
Fearnhead, Warrington,
Cheshire WA2 0DB
(Tel: 0925 814343)

C&G 585 Carpentry and Joinery
Craft

- Day Release

C&G 585 Advanced Craft
(Subjects not specified)

- Day Release

North Devon College
Old Sticklepath Hill, Barnstaple,
Devon EX31 2BQ
(Tel: 0271 45291)

C&G 585 Carpentry and Joinery
Craft

- Block Release

C&G 585 Advanced Craft,
Site Practice

- Day Release

C&G 585 Advanced Craft,
Purpose Made Joinery

- Block Release

North Down and Ards College of Further Education
Castle Park Road, Bangor,
County Down,
Northern Ireland BT20 4TF
(Tel: 0247 271254/5)

C&G 585 Carpentry and Joinery
Craft

- Day Release

C&G 585 Advanced Craft,
Purpose Made Joinery

- Day Release

North East Derbyshire College of Further Education
Rectory Road, Clowne,
Chesterfield,
Derbyshire S43 4BQ
(Tel: 0246 810332)

C&G 585 Carpentry and Joinery
Craft

- Day Release

North East London College Park Road, Bonds Green, London N11 2QF (Tel: 081-888 7123)	C&G 585 Carpentry and Joinery Craft	- Full Time/ Day Release
North East Surrey College of Technology Reigate Road, Ewell, Surrey KT17 3DS (Tel: 081-394 1731)	C&G 585 Carpentry and Joinery Craft C&G 585 Advanced Craft, Site Practice C&G 585 Advanced Craft, Purpose Made Joinery	- Day Release/ Evening - Block Release/ Day Release - Day Release/ Evening
North East Wales Institute of Higher Education Deeside, Connah's Quay, Clwyd CH5 4BR (Tel: 0244 817531)	C&G 585 Carpentry and Joinery Craft C&G 585 Advanced Craft, (Subjects not specified)	- Day Release - Day Release
North Hertfordshire College Cambridge Road, Hitchin, Hertfordshire SG4 0JD (Tel: 0462 422882)	C&G 585 Carpentry and Joinery Craft C&G 585 Advanced Craft (Subjects not specified)	- Day Release/ Evening - Day Release
North Lincolnshire College Gainsborough Centre, Morton Terrace, Gainsborough DN21 2SU (Tel: 0427 617471)	C&G 585 Carpentry and Joinery Craft C&G 585 Advanced Crafts, (Subjects not specified)	- Day Release/ Block Release - Day Release
North Lincolnshire College Lincoln Site, Cathedral Street, Lincoln, Lincolnshire LN2 5HQ (Tel: 0522 510530)	C&G 585 Carpentry and Joinery Craft C&G 585 Advanced Craft, Site Practice CITB 'Off the Job' Carpentry and Joinery	- Block Release/ Day Release/ Evening - Day Release - Block Release
North Lindsey College Kingsway, Scunthorpe, South Humberside DN17 1AJ (Tel: 0724 281111)	C&G 585 Carpentry and Joinery Craft C&G 585 Advanced Craft, Site Practice	- Day Release - Day Release
North Nottinghamshire College of Further Education Carlton Road, Worksop, Nottinghamshire S81 7HP (Tel: 0909 473561)	C&G 585 Carpentry and Joinery Craft C&G 585 Advanced Craft, Purpose Made Joinery	- Day Release - Day Release
North Oxfordshire Technical College & School of Art Broughton Road, Banbury, Oxfordshire OX16 9QA (Tel: 0295 252221)	C&G 585 Carpentry and Joinery Craft C&G 585 Advanced Craft, Site Practice C&G 585 Advanced Craft, Purpose Made Joinery	- Day Release - Day Release - Day Release

CARPENTRY AND JOINERY

North Tyneside College of Further Education
Embleton Avenue, Wallsend,
Tyne and Wear NE28 9NJ
(Tel: 091 262 4081)

C&G 585 Carpentry and Joinery Craft — Block Release

Northumberland College of Art & Technology
College Road, Ashington,
Northumberland NE26 9RG
(Tel: 0670 813248)

C&G 585 Carpentry and Joinery Craft — Day Release
C&G 585 Advanced Craft, Purpose Made Joinery — Day Release

North Warwickshire College of Technology & Art
Hinckley Road, Nuneaton,
Warwickshire CV11 6BH
(Tel: 0203 349321)

C&G 585 Carpentry and Joinery Craft — Day Release/ Evening
C&G 585 Advanced Craft, Site Practice — Day Release
C&G 585 Advanced Craft, Purpose Made Joinery — Day Release

North West College of Technology
Strand Road, Londonderry,
Northern Ireland BT48 7BY
(Tel: 0504 266711)

C&G 585 Carpentry and Joinery Craft — Day Release
C&G 585 Advanced Craft, Site Practice — Block Release

North West Kent College of Technology
Miskin Road, Dartford,
Kent DA1 2LU
(Tel: 0322 225471)

C&G 585 Carpentry and Joinery Craft — Day Release

Norwich City College of Further & Higher Education
Ipswich Road, Norwich,
Norfolk NR2 2LJ
(Tel: 0603 660011)

C&G 585 Carpentry and Joinery Craft — Block Release/ Day Release/ Evening
C&G 585 Advanced Craft, Site Practice — Block Release/ Evening

Oldham College of Technology
Rochdale Road, Oldham,
Lancashire OL9 6AA
(Tel: 061-624 5214)

C&G 585 Carpentry and Joinery Craft — Day Release
C&G 585 Advanced Craft, Site Practice — Day Release
C&G 585 Advanced Craft, Purpose Made Joinery — Day Release

Omagh College of Further Education
Omagh, County Tyrone,
Northern Ireland BT79 7AH
(Tel: 0662 45433)

C&G 585 Carpentry and Joinery Craft — Day Release
C&G 585 Advanced Craft, Site Practice — Day Release

Oswestry College
College Road, Oswestry,
Shropshire SY11 2SA
(Tel: 0691 653067)

C&G 585 Carpentry and Joinery Craft — Day Release

CARPENTRY AND JOINERY

Oxford College of Further Education
Oxpens Road, Oxford,
Oxfordshire OX1 1SA
(Tel: 0865 245871)

C&G 585 Carpentry and Joinery Craft — Block Release/ Day Release
C&G 585 Advanced Craft, Site Practice — Day Release
C&G 585 Advanced Craft, Purpose Made Joinery — Day Release

Parkwood College
Shirecliffe Road, Sheffield,
South Yorkshire S5 8XZ
(Tel: 0742 768301)

C&G 585 Carpentry and Joinery Craft — Full Time/ Block Release/ Day Release
C&G 585 Advanced Craft, Site Practice — Block Release/ Day Release
C&G 585 Advanced Craft, Purpose Made Joinery — Block Release/ Day Release

Pembrokeshire College
Merlins Bridge, Haverfordwest,
Dyfed
(Tel: 0437 765247)

C&G 585 Carpentry and Joinery Craft — Block Release
C&G 585 Advanced Craft, (Subjects not specified) — Day Release
CITB 'Off the Job' Carpentry and Joinery Craft — Day Release

Percival Whitley College of Further Education
Francis Street, Halifax,
West Yorkshire HX1 3UZ
(Tel: 0422 358221)

C&G 585 Advanced Craft, Purpose Made Joinery — Day Release

Perth College of Further Education
Brahan Estate, Creiff Road,
Perth PH1 2NX
(Tel: 0738 21171)

C&G 585 Advanced Craft, Site Practice — Block Release
C&G 585 Advanced Craft, Purpose Made Joinery — Day Release

Peterborough Regional College
Park Crescent, Peterborough,
Cambridgeshire PE1 4DZ
(Tel: 0733 67366)

C&G 585 Carpentry and Joinery Craft — Day Release
C&G 585 Advanced Craft, Site Practice — Day Release
C&G 585 Advanced Craft, Purpose Made Joinery — Day Release

Plymouth College of Further Education
King's Road, Plymouth,
Devon PL1 5QG
(Tel: 0752 264786)

C&G 585 Carpentry and Joinery Craft — Block Release/ Day Release/ Evening
C&G 585 Advanced Craft, Site Practice — Block Release/ Day Release/ Evening

Pontypool College
Blaendare Road, Pontypool,
Gwent NP4 5YE
(Tel: 049 55 55141)

C&G 585 Carpentry and Joinery Craft — Full Time/ Day Release/ Evening
C&G 585 Advanced Craft, Site Practice — Block Release
C&G 585 Advanced Craft, Purpose Made Joinery — Day Release

DIRECTORY OF COURSES

CARPENTRY AND JOINERY

Pontypridd Technical College
Ynys Terrace, Rhydyfelin,
Pontypridd, Mid-Glamorgan
CF37 5RN
(Tel: 0443 400121)

C&G 585 Carpentry and Joinery Craft — Day Release/ Evening

C&G 585 Advanced Craft, Site Practice — Block Release/ Day Release/ Evening

C&G 585 Advanced Craft, Purpose Made Joinery — Day Release/ Evening

Portadown College of Further Education
26-44 Lurgan Road, Portadown,
Craigavon, County Armagh,
Northern Ireland BT63 5BL
(Tel: 0762 337111)

C&G 585 Carpentry and Joinery Craft — Day Release

C&G 585 Advanced Craft, Purpose Made Joinery — Day Release

Reading College of Technology
Crescent Road, Reading,
Berkshire RG1 5RQ
(Tel: 0734 583501)

C&G 585 Carpentry and Joinery Craft — Block Release/ Day Release

C&G 585 Advanced Craft, Site Practice — Day Release

C&G 585 Advanced Craft, Purpose Made Joinery — Day Release

Reid Kerr College
Renfrew Road, Paisley,
Renfrewshire PA3 4DR
(Tel: 041-889 4225)

C&G 585 Advanced Craft, Purpose Made Joinery — Block Release

Rhondda College of Further Education
Llwynypia, Tonypandy, Rhondda,
Mid-Glamorgan CF40 2TQ
(Tel: 0443 432187)

C&G 585 Carpentry and Joinery Craft — Day Release

C&G 585 Advanced Craft, Site Practice — Block Release

C&G 585 Advanced Craft, Purpose Made Joinery — Day Release

Richmond upon Thames College
Egerton Road, Twickenham,
Middlesex TW2 7SJ
(Tel: 081-892 6656)

C&G 585 Carpentry and Joinery Craft — Day Release

C&G 585 Advanced Craft, Site Practice — Day Release

C&G 585 Advanced Craft, Purpose Made Joinery — Day Release

Rother Valley College of Further Education
Doe Quarry Lane, Dinnington,
Sheffield, South Yorkshire
S31 7NH
(Tel: 0909 550550)

C&G 585 Carpentry and Joinery Craft — Day Release

Rotherham College of Art & Technology
Eastwood Lane, Rotherham,
South Yorkshire S65 1EG
(Tel: 0709 362111)

C&G 585 Carpentry and Joinery Craft — Day Release

C&G 585 Advanced Craft, Site Practice — Day Release

C&G 585 Advanced Craft, Purpose Made Joinery — Day Release

CARPENTRY AND JOINERY

Royal Forest of Dean College Cinderford, Gloucestershire GL14 2JY (Tel: 0594 22191/33416)	C&G 585 Carpentry and Joinery Craft CITB 'Off the Job' Carpentry and Joinery	- Block Release/ Day Release - Block Release
St. Helens College Water Street, St Helens, Merseyside WA10 1PZ (Tel: 0744 33766)	C&G 585 Carpentry and Joinery Craft C&G 585 Advanced Craft, Purpose Made Joinery	- Day Release - Day Release
St. Loye's College Fairfield House, Topsham Road, Exeter, Devon EX2 6EP (Tel: 0392 55428)	C&G 585 Carpentry and Joinery Craft	- Day Release
Salford College of Further Education The Crescent Campus, Windsor Building, Withington Street, Salford Lancashire M6 5BG (Tel: 061-745 8520)	C&G 585 Carpentry and Joinery Craft C&G 585 Advanced Craft, (Subjects not specified)	- Day Release - Day Release
Salisbury College of Technology Southampton Road, Salisbury, Wiltshire SP1 2LW (Tel: 0722 23711)	C&G 585 Carpentry and Joinery Craft C&G 585 Advanced Craft, Site Practice C&G 585 Advanced Craft, Purpose Made Joinery	- Day Release - Day Release - Day Release
Sandwell College of Further & Higher Education Woden Road South, Wednesbury, West Midlands WS10 0PE (Tel: 021-556 6000)	C&G 585 Carpentry and Joinery Craft C&G 585 Advanced Craft, Site Practice C&G 585 Advanced Craft, Purpose Made Joinery	- Day Release - Day Release - Day Release
Scarborough Technical College Lady Edith's Drive, Scarborough, North Yorkshire YO12 5RN (Tel: 0723 372105)	C&G 585 Carpentry and Joinery Craft C&G 585 Advanced Craft, Site Practice	- Day Release - Day Release
Selby Tertiary College Abbot's Road, Selby, North Yorkshire YO8 8AT (Tel: 0757 702606)	C&G 585 Carpentry and Joinery Craft	- Day Time
Shetland College of Further Education Gressy Loan, Lerwick, Shetland ZE1 0BB (Tel: 0595 5514)	C&G 585 Carpentry and Joinery Craft C&G 585 Advanced Craft, Formwork C&G 585 Advanced Craft, Purpose Made Joinery	- Day Release - Day Release - Day Release

DIRECTORY OF COURSES

CARPENTRY AND JOINERY

Shrewsbury College of Art & Technology London Road, Shrewsbury, Shropshire SY2 6PR (Tel: 0743 231544)	C&G 585 Carpentry and Joinery Craft C&G 585 Advanced Craft, Site Practice C&G 585 Advanced Craft, Purpose Made Joinery	- Day Release - Day Release - Day Release
Somerset College of Arts & Technology Wellington Road, Taunton, Somerset TA1 5AX (Tel: 0823 83403)	C&G 585 Carpentry and Joinery Craft C&G 585 Advanced Craft, Site Practice	- Block Release - Day Release
Somerset Training Centre 58 Salmon Parade, Bridgwater, Somerset TA6 5JT (Tel: 0278 428494)	C&G 585 Carpentry and Joinery Craft	- Day Time
Southall College of Technology Beaconsfield Road, Southall, Middlesex UB1 1DP (Tel: 081-574 3448)	C&G 585 Carpentry and Joinery Craft C&G 585 Advanced Craft, Purpose Made Joinery	- Day Release/ Evening - Day Release/ Evening
Southampton Technical College St Mary Street, Southampton, Hampshire SO9 4WX (Tel: 0703 635222)	C&G 585 Carpentry and Joinery Craft C&G 585 Advanced Craft, Purpose Made Joinery C&G 585 Advanced Craft, Maintenance Work	- Block Release/ Day Release/ Evening - Day Release/ Evening - Full Time/ Day Release
South Cheshire College Dane Bank Avenue, Crewe, Cheshire CW2 8AB (Tel: 0270 69133)	C&G 585 Carpentry and Joinery Craft C&G 585 Advanced Craft, Purpose Made Joinery	- Day Release/ Evening - Day Release/ Evening
South Devon College of Arts & Technology Newton Road, Torquay, Devon TQ2 5BY (Tel: 0803 213242/217512)	C&G 585 Carpentry and Joinery Craft C&G 585 Advanced Craft, Site Practice C&G 585 Advanced Craft, Purpose Made Joinery	- Block Release - Block Release - Block Release
South East Derbyshire College Field Road, Ilkeston, Derbyshire DE7 5RS (Tel: 0602 324212)	C&G 585 Carpentry and Joinery Craft C&G 585 Advanced Craft, Site Practice C&G 585 Advanced Craft, Purpose Made Joinery CITB 'Off the Job' Carpentry and Joinery	- Block Release/ Day Release - Day Release - Day Release - Block Release/ Day Release/ Evening

CARPENTRY AND JOINERY

Southend College of Technology Carnarvon Road, Southend on Sea, Essex SS2 6LS (Tel: 0702 432205)	C&G 585 Carpentry and Joinery Craft C&G 585 Advanced Craft, Site Practice C&G 585 Advanced Craft, Purpose Made Joinery CITB 'Off the Job' Carpentry and Joinery	- Day Release - Day Release - Day Release - Block Release/ Evenings
South Fields College of Further Education Aylestone Road, Leicester, Leicestershire LE2 7LW (Tel: 0533 541818)	C&G 585 Carpentry and Joinery Craft C&G 585 Advanced Craft, Site Practice C&G 585 Advanced Craft, Purpose Made Joinery	- Day Release - Day Release - Day Release
South Kent College of Technology The Grange, Shorncliffe Road, Folkestone, Kent CT20 2NA (Tel: 0303 850061)	C&G 585 Carpentry and Joinery Craft C&G 585 Advanced Craft, Site Practice C&G 585 Advanced Craft, Purpose Made Joinery	- Block Release/ Day Release - Day Release - Day Release
South Mersey College Riversdale Road, Liverpool, Merseyside L19 3QR (Tel: 051-427 1227)	C&G 585 Carpentry and Joinery Craft C&G 585 Advanced Craft, Site Practice C&G 585 Advanced Craft, Formwork C&G 585 Advanced Craft, Purpose Made Joinery C&G 585 Advanced Craft, Maintenance Work	- Block Release/ Day Release - Block Release/ Day Release - Block Release/ Day Release - Block Release/ Day Release - Block Release/ Day Release
Southport College of Art & Technology Mornington Road, Southport, Merseyside PR9 0TT (Tel: 0704 542411)	C&G 585 Carpentry and Joinery Craft C&G 585 Advanced Craft, (Subjects not specified)	- Day Release/ Evening - Day Release
South Tyneside College St George's Avenue, South Shields, Tyne and Wear NE34 6ET (Tel: 091-456 0403)	C&G 585 Carpentry and Joinery Craft C&G 585 Advanced Craft, Site Practice	- Day Release - Day Release
Stafford College Earl Street, Stafford, Staffordshire ST16 2QR (Tel: 0785 223800)	C&G 585 Carpentry and Joinery Craft C&G 585 Advanced Craft, Site Practice CITB 'Off the Job' Carpentry and Joinery	- Full Time/ Day Release - Day Release - Full Time/ Block Release/ Day Release

CARPENTRY AND JOINERY

Stockport College of Further & Higher Education	C&G 585 Advanced Craft, Site Practice	- Day Release
Wellington Road South,	C&G 585 Advanced Craft,	- Day Release
Stockport, Cheshire SK1 3UQ	Purpose Made Joinery	
(Tel: 061-480 7331)		
Stoke-on-Trent College	C&G 585 Carpentry and Joinery Craft	- Full Time/ Day Release/ Evening
Stoke Road, Shelton,		
Stoke-on-Trent,	C&G 585 Advanced Craft,	- Day Release/
Staffordshire ST4 2DG	Site Practice	Evening
(Tel: 0782 208208)	C&G 585 Advanced Craft,	- Day Release/
	Purpose Made Joinery	Evening
Stourbridge College of Technology & Art	C&G 585 Carpentry and Joinery Craft	- Day Release
Hagley Road, Stourbridge,	C&G 585 Advanced Craft,	- Day Release
West Midlands DY8 1LY	Site Practice	
(Tel: 038 43 78531)	C&G 585 Advanced Craft, Purpose Made Joinery	- Day Release
	CITB 'Off the Job' Carpentry and Joinery Craft	- Sandwich/Block
Stroud College	C&G 585 Carpentry and Joinery Craft	- Day Release
Stratford Road, Stroud,	C&G 585 Advanced Craft,	- Day Release
Gloucestershire GL5 4AH	Purpose Made Joinery	
(Tel: 0453 763424)	CITB/NTI 'Off the Job' Carpentry and Joinery	- Block Release
Suffolk College of Higher & Further Education	C&G 585 Carpentry and Joinery Craft	- Block Release
Rope Walk, Ipswich,	C&G 585 Advanced Craft,	- Day Release
Suffolk IP4 1LT	Site Practice	
(Tel: 0473 55885)		
Swindon College	C&G 585 Carpentry and Joinery Craft	- Block Release/ Day Release
Regent Circus, Swindon,	C&G 585 Advanced Craft,	- Day Release
Wiltshire SN1 1PT	Site Practice	
(Tel: 0793 491591)	C&G 585 Advanced Craft, Formwork	- Day Release
	C&G 585 Advanced Craft, Purpose Made Joinery	- Day Release
Tameside College of Technology	C&G 585 Carpentry and Joinery Craft	- Day Release
Beaufort Road,	C&G 585 Advanced Craft,	- Day Release
Ashton under Lyne,	Purpose Made Joinery	
Lancashire OL6 6NX		
(Tel: 061-330 6911)		
Telford College of Art & Technology	C&G 585 Carpentry and Joinery Craft	- Day Release
Haybridge Road, Wellington,		
Telford, Shropshire TF1 2NP		
(Tel: 0952 612505)		

CARPENTRY AND JOINERY

Telford College of Further Education
Crewe Toll, Edinburgh EH4 2NZ
(Tel: 031-332 2491)

C&G 585 Advanced Craft, Site Practice — Block Release

Thanet Technical College
Ramsgate Road, Broadstairs,
Kent CT10 1PN
(Tel: 0843 65111)

C&G 585 Carpentry and Joinery Craft — Block Release
C&G 585 Advanced Craft, Purpose Made Joinery — Day Release
C&G 6111 Basic Carpentry and Joinery Skills Test — Evenings

Thurrock Technical College
Woodview, Grays,
Essex RM16 4YR
(Tel: 0375 391199)

C&G 585 Carpentry and Joinery Craft — Full Time/ Day Release/ Evening
C&G 585 Advanced Craft, Purpose Made Joinery — Day Release

Thurso Technical College
Ormlie Road, Thurso,
Caithness KW14 7EE
(Tel: 0847 66161)

C&G 585 Advanced Craft, Purpose Made Joinery — Day Release
CITB 'Off the Job' Carpentry and Joinery — Day Release

TICC Skillcentres Ltd
Cumbria Skillcentre,
Glasson Industrial Estate,
Maryport, Cumbria CA15 8NY
(Tel: 0900 812771)

C&G 585 Carpentry and Joinery Craft — Day Time

TICC Skillcentres Ltd
East Lancs Skillcentre,
Eagle Street, Accrington,
Lancashire BB5 1NS
(Tel: 0254 395521)

C&G 585 Carpentry and Joinery Craft — Full Time

TICC Skillcentres Ltd
White House Road, Ipswich,
Suffolk IP1 5NX
(Tel: 0473 47464)

C&G 585 Carpentry and Joinery Craft — Day Time

Tottenham College of Technology
High Road, Tottenham,
London N15 4RU
(Tel: 081-802 3111)

C&G 585 Carpentry and Joinery Craft — Day Release/ Evening
C&G 585 Advanced Craft, Site Practice — Day Release/ Evening
C&G 585 Advanced Craft, Formwork — Day Release/ Evening
C&G 585 Advanced Craft, Purpose Made Joinery — Day Release/ Evening
C&G 585 Advanced Craft, Maintenance Work — Day Release/ Evening

---

Tralee Regional Technical College
Clash, Tralee, County Kerry, Eire
(Tel: 010 353 66 22319)

C&G 585 Carpentry and Joinery Craft — Day Release

CARPENTRY AND JOINERY

Tresham College
St Mary's Road, Kettering,
Northamptonshire NN15 7BS
(Tel: 0536 85353)

C&G 585 Carpentry and Joinery Craft	- Day Release
C&G 585 Advanced Craft, Purpose Made Joinery	- Day Release/ Evening

Trowbridge College
College Road, Trowbridge,
Wiltshire BA14 0ES
(Tel: 0225 766241)

C&G 585 Carpentry and Joinery Craft	- Day Release
C&G 585 Advanced Craft, Site Practice	- Day Release
C&G 585 Advanced Craft, Purpose Made Joinery	- Day Release

Vauxhall College of Building & Further Education
Belmore Street,
London SW8 2JY
(Tel: 071-498 1234)

C&G 585 Carpentry and Joinery Craft	- Block Release/ Day Release/ Evening
C&G 585 Advanced Craft, Site Practice	- Day Release/ Evening
C&G 585 Advanced Craft, Purpose Made Joinery	- Day Release/ Evening

Wakefield District College
Margaret Street, Wakefield,
West Yorkshire WF1 2DH
(Tel: 0924 370501)

C&G 585 Carpentry and Joinery Craft	- Day Release
C&G 585 Advanced Craft, Site Practice	- Day Release/ Evening
C&G 585 Advanced Craft, Purpose Made Joinery	- Day Release/ Evening

Walsall College of Technology
St Pauls Street, Walsall,
West Midlands WS1 1XN
(Tel: 0922 720824)

C&G 585 Carpentry and Joinery Craft	- Day Release
C&G 585 Advanced Craft, Site Practice	- Day Release

Waltham Forest College
Forest Road, London E17 4JB
(Tel: 081-527 2311)

C&G 585 Carpentry and Joinery Craft	- Day Release/ Evening
C&G 585 Advanced Craft, Site Practice	- Day Release/ Evening
C&G 585 Advanced Craft, Purpose Made Joinery	- Day Release/ Evening

Waterford Regional Technical College
Cork Road, Waterford, Eire
(Tel: 010 353 51 75934)

C&G 585 Carpentry and Joinery Craft	- Day Release/ Evening
C&G 585 Advanced Craft, (Subjects not specified)	- Day Release/ Evening

Wearside College of Further Education
Sea View Road West,
Grangetown, Sunderland,
Tyne and Wear SR2 9LH
(Tel: 091 5670794)

C&G 585 Advanced Craft, Site Practice	- Day Release
C&G 585 Advanced Craft, Formwork	- Day Release
C&G 585 Advanced Craft, Purpose Made Joinery	- Day Release

West Cheshire College
Handbridge Centre, Eaton Road,
Handbridge, Chester,
Cheshire CH4 7ER
(Tel: 0244 677677)

C&G 585 Carpentry and Joinery Craft	- Day Release
C&G 585 Advanced Craft, Site Practice	- Day Release

CARPENTRY AND JOINERY

West Cumbria College
Park Lane, Workington,
Cumbria CA14 2RW
(Tel: 0900 64331)

C&G 585 Carpentry and Joinery Craft	- Day Release
C&G 585 Advanced Craft, Site Practice	- Day Release
C&G 585 Advanced Craft, Purpose Made Joinery	- Day Release
YTS Carpentry and Joinery Craft	- Block Release
YTS Carpentry and Joinery Advanced Craft	- Day Release

West Glamorgan Institute of Higher Education
Mount Pleasant, Swansea,
West Glamorgan SA1 6ED
(Tel: 0792 469004)

C&G 585 Carpentry and Joinery Craft	- Day Release
C&G 585 Advanced Craft, Purpose Made Joinery	- Day Release
C&G 585 Advanced Craft, Site Practice	- Day Release

West Kent College of Further Education
Brook Street, Tonbridge,
Kent TN9 2PW
(Tel: 0732 358101)

C&G 585 Carpentry and Joinery Craft	- Day Release
C&G 585 Advanced Craft, (Subjects not specified)	- Day Release

West Lothian College of Further Education
Marjoribanks Street, Bathgate,
West Lothian EH48 1QJ
(Tel: 0506 634300)

C&G 585 Advanced Craft, Site Practice	- Block Release/ Day Release/ Distance Learning

West Nottinghamshire College of Further Education
Derby Road, Mansfield,
Nottinghamshire NG18 5BH
(Tel: 0623 27191)

C&G 585 Advanced Craft, Site Practice	- Day Release
C&G 585 Advanced Craft, Purpose Made Joinery	- Day Release

Weston Super Mare College of Further Education
Knightstone Road,
Weston Super Mare,
Avon BS23 2AL
(Tel: 0934 621301)

C&G 585 Carpentry and Joinery Craft	- Day Release

West Suffolk College of Further Education
Out Risbygate, Bury St Edmunds,
Suffolk IP33 3RL
(Tel: 0284 701301)

C&G 585 Carpentry and Joinery Craft	- Block Release
C&G 585 Advanced Craft, Site Practice	- Day Release
C&G 585 Advanced Craft, Purpose Made Joinery	- Day Release

CARPENTRY AND JOINERY

Weymouth College
Cranford Avenue, Weymouth,
Dorset DT4 7LQ
(Tel: 030 57 761100)

C&G 585 Carpentry and Joinery Craft	- Day Release/ Evening
C&G 585 Advanced Craft, Site Practice	- Day Release
C&G 585 Advanced Craft, Formwork	- Day Release
C&G 585 Advanced Craft, Purpose Made Joinery	- Day Release
C&G 585 Advanced Craft, Maintenance Work	- Day Release

Wigan College of Technology
Parsons Walk, Wigan,
Lancashire WN1 1RR
(Tel: 0942 494911)

C&G 585 Carpentry and Joinery Craft	- Day Release
C&G 585 Advanced Craft, Site Practice	- Day Release

Willesden College of Technology
Denzil Road,
London NW10 2XD
(Tel: 081-451 3411)

C&G 585 Carpentry and Joinery Craft	- Day Release/ Evening
C&G 585 Advanced Craft, Site Practice	- Day Release/ Evening

Wimpey Craft Training Centre
Stockwood Road, Brislington,
Bristol, Avon BS4 5LT
(Tel: 0272 725280)

C&G 585 Carpentry and Joinery Craft	- Full Time

Wimpey Craft Training Centre
High Street, Westend,
Southampton, Hampshire
SO3 3JJ
(Tel: 0703 475361)

C&G 585 Carpentry and Joinery Craft	- Day Time

Wirral Metropolitan College
Borough Road, Birkenhead,
Wirral L42 9QD
(Tel: 051-653 5555)

C&G 585 Carpentry and Joinery Craft	- Day Release
C&G 585 Advanced Craft, (Subjects not specified)	- Day Release

Worcester Technical College
Deansway, Worcester,
Hereford and Worcester
WR1 2JF
(Tel: 0905 723383)

C&G 585 Carpentry and Joinery Craft	- Day Release
C&G 585 Advanced Craft, Site Practice	- Day Release
C&G 585 Advanced Craft, Purpose Made Joinery	- Day Release

W R Tuson College
St Vincent's Road, Fulwood,
Preston, Lancashire PR2 4UR
(Tel: 0772 53558)

C&G 585 Carpentry and Joinery Craft	- Day Release/ Evening
C&G 585 Advanced Craft, Site Practice	- Day Release/ Evening
C&G 585 Advanced Craft, Purpose Made Joinery	- Day Release/ Evening
CITB 'Off the Job' Carpentry and Joinery	- Block Release

Yeovil College
Ilchester Road, Yeovil,
Somerset BA21 3BA
(Tel: 0935 23921)

C&G 585 Carpentry and Joinery Craft	- Block Release
C&G 585 Advanced Craft, Site Practice	- Day Release

CARPENTRY AND JOINERY

York College of Arts & Technology
Dringhouses, York,
North Yorkshire YO2 1UA
(Tel: 0904 704141)

Ystrad Mynach College of Further Education
Twyn Road, Ystrad Mynach,
Hengoed, Mid-Glamorgan
CF8 7XR
(Tel: 0443 816888)

C&G 585 Carpentry and Joinery Craft — Day Release/ Block Release
C&G 585 Advanced Craft, Purpose Made Joinery — Day Release
C&G 585 Advanced Craft, Site Practice — Day Release

C&G 585 Advanced Craft, Purpose Made Joinery — Day Release

CARPENTRY, WOOD AND TIMBER TRADES

CNAA - Council for National Academic Awards
BSC in Timber Technology
BSC (Hons) in Wood Technology
BA (Hons) in Three-Dimensional Design (Wood/Metal/Plastics)
BA (Hons) in Three-Dimensional Design (Wood/Metal/Ceramics)
BA (Hons) in Three-Dimensional Deisgn (Wood/Metal/Ceramics/Plastics)

Institute of Carpenters: Intermediate
Institute of Carpenters: Craftsman (CIOC)
Institute of Carpenters: Associateship (AIOC)
Institute of Carpenters: Fellowship (FIOC)
Institute of Wood Science: Intermediate, Certificate (CMIWSC)
Institute of Wood Science: Final, Associate (AIWSC)

SCOTVEC: NC Modules, Built Environment Group (Carpentry and Joinery)
SCOTVEC: NC Modules, Built Environment Group (Machine Woodworking)

EITB - Engineering Industry Training Board

Regional Award: 585 Carpentry and Joinery, Craft

College Award: Certificate in Saw Doctoring
College Award: Certificate in Timber Infestation
College Award: Certificate in Wood Machine Tool Maintenance
College Award: Diploma in Stage Carpentry
College Award: Diploma in Timber Studies
College Award: Craft Diploma in Carving and Gilding
College Based: Practical Woodwork
College Based: Women Only Workshop/Carpentry
College Based: Use of Portable Woodworking Power Tools
College Based: Woodwork for the Hearing Impaired
College Based: Basic Skills, Carpentry
College Based: Timber Formwork

GCE A-Level Design and Craftwood (Wood)

C&G 785 Toymaking
C&G 171 Patternmaking and Modelmaking

Non-vocational courses

DIRECTORY OF COURSES

CARPENTRY, WOOD AND TIMBER TRADES

Aberdeen Technical College
Gallowgate, Aberdeen,
Grampian AB9 1DN
(Tel: 0224 640366)

SCOTVEC: NC Modules,
   Built Environment Group
   Carpentry and Joinery
SCOTVEC: NC Modules,
   Built Environment Group
   Machine Woodworking

- Block Release

- Day Release

Angus Technical College
Keptie Road, Arbroath,
Angus DD11 3EA
(Tel: 0241 72056)

SCOTVEC: NC Modules,
   Built Environment Group
   Carpentry and Joinery

- Block Release

Anniesland College
Hatfield Drive, Glasgow
G12 0YE
(Tel: 041-357 3969)

SCOTVEC: NC Modules,
   Built Environment Group
   Carpentry and Joinery

- Day Release

Ayr College
Dam Park, Ayr KA8 0EU
(Tel: 0292 265184)

SCOTVEC: NC Modules,
   Built Environment Group
   Carpentry and Joinery

- Block Release

Ballymena Technical College
Farm Lodge Avenue, Ballymena,
County Antrim, Northern Ireland
BT43 7DJ
(Tel: 0266 652871)

College Based: Practical
   Woodwork

- Evening

**Banff & Buchan College of
Further Education**
Argyll Road, Fraserburgh,
Aberdeenshire AB4 5RF
(Tel: 03465 5777)

SCOTVEC: NC Modules,
   Built Environment Group
   Carpentry and Joinery

- Day Release

Barking College of Technology
Dagenham Road, Romford,
Essex RM7 0XU
(Tel: 0708 766841)

College Based: Basic Skills,
   Carpentry

- Evening

Barmulloch College
Rye Road, Glasgow G21 3JY
(Tel: 041-558 9071)

SCOTVEC: NC Modules,
   Built Environment Group
   Carpentry and Joinery

- Block Release

**Barrow College of Further
Education**
Howard Street, Barrow in Furness,
Cumbria LA14 1NB
(Tel: 0229 825017)

College Based: Practical
   Woodwork

- Evening

**Barry College of Further
Education**
Colcot Road, Barry,
South Glamorgan CF6 8YJ
(Tel: 0446 733251)

BTEC: First Diploma in
   Construction
BTEC: First Certificate in
   Construction

- Full Time

- Part Time

CARPENTRY, WOOD AND TIMBER TRADES

Basford Hall College of Further Education Stockhill Lane, Nottingham, Nottinghamshire NG6 0NB (Tel: 0602 704541)	Institute of Wood Science: TRADA Product Knowledge Timber Institute of Wood Science: Final, Associate (AIWSC)	- Open Learning - Day Release
Blackpool & The Fylde College Palatine Road, Blackpool, Lancashire FY2 0HB (Tel: 0253 52352)	Institute of Carpenters: Associateship (AIOC)	- Day Release/ Evening
Borders College of Further Education Thorniedean, Melrose Road, Galashiels TD1 2AF (Tel: 0896 57755)	SCOTVEC: NC Modules, Built Environment Group Carpentry and Joinery	- Full Time
Bournemouth & Poole College of Further Education North Road, Poole, Dorset BH14 0LS (Tel: 0202 747600)	College Based: Timber Formwork	- Evening
Bradford & Ilkley Community College Great Horton Road, Bradford, West Yorkshire BD7 1AY (Tel: 0274 753080)	Regional Award: 585 Carpentry and Joinery, Craft	- Day Release
Bridgwater College Bath Road, Bridgwater, Somerset TA6 4PZ (Tel: 0278 455464)	C&G 785 Toymaking C&G 171 Patternmaking and Modelmaking	- Evening - Evening
Brighton Polytechnic Moulsecoomb, Brighton, East Sussex BN2 4AT (Tel: 0273 667788)	CNAA: BA in Three-Dimensional Design (Wood/Metal/ Ceramics/Plastic)	- Full Time
Bristol Polytechnic Faculty of Art and Design, Clanage Road, Bower Ashton, Bristol, Avon BS3 2JU (Tel: 0272 660222)	CNAA: BA (Hons) in Three- Dimensional Design (Wood/ Metal/Plastics)	- Full Time
Buckinghamshire College of Higher Education Queen Alexandra Road, High Wycombe, Buckinghamshire HP11 2JZ (Tel: 0494 22141)	CNAA: BSC in Timber Technology CNAA: BSC (Hons) in Wood Technology Institute of Carpenters: Associateship (AIOC)	- Full Time - Full Time - Day Release

CARPENTRY, WOOD AND TIMBER TRADES

Buckinghamshire College of Higher Education *Continued*	Institute of Wood Science: Intermediate, Certificate (CMIWSC)	- Block Release
	Institute of Wood Science: Final, Associate (AIWSC)	- Block Release
	College Award: Certificate in Saw Doctoring	- Full Time
	College Award: Certificate in Timber Infestation	- Block Release
	College Award: Diploma in Timber Studies	- Full Time
Building Crafts Training School 153 Great Titchfield Street, London W1P 7FR (Tel: 071-636 0480)	Wood Turning	- Evening
Cambuslang College Hamilton Road, Cambuslang, Glasgow G72 7NY (Tel: 041-641 6600)	SCOTVEC: NC Modules, Built Environment Group Carpentry and Joinery	- Block Release/ Evening
Cardonald College of Further Education 690 Mosspark Drive, Glasgow G52 3AY (Tel: 041-883 6151/1119)	SCOTVEC: NC Modules, Built Environment Group Carpentry and Joinery	- Block Release
Ceredigion College of Further Education Llanbadarn Campus, Llanbadarn Fawr, Dyfed SY23 2BP (Tel: 0970 4511)	Institute of Carpenters: Associateship (AIOC) Regional Award: 585 Carpentry and Joinery, Craft	- Day Release - Day Release
City & East London College Rochelle Street Arnold Circus, London E2 7ES (Tel: 071-739 7123 Fax: 071-588 9024)	C&G 6135 Basic Woodwork Skills College Based: Women only Workshop	- Day Release - Evening
City & Guilds of London Art School 124 Kennington Park Road, London SE11 4DJ (Tel: 071-735 2306/5210)	College Award: Diploma in Carving and Gilding	- Full Time
Clackmannan College of Further Education Branshill Road, Alloa, Clackmannanshire FK10 3BT (Tel: 0259 215121)	SCOTVEC: NC Modules, Built Environment Group Carpentry and Joinery	- Full Time/ Day Release

CARPENTRY, WOOD AND TIMBER TRADES

Cleveland Technical College
Corporation Road, Redcar,
Cleveland TS10 1EZ
(Tel: 0642 473132)
	Institute of Carpenters:
	  Intermediate
	Institute of Carpenters: Craftsman
	  (CIOC)
	Institute of Carpenters:
	  Associateship (AIOC)
	Institute of Carpenters: Fellowship
	  (FIOC)
		- Day Release
		
		- Day Release
		
		- Block Release/
		  Day Release
		- Day Release

Clydebank College
Kilbowie Road, Clydebank,
Dunbartonshire G81 2AA
(Tel: 041-952 7771)
	SCOTVEC: NC Modules,
	  Built Environment Group
	  Carpentry and Joinery
		- Full Time/
		  Block Release

Coalville Technical College
Bridge Road, Coalville, Leicester,
Leicestershire LE6 2QR
(Tel: 0530 36136)
	Regional Award: 585 Carpentry
	  and Joinery, Craft
	College Based: Basic Skills,
	  Carpentry
	Non-vocational Woodturning
		- Day Release
		
		- Day Release
		
		- Evening

Connemara West Centre Letterfrack, Co Galway, Ireland (Tel: 095-41047/41044 Fax: 095 41112)	National Certificate in Fine Woodworking and Design	- Day Release
Dewsbury College Halifax Road, Dewsbury, West Yorkshire WF13 2AS (Tel: 0924 465916)	Regional Award: 585 Carpentry and Joinery, Craft	- Day Release

**Dumfries & Galloway College
of Technology**
Heathhall, Dumfries DG1 3QZ
(Tel: 0387 61261
Fax: 0387 50006)
	SCOTVEC: NC Modules, Wood-
	  working (Including Carpentry
	  and Joinery)
		- Block Release/
		  Day Release/
		  Infill (any pattern)

**Dundee College of Further
Education**
Old Glamis Road, Dundee
DD3 8LE
(Tel: 0382 819021)
	SCOTVEC: NC Modules,
	  Built Environment Group
	  Carpentry and Joinery
	SCOTVEC: NC Modules,
	  Built Environment Group
	  Machine Woodworking
		- Block Release/
		  Day Release/
		  Evening
		- Day Release

East Hertfordshire College
Turnford, Broxbourne,
Hertfordshire EN10 6AF
(Tel: 0992 466451)
	Institute of Carpenters:
	  Intermediate
	Institute of Carpenters: Craftsman
	  (CIOC)
		- Day Release/
		  Evening
		- Day Release/
		  Evening

**East Yorkshire College of
Further Education**
St Mary's Walk, Bridlington,
North Humberside YO16 5JW
(Tel: 0262 672676)
	Institute of Wood Science:
	  Intermediate, Certificate
	  (CMIWSC)
		- Evening

CARPENTRY, WOOD AND TIMBER TRADES

Ebbw Vale College of Further Education
Ebbw Vale, Gwent NP3 6LE
(Tel: 0495 302083)

College Based: Basic Skills, Carpentry — Day Release

Falkirk College of Technology
Grangemouth Road, Falkirk,
Central Region FK2 9AD
(Tel: 0324 24981)

SCOTVEC: NC Modules, Built Environment Group Carpentry and Joinery — Block Release

SCOTVEC: NC Modules, Built Environment Group Machine Woodworking — Block Release

Fife College of Technology
St Brycedale Avenue, Kirkcaldy,
Fife KY1 1EX
(Tel: 0592 268591/7)

SCOTVEC: NC Modules, Built Environment Group Carpentry and Joinery — Block Release

Glasgow College of Building & Printing
60 North Hanover Street,
Glasgow G1 2BP
(Tel: 041-332 9969)

Institute of Wood Science: Intermediate, Certificate (CMIWSC) — Day Release

Institute of Wood Science: Final, Associate (AIWSC) — Day Release

SCOTVEC: NC Modules, Built Environment Group Machine Woodworking — Block Release

College Award: Certificate in Wood Machine Tool Maintenance — Day Release

Gloucestershire College of Art & Technology
Brunswick Campus,
Brunswick Road, Gloucester,
Gloucestershire GL1 1HU
(Tel: 0452 426500)

Institute of Wood Science Intermediate, Certificate (CMIWSC) — Day Release/ Distance Learning

Institute of Wood Science: Final, Associate (AIWSC) — Day Release

Hall Green College
Cole Bank Road, Birmingham,
West Midlands, B28 8ES
(Tel: 021-778 2311)

Institute of Carpenters: Associateship (MIOC) — Day Release

Institute of Carpenters: Fellowship (FIOC) — Day Release

Herefordshire Technical College
Folly Lane, Hereford HR1 1LS
(Tel: 0432 352235)

GCE A-Level Design and Craft-work (Wood) — Full Time

Highlands College
PO Box 142, St Saviour, Jersey
(Tel: 0534 71800)

Regional Award: 585 Carpentry and Joinery, Craft — Day Release

Huddersfield Technical College
New North Road, Huddersfield,
West Yorkshire HD1 5NN
(Tel: 0484 36521)

Regional Award: 585 Carpentry and Joinery, Craft — Block Release/ Day Release

CARPENTRY, WOOD AND TIMBER TRADES

Inverness College of Further & Higher Education
3 Longman Road,
Inverness IV1 1SA
(Tel: 0463 236681)

SCOTVEC: NC Modules, - Block Release
    Built Environment Group
    Carpentry and Joinery

James Watt College
Finnart Street, Greenock,
Renfrewshire PA16 8HF
(Tel: 0475 24433)

SCOTVEC: NC Modules, - Day Release
    Built Environment Group
    Carpentry and Joinery

Jewel & Esk Valley College
Newbattle Road, Dalkeith,
Mid-Lothian EH22 3AE
(Tel: 031-663 1951)

SCOTVEC: NC Modules, - Block Release/
    Built Environment Group   Day Release
    Carpentry and Joinery

Kendal College of Further Education
Milnthorpe Road, Kendal,
Cumbria LA9 5AY
(Tel: 0539 724313)

Regional Award: 585 Carpentry - Day Release
    and Joinery, Craft

Kirkwall Further Education Centre
Kirkwall Grammar School,
Kirkwall, Orkney KW15 1JG
(Tel: 0856 2102)

SCOTVEC: Modules, - Block Release
    Carpentry and Joinery

Langside College
50 Prospecthill Road, Glasgow
G42 9LB
(Tel: 041-649 4991)

SCOTVEC: NC Modules, - Block Release
    Built Environment Group
    Carpentry and Joinery

Lauder Technical College
Halbeath, Dunfermline,
Fife KY11 5DY
(Tel: 0383 726201)

SCOTVEC: NC Modules, - Day Release
    Built Environment Group
    Carpentry and Joinery

Lews Castle College
Stornoway, Isle of Lewis
PA86 0XR
(Tel: 0851 3311)

SCOTVEC: NC Modules, - Block Release
    Built Environment Group
    Carpentry and Joinery

Luton College of Higher Education
Park Square, Luton,
Bedfordshire LU1 3JU
(Tel: 0582 34111)

Institute of Carpenters: - Day Release
    Intermediate

Manchester Polytechnic
All Saints, Manchester,
Gt Manchester M15 6BH
(Tel: 061-228 6171)

CNAA: BA (Hons) in Three- - Full Time
    Dimensional Design (Wood/
    Metal/Ceramics)

CARPENTRY, WOOD AND TIMBER TRADES

Meirionnydd College
Dolgellau, Gwynedd LL40 2YF
(Tel: 0341 422827)

Regional Award: 585 Carpentry
and Joinery, Craft

- Day Release

Merthyr Tydfil Technical College
Ynysfach, Merthyr Tydfil,
Mid-Glamorgan CF48 1AR
(Tel: 0685 723663)

Recreational Woodwork

- Evening

Mid-Kent College of Higher & Further Education
Horsted, Maidstone Road,
Chatham, Kent ME5 9UQ
(Tel: 0634 44470)

Institute of Carpenters:
Associateship (AIOC)

- Day Release

Mid-Warwickshire College of Further Education
Warwick New Road,
Leamington Spa, Warwickshire
CV32 5JE
(Tel: 0926 311711)

Institute of Wood Science:
Intermediate, Certificate
(CMIWSC)
Institute of Wood Science: Final,
Associate (AIWSC)

- Block Release/
Day Release
- Block Release/
Day Release

Moray College of Further Education
Hay Street, Elgin,
Morayshire IV30 2NN
(Tel: 0343 543425)

SCOTVEC: NC Modules,
Built Environment Group
Carpentry and Joinery

- Full Time/
Block Release/
Day Release/
Evening

Motherwell College
Dalzell Drive, Motherwell,
Lanarkshire ML1 2DD
(Tel: 0698 59641/7)

SCOTVEC: NC Modules,
Built Environment Group
Carpentry and Joinery

- Full Time/
Day Release

Newark Technical College
Chauntry Park, Newark,
Nottinghamshire
NG24 1BP
(Tel: 0636 705921)

Institute of Carpenters:
Associateship (AIOC)
Institute of Carpenters: Fellowship
(FIOC)

- Day Release/
Evening
- Evening

Newport College of Further Education
Nash Road, Newport,
Gwent NP6 2BR
(Tel: 0633 274861)

Regional Award: 585 Carpentry
and Joinery, Craft

- Full Time/
Day Release

New Technical College
Coleraine Road, Ballymoney,
County Antrim, Northern Ireland
BT53 6BT
(Tel: 026 56 62258/62339)

GCE A-Level Design and Craft-
work (Wood)

- Full Time

Newtownabbey Technical College Shore Road, Newtownabbey, County Antrim, Northern Ireland BT37 9RS (Tel: 0232 864331)	Institute of Wood Science: Intermediate, Certificate (CMIWSC)	- Day Release
North Hertfordshire College Cambridge Road, Hitchin, Hertfordshire SG4 0JD (Tel: 0462 422882)	EITB Woodworking Training	- Full Time
North Nottinghamshire College of Further Education Carlton Road, Worksop, Nottinghamshire S81 7HP (Tel: 0909 473561)	GCE A-Level Design and Craft- work (Wood)	- Full Time
Northumberland College of Art & Technology College Road, Ashington, Northumberland NE26 9RG (Tel: 0670 813248)	GCE A-Level Design and Craft- work (Wood)	- Day Release
Oldham College of Technology Rochdale Road, Oldham, Lancashire OL9 6AA (Tel: 061-624 5214)	Regional Award: 585 Carpentry and Joinery, Craft	- Day Release
Oswestry College College Road, Oswestry, Shropshire SY11 2SA (Tel: 0691 653067)	Regional Award: 585 Carpentry and Joinery, Craft Wood Carving and Wood Sculpture	- Day Release - Evening
Percival Whitley College of Further Education Francis Street, Halifax, West Yorkshire HX1 3UZ (Tel: 0422 358221)	Regional Award: 585 Carpentry and Joinery, Craft	- Day Release
Perth College of Further Education Brahan Estate, Creiff Road, Perth PH1 2NX (Tel: 0738 21171)	SCOTVEC: NC Modules, Built Environment Group Carpentry and Joinery	- Full Time/ Block Release
Reading College of Technology Crescent Road, Reading, Berkshire RG1 5RQ (Tel: 0734 583501)	Institute of Carpenters Practical and Technology (IOC) Timber Technology and Associated Practices	- Evening - Evening

CARPENTRY, WOOD AND TIMBER TRADES

Reid Kerr College
Renfrew Road, Paisley,
Renfrewshire PA3 4DR
(Tel: 041-889 4225)

SCOTVEC: NC Modules,
    Built Environment Group
    Carpentry and Joinery

- Block Release

Royal Academy of Dramatic Art
62-64 Gower Street,
London WC1E 6ED
(Tel: 071-636 7076)

College Award: Diploma in Stage
    Carpentry

- Full Time

St. Helens College
Water Street, St Helens,
Merseyside WA10 1PZ
(Tel: 0744 33766)

Wood Carving
Wood Turning

- Non-vocational
- Non-vocational

Scarborough Technical College
Lady Edith's Drive, Scarborough,
North Yorkshire YO12 5RN
(Tel: 0723 372105)

Regional Award: 585 Carpentry
    and Joinery, Craft

- Day Release

Shetland College of Further Education
Gressy Loan, Lerwick,
Shetland ZE1 0BB
(Tel: 0595 5514)

SCOTVEC: NC Modules,
    Built Environment Group
    Carpentry and Joinery

- Full Time/
   Block Release

South Devon College of Arts & Technology
Newton Road, Torquay,
Devon TQ2 5BY
(Tel: 0803 213242/217512)

Institute of Carpenters:
    Associateship (AIOC)

- Block Release

Stoke-on-Trent College
Stoke Road, Shelton,
Stoke-on-Trent,
Staffordshire ST4 2DG
(Tel: 0782 208208)

Institute of Carpenters:
    Associateship (AIOC)

- Day Release

Swindon College
Regent Circus, Swindon,
Wiltshire SN1 1PT
(Tel: 0793 491591)

Non-vocational Wood Turning

- Evening

Telford College of Further Education
Crewe Toll, Edinburgh EH4 2NZ
(Tel: 031-332 2491)

SCOTVEC: NC Modules,
    Built Environment Group
    Carpentry and Joinery
SCOTVEC: NC Modules,
    Built Environment Group
    Machine Woodworking

- Block Release

- Block Release/
   Day Release

CARPENTRY, WOOD AND TIMBER TRADES

Thanet Technical College Ramsgate Road, Broadstairs, Kent CT10 1PN (Tel: 0843 65111)	Wood Carving	- Short Course

Thurso Technical College
Ormlie Road, Thurso,
Caithness KW14 7EE
Tel: 0847 66161)
	SCOTVEC: NC Modules,
	    Built Environment Group
	    Carpentry and Joinery
		- Block Release

Vauxhall College of Building & **Further Education** Belmore Street, London SW8 2JY (Tel: 071-498 1234)	College Award: Certificate in Saw Doctoring	- Evening
Wearside College of Further **Education** Sea View Road West, Grangetown, Sunderland, Tyne and Wear SR2 9LH (Tel: 091 5670794)	Regional Award: 585 Carpentry and Joinery, Craft	- Day Release

West Lothian College of Further
Education
Marjoribanks Street, Bathgate,
West Lothian EH48 1QJ
(Tel: 0506 634300)
	SCOTVEC: NC Modules,
	    Built Environment Group
	    Carpentry and Joinery
		- Block Release/
		  Day Release

West Nottinghamshire College **of Further Education** Derby Road, Mansfield, Nottinghamshire NG18 5BH (Tel: 0623 27191)	Regional Award: 585 Carpentry and Joinery, Craft	- Day Release
Weston Super Mare College of **Further Education** Knightstone Road, Weston Super Mare, Avon BS23 2AL (Tel: 0934 621301)	Woodwork (non-vocational) Woodturning (non-vocational)	- Evening - Evening
Wigan College of Technology Parsons Walk, Wigan, Lancashire WN1 1RR (Tel: 0942 494911)	Institute of Carpenters: Associateship (AIOC)	- Evening
Wirral Metropolitan College Borough Road, Birkenhead, Wirral L42 9QD (Tel: 051-653 5555)	Regional Award: 585 Carpentry and Joinery, Craft	- Day Release

CARPENTRY, WOOD AND TIMBER TRADES

Wolverhampton Polytechnic
Molineux Street, Wolverhampton,
West Midlands WV1 1SB
(Tel: 0902 313000)

CNAA: BA (Hons) in Three-
   Dimensional Design
   (Wood/Metal/Plastics)

- Full Time

**Ystrad Mynach College of
Further Education**
Twyn Road, Ystrad Mynach,
Hengoed, Mid-Glamorgan
CF8 7XR
(Tel: 0443 816888)

Institute of Carpenters:
   Associateship (AIOC)
Regional Award: 585 Carpentry
   and Joinery, Craft

- Day Release

- Day Release

FURNITURE CRAFTS

City and Guilds of London Institute Certificates:
555 Furniture Craft Subjects Part I
555 Furniture Craft Subjects Part II (Subject not Specified)
555 Furniture Craft Subjects Part II Timber Preparation
555 Furniture Craft Subjects Part II Upholstery and Bedding Preparation
555 Furniture Craft Subjects Part II Finishing Preparation
555 Furniture Craft Subjects Part II Carcase and Wooden Frame Construction
555 Furniture Craft Subjects Part II Modern Upholstery and Bedding Construction
555 Furniture Craft Subjects Part II Traditional Upholstery
555 Furniture Craft Subjects Part II Traditional Finishing
555 Furniture Craft Subjects Part II Modern Finishing
555 Furniture Craft Subjects Part II Soft Furnishing
555 Furniture Craft Subjects Part II Hand-made Furniture Construction
555 Furniture Advanced Studies: Advanced Crafts in Furniture
555 Furniture Advanced Studies: Advanced Industrial Studies in Furniture
564 Furniture Crafts: Cabinet Making (Special)
564 Furniture Crafts: Upholstery (Special)
564 Furniture Crafts: Fine Craftsmanship (Furniture and Allied Subjects)
   (Special)
579 Furniture Subjects: Advanced, Design and Construction

**Basford Hall College of Further
Education**
Stockhill Lane, Nottingham,
Nottinghamshire NG6 0NB
(Tel: 0602 704541)

C&G 555 Furniture Craft Subjects:
   Part 1
C&G 555 Furniture Craft Subjects:
   Part II Timber Preparation
C&G 555 Furniture Craft Subjects:
   Part II Upholstery and Bedding
   Preparation
C&G 555 Furniture Craft Subjects
   Part II Finishing Preparation
C&G 555 Furniture Craft Subjects:
   Part II Carcase and Wooden
   Frame Construction
C&G 555 Furniture Craft Subjects:
   Part II Modern Upholstery
   and Bedding Construction
C&G 555 Furniture Craft Subjects:
   Part II Traditional Upholstery

- Day Release

- Day Release

- Day Release

- Day Release

- Day Release

- Day Release

- Day Release

Basford Hall College of Further Education
Continued

C&G 555 Furniture Craft Subjects:
Part II Traditional Finishing — Day Release

C&G 555 Furniture Craft Subjects:
Part II Modern Finishing — Day Release

C&G 555 Furniture Craft Subjects:
Part II Soft Furnishing — Day Release

C&G 555 Furniture Craft Subjects:
Part II Hand-made Furniture
Construction — Day Release

C&G 555 Furniture Advanced
Studies: Advanced Crafts in
Furniture — Day Release

C&G 555 Furniture Advanced
Studies: Advanced Industrial
Studies in Furniture — Day Release

C&G 564 Furniture Crafts:
Cabinet Making (Special) — Day Release

C&G 579 Furniture Subjects:
Advanced, Design and
Construction — Day Release

Birmingham Polytechnic
Perry Barr, Birmingham,
West Midlands B42 2SU
(Tel: 021-331 5000)

C&G 555 Furniture Craft Subjects:
Part I — Day Release

C&G 555 Furniture Craft Subjects:
Part II (Subject not specified) — Day Release

Bournemouth & Poole College of Further Education
North Road, Poole,
Dorset BH14 0LS
(Tel: 0202 747600)

C&G 555 Furniture Craft Subjects:
Part I — Full Time

Bridgend College of Technology
Cowbridge Road, Bridgend,
Mid-Glamorgan CF31 3DF
(Tel: 0656 55588)

C&G 555 Furniture Craft Subjects:
Part I — Day Release

C&G 555 Furniture Craft Subjects:
Part II Timber Preparation — Day Release

C&G 555 Furniture Craft Subjects:
Part II Upholstery and Modern
Upholstery — Day Release

C&G 555 Furniture Craft Subjects:
Part II Modern Upholstery
and Bedding Construction — Day Release

C&G 555 Furniture Craft Subjects:
Part II Traditional Upholstery — Day Release

C&G 555 Furniture Craft Subjects:
Part II Carcase and Wooden
Frame Construction — Day Release

C&G 555 Furniture Craft Subjects:
Part II Hand-made Furniture
Construction — Day Release

FURNITURE

Bridgwater College
Bath Road, Bridgwater,
Somerset TA6 4PZ
(Tel: 0278 455464)

C&G 555 Furniture Craft Subjects: - Day Release
Part I

Brighton College of Technology
Pelham Street, Brighton,
East Sussex BN1 4FA
(Tel: 0273 667788)

C&G 555 Furniture Craft Subjects: - Block Release
Part I
C&G 555 Furniture Craft Subjects: - Block Release
Part II (Subject not specified)

Brunel Technical College
Ashley Down, Bristol,
Avon BS7 9BU
(Tel: 0272 241241)

C&G 555 Furniture Craft Subjects: - Full Time/
Part I   Block Release
C&G 555 Furniture Craft Subjects: - Full Time/
Part II (Subject not specified)   Block Release
C&G 555 Furniture Craft Subjects: - Block Release
Part II Soft Furnishing
C&G 555 Furniture Advanced - Full Time/
Studies: Advanced Crafts in   Block Release
Furniture

Buckinghamshire College of
Higher Education
Queen Alexandra Road,
High Wycombe,
Buckinghamshire HP11 2JZ
(Tel: 0494 22141)

C&G 555 Furniture Craft Subjects: - Block Release
Part I
C&G 555 Furniture Craft Subjects: - Block Release
Part II Timber Preparation
C&G 555 Furniture Craft Subjects: - Block Release
Part II Upholstery and Bedding
Preparation
C&G 555 Furniture Craft Subjects: - Block Release
Part II Carcase and Wooden
Frame Construction
C&G 555 Furniture Craft Subjects: - Block Release
Part II Modern Upholstery
and Bedding Construction
C&G 555 Furniture Craft Subjects: - Block Release
Part II Traditional Upholstery
C&G 555 Furniture Craft Subjects: - Block Release
Part II Soft Furnishing
C&G 555 Furniture Craft Subjects: - Block Release
Part II Hand-made Furniture
Construction
C&G 555 Furniture Advanced - Block Release
Studies: Advanced Crafts in
Furniture
C&G 555 Furniture Advanced - Block Release
Studies: Advanced Industrial
Studies in Furniture
C&G 564 Furniture Crafts: Fine
Craftsmanship Furniture and
Allied Subjects (Special)

Burnley College
Shorey Bank, Ormerod Road,
Burnley, Lancashire BB11 2RX
(Tel: 0282 36111)

C&G 555 Furniture Craft Subjects:
    Part I
        - Block Release/
          Day Release

C&G 555 Furniture Craft Subjects:
    Part II (Subject not specified)
        - Block Release/
          Day Release

C&G 555 Furniture Advanced
    Studies: Advanced Crafts in
    Furniture
        - Day Release/
          Evening

C&G 579 Furniture Subjects:
    Advanced, Design and
    Construction
        - Day Release/
          Evening

Cambridge Regional College
Newmarket Road, Cambridge,
Cambridgeshire CB5 8EG
(Tel: 0223 357545)

C&G 555 Furniture Craft Subjects:
    Part I
        - Day Release/
          Evening

C&G 555 Furniture Craft Subjects:
    Part II Timber Preparation
        - Day Release

C&G 555 Furniture Craft Subjects:
    Part II Carcase and Wooden
    Frame Construction
        - Day Release

C&G 555 Furniture Craft Subjects:
    Part II Hand-made Furniture
        - Day Release

C&G 555 Furniture Craft Subjects:
    Part II Furniture Finishing
    Preparation

Central Manchester College
Lower Hardman Street,
Manchester,
Gt Manchester M3 3ER
(Tel: 061-831 7791)

C&G 555 Furniture Craft Subjects:
    Part I
        - Block Release/
          Day Release

C&G 555 Furniture Craft Subjects:
    Part II (Subject not specified)
        - Block Release/
          Day Release

C&G 555 Furniture Advanced
    Studies: Advanced Crafts in
    Furniture
        - Full Time

**Ceredigion College of Further
Education**
Llanbadarn Campus,
Llanbadarn Fawr,
Dyfed SY23 2BP
(Tel: 0970 4511)

C&G 555 Furniture Craft Subjects:
    Part I
        - Day Release

C&G 555 Furniture Craft Subjects:
    Part II (Subject not specified)
        - Day Release

Chippenham Technical College
Cocklebury Road, Chippenham,
Wiltshire SN15 3QD
(Tel: 0249 444501)

C&G 555 Furniture Craft Subjects:
    Part I
        - Day Release

City College
Abercrombie Campus,
Clarence Street, Liverpool,
Merseyside L1 4DB
(Tel: 051-708 0423)

C&G 555 Furniture Craft Subjects:
    Part I
        - Day Release

C&G 555 Furniture Craft Subjects:
    Part II Timber Preparation
        - Day Release

C&G 555 Furniture Advanced
    Studies: Advanced Crafts in
    Furniture
        - Day Release

FURNITURE

City College *Continued*	C&G 555 Furniture Advanced Studies: Advanced Industrial Studies in Furniture	- Day Release
	C&G 579 Furniture Subjects: Advanced, Design and Construction	- Day Release
City & East London College Rochelle Street, Arnold Circus, London E2 7ES (Tel: 071-739 7123/ Fax: 071-588 9024)	C&G 555 Furniture Craft Subjects: Part I C&G 555 Furniture Craft Subjects: Part II	- Part-time (Women only) - Day Release
City of London Polytechnic 41-71 Commercial Road, London E1 1LA (Tel: 071-247 1953)	C&G 555 Furniture Craft Subjects: Part I	- Day Release
	C&G 555 Furniture Craft Subjects: Part II (Subject not specified)	- Full Time
	C&G 555 Furniture Craft Subjects: Part II Timber Preparation	- Day Release
	C&G 555 Furniture Craft Subjects: Part II Upholstery and Bedding Preparation	- Day Release
	C&G 555 Furniture Craft Subjects: Part II Carcase and Wooden Frame Construction	- Day Release
	C&G 555 Furniture Craft Subjects: Part II Modern Upholstery and Bedding Construction	- Day Release
	C&G 555 Furniture Craft Subjects: Part II Traditional Upholstery	- Day Release
	C&G 555 Furniture Craft Subjects: Part II Soft Furnishing	- Day Release
	C&G 555 Furniture Craft Subjects: Part II Hand-made Furniture Construction	- Day Release
	C&G 555 Furniture Advanced Studies: Advanced Crafts in Furniture	- Full Time/ Day Release/ Evening
	C&G 555 Furniture Advanced Studies: Advanced Industrial Studies in Furniture	- Day Release/ Evening
	C&G 564 Furniture Crafts: Cabinet Making (Special)	- Full Time/ Day Release/ Evening
	C&G 564 Furniture Crafts: Upholstery (Special)	- Full Time
	C&G 579 Furniture Subjects: Advanced, Design and Construction	- Day Release

Connemara West Centre Letterfrack, Co Galway, Ireland (Tel: 095-41047/41044 Fax: 095 41112)	C&G 555 Furniture Craft Subjects: Part I C&G 555 Furniture Craft Subjects: Part II	- Full Time - Full Time
Cornwall College of Further & Higher Education Falmouth Marine Centre, Killigrew Street, Falmouth, Cornwall TR11 3QS (Tel: 0326 313326)	C&G 555 Furniture Craft Subjects: Part I C&G 555 Furniture Craft Subjects: Part II Timber Preparation C&G 555 Furniture Craft Subjects: Part II Upholstery and Bedding Preparation C&G 555 Furniture Craft Subjects: Part II Hand-made Furniture Construction	- Full Time - Block Release - Block Release - Block Release
Darlington College of Technology Cleveland Avenue, Darlington, Co Durham DL3 7BB (Tel: 0325 467651)	C&G 555 Furniture Craft Subjects: Part I C&G 555 Furniture Craft Subjects: Part II	- Day Release - Day Release
Dublin College of Technology Bolton Street, Dublin, Eire (Tel: 0001 727177)	C&G 555 Furniture Craft Subjects: Part I C&G 555 Furniture Craft Subjects: Part II (Subject not specified)	- Day Release - Day Release
Dun Laoghaire Community College Cumberland Street, Dun Laoghaire, Co Dublin, Ireland (Tel: 001 809676)	C&G 555 Furniture Craft Subjects: Part II	- Day Release
East Yorkshire College of Further Education St Mary's Walk, Bridlington, North Humberside YO16 5JW (Tel: 0262 672676)	C&G 555 Furniture Craft Subjects: Part I	- Full Time/ Day Release
Exeter College Hele Road, Exeter, Devon EX4 4JS (Tel: 0392 53514)	C&G 555 Furniture Craft Subjects: Part I	- Day Release
Fife College of Technology St Brycedale Avenue, Kirkcaldy, Fife KY1 1EX (Tel: 0592 268591/7)	C&G 555 Furniture Craft Subjects: Part II (Subject not specified)	- Day Release
Galway Regional Technical College Dublin Road, Galway, Eire (Tel: 010 353 91 53161)	C&G 555 Furniture Craft Subjects: Part I C&G 555 Furniture Craft Subjects: Part II Timber Preparation	- Day Release - Day Release

FURNITURE

Galway Regional Technical College *Continued*	C&G 555 Furniture Craft Subjects: Part II Carcase and Wooden Frame Construction	- Day Release
	C&G 555 Furniture Craft Subjects: Part II Hand-made Furniture Construction	- Day Release
Glasgow College of Building & Printing 60 North Hanover Street, Glasgow G1 2BP (Tel: 041-332 9969)	C&G 555 Furniture Craft Subjects: Part I	- Full Time
	C&G 555 Furniture Craft Subjects: Part II Timber Preparation	- Block Release
	C&G 555 Furniture Craft Subjects: Part II Upholstery and Bedding Preparation	- Block Release
	C&G 555 Furniture Advanced Studies: Advanced Crafts in Furniture	- Day Release
Gloucestershire College of Arts & Technology Brunswick Campus, Brunswick Road, Gloucester, Gloucestershire GL1 1HU (Tel: 0452 426500)	C&G 555 Furniture Craft Subjects: Part I	- Day Release
Halton College of Further Education Kingsway, Widnes, Cheshire WA8 7QQ (Tel: 051-423 1391)	C&G 555 Furniture Craft Subjects: Part II Hand-made Furniture Construction	- Day Release
Harlow College College Gate, The High, Harlow, Essex CM20 1LT (Tel: 0279 441288)	C&G 555 Furniture Craft Subjects: Part I	- Day Release
	C&G 555 Furniture Craft Subjects: Part II (Subject not specified)	- Day Release
	C&G 555 Furniture Advanced Studies: Advanced Crafts in Furniture	- Day Release
Hastings College of Art & Technology Archery Road, St Leonards on Sea, East Sussex TN38 0HX (Tel: 0424 423847)	C&G 555 Furniture Craft Subjects: Part I	- Day Release
Herefordshire Technical College Folly Lane, Hereford, HR1 1LS (Tel: 0432 352235)	C&G 555 Furniture Craft Subjects: Part I	- Full Time/ Day Release
	C&G 555 Furniture Craft Subjects: Part II	- Full Time/ Day Release
	C&G 555 Furniture Craft Subjects: Part III	- Full Time/ Day Release

FURNITURE

Hertfordshire Centre for Building Studies	C&G 555 Furniture Craft Subjects: Part I	- Day Release
St Peter's Road, St Albans, Hertfordshire AL1 3RX	C&G 555 Furniture Craft Subjects: Part II Timber Preparation	- Day Release
(Tel: 0727 47074)	C&G 555 Furniture Craft Subjects: Part II Carcase and Wooden Frame Construction	- Day Release
	C&G 555 Furniture Craft Subjects: Part II Hand-made Furniture Construction	- Day Release
	C&G 555 Furniture Advanced Studies: Advanced Crafts in Furniture	- Full Time
Highbury College of Technology	C&G 555 Furniture Craft Subjects: Part I	- Full Time/ Day Release
Dovercourt Road, Cosham, Portsmouth, Hampshire PO6 2SA	C&G 555 Furniture Craft Subjects: Part II Timber Preparation	- Full Time
(Tel: 0705 383131)	C&G 555 Furniture Craft Subjects: Part II Upholstery and Bedding Preparation	- Full Time
	C&G 555 Furniture Craft Subjects: Part II Carcase and Wooden Frame Construction	- Full Time
	C&G 555 Furniture Craft Subjects: Part II Modern Upholstery and Bedding Construction	- Full Time
	C&G 555 Furniture Craft Subjects: Part II Traditional Upholstery	- Full Time
	C&G 555 Furniture Craft Subjects: Part II Traditional Finishing	- Full Time
	C&G 555 Furniture Craft Subjects: Part II Soft Furnishing	- Full Time
	C&G 555 Furniture Craft Subjects: Part II Hand-made Furniture Construction	- Full Time
	C&G 555 Furniture Advanced Studies: Advanced Crafts in Furniture	- Full Time/ Day Release
Huddersfield Technical College	C&G 555 Furniture Craft Subjects: Part I	- Day Release
New North Road, Huddersfield, West Yorkshire HD1 5NN	C&G 555 Furniture Craft Subjects: Part II Timber Preparation	- Day Release/ Evening
(Tel: 0484 36521)	C&G 555 Furniture Craft Subjects Part II Finishing Preparation	- Day Release/ Evening
	C&G 555 Furniture Craft Subjects: Part II Carcase and Wooden Frame Construction	- Day Release/ Evening
	C&G 555 Furniture Craft Subjects: Part II Traditional Upholstery	- Day Release/ Evening

FURNITURE

Huddersfield Technical College *Continued*	C&G 555 Furniture Craft Subjects: Part II Hand-made Furniture Construction	- Day Release/ Evening
	C&G 555 Furniture Advanced Studies: Advanced Crafts in Furniture	- Day Release
Hull College of Further Education Queen's Gardens, Hull, North Humberside HU1 3DG (Tel: 0482 29943)	C&G 555 Furniture Craft Subjects: Part II Timber Preparation	- Day Release
	C&G 555 Furniture Craft Subjects: Part II Upholstery and Bedding Preparation	- Day Release
	C&G 555 Furniture Craft Subjects Part II Finishing Preparation	- Day Release
	C&G 555 Furniture Craft Subjects: Part II Carcase and Wooden Frame Construction	- Day Release
	C&G 555 Furniture Craft Subjects: Part II Traditional Upholstery	- Day Release
	C&G 555 Furniture Craft Subjects: Part II Modern Finishing	- Day Release
	C&G 555 Furniture Craft Subjects: Part II Soft Furnishing	- Day Release
	C&G 555 Furniture Craft Subjects: Part II Hand-made Furniture Construction	- Day Release
	C&G 555 Furniture Advanced Studies: Advanced Crafts in Furniture	- Day Release
Isle College Ramnoth Road, Wisbech, Cambridgeshire PE13 2JE (Tel: 0945 582561)	C&G 555 Furniture Craft Subjects: Part I	- Full Time
	C&G 555 Furniture Craft Subjects: Part II (Subject not specified)	- Full Time
Jacob Kramer College Vernon Street, Leeds, West Yorkshire LS2 8PH (Tel: 0532 439931)	C&G 555 Furniture Craft Subjects: Part II Timber Preparation	- Block Release
	C&G 555 Furniture Craft Subjects: Part II Upholstery and Bedding Preparation	- Block Release
	C&G 555 Furniture Craft Subjects: Part II Carcase and Wooden Frame Construction	- Block Release
	C&G 555 Furniture Craft Subjects: Part II Modern Upholstery and Bedding Construction	- Block Release
	C&G 555 Furniture Craft Subjects: Part II Traditional Upholstery	- Block Release
	C&G 555 Furniture Craft Subjects: Part II Soft Furnishing	- Block Release

Jacob Kramer College *Continued*	C&G 555 Furniture Craft Subjects: Part II Hand-made Furniture Construction	- Block Release
	C&G 555 Furniture Advanced Studies: Advanced Crafts in Furniture	- Block Release
	C&G 579 Furniture Subjects: Advanced, Design and Construction	- Day Release
Keighley College Cavendish Street, Keighley, West Yorkshire BD21 3DF (Tel: 0274 758555)	C&G 555 Furniture Craft Subjects: Part I	- Day Release
	C&G 555 Furniture Craft Subjects: Part II Timber Preparation	- Day Release
Little Surrenden Workshops Ashford Road, Bethersden, Nr Ashford, Kent TN26 3BG (Tel: 023 382 589)	C&G 555 Furniture Craft Subjects: Part I	- Full Time
	C&G 555 Furniture Craft Subjects: Part II	- Full Time
Lurgan College of Further Education Kitchen Hill, Lurgan, County Armagh, Northern Ireland BT66 6AZ (Tel:076 22 6135)	C&G 555 Furniture Craft Subjects: Part I	- Day Release
Marine Builders Training Trust Hazel Road, Woolston, Southampton, Hampshire SO2 7GB (Tel: 0703 446824)	C&G 555 Furniture Craft Subjects	- Full Time
Mid-Kent College of Higher & Further Education Horsted, Maidstone Road, Chatham, Kent ME5 9UQ (Tel: 0634 44470)	C&G 555 Furniture Craft Subjects: Part I	- Day Release
	C&G 555 Furniture Craft Subjects: Part II (Subject not specified)	- Day Release
Mid-Warwickshire College of Further Education Warwick New Road, Leamington Spa, Warwickshire CV32 5JE (Tel: 0926 311711)	C&G 555 Furniture Craft Subjects: Part I	- Day Release
Moray College of Further Education Hay Street, Elgin, Morayshire IV30 2NN (Tel: 0343 543425)	Non-vocational Furniture Making, French Polishing, Finishing, Restoration	- Evenings

FURNITURE

Newcastle College
Maple Terrace,
Newcastle upon Tyne,
Tyne & Wear NE4 7SA
(Tel: 091-273 8866)

C&G 555 Furniture Craft Subjects: Part I	- Day Release
C&G 555 Furniture Craft Subjects: Part II Timber Preparation	- Day Release
C&G 555 Furniture Craft Subjects: Part II Upholstery and Bedding Preparation	- Day Release
C&G 555 Furniture Craft Subjects: Part II Carcase and Wooden Frame Construction	- Day Release
C&G 555 Furniture Craft Subjects: Part II Modern Upholstery and Bedding Construction	- Day Release
C&G 555 Furniture Craft Subjects: Part II Soft Furnishing	- Day Release
C&G 555 Furniture Craft Subjects: Part II Hand-made Furniture Construction	- Day Release

Norwich City College of Further & Higher Education
Ipswich Road, Norwich,
Norfolk NR2 2LJ
(Tel: 0603 660011)

C&G 555 Furniture Craft Subjects: Part I	- Full Time/ Day Release
C&G 555 Furniture Craft Subjects: Part II Timber Preparation	- Full Time/ Day Release
C&G 555 Furniture Advanced Studies: Advanced Crafts in Furniture	- Day Release/ Evening

Oldham College of Technology
Rochdale Road, Oldham,
Lancashire OL9 6AA
(Tel: 061-624 5214)

C&G 555 Furniture Craft Subjects: Part I	- Day Release

OTJ Training
198 Prescot Road, Aughton,
Lancashire L39 5AG
(Tel: 0695 421646)

C&G 555 Furniture Craft Subjects: Part I	- Day Release

Parkwood College
Shirecliffe Road, Sheffield,
South Yorkshire S5 8XZ
(Tel: 0742 768301)

C&G 555 Furniture Craft Subjects: Part II Timber Preparation	- Full Time/ Part Time Day Release
C&G 555 Furniture Craft Subjects: Part II Upholstery and Bedding Preparation	- Full Time/ Part Time Day Release
C&G 555 Furniture Craft Subjects: Part II Carcase and Wooden Frame Construction	- Part Time Day Release
C&G 555 Furniture Craft Subjects: Part II Modern Upholstery and Bedding Construction	- Full Time/ Part Time Day Release
C&G 555 Furniture Craft Subjects: Part II Hand-made Furniture Construction	- Full Time/ Part Time Day Release

Parkwood College
Continued

C&G 555 Furniture Advanced Studies: Advanced Crafts in Furniture — Full Time/ Part Time Day Release

C&G 555 Furniture Advanced Studies: Traditional Upholstery Construction — Full Time/ Part Time Day Release

C&G 555 Furniture Advanced Studies: Wood Finishing Preparation — Full Time/ Part Time Day Release

C&G 555 Furniture Advanced Studies: Traditional Wood Finishing Construction — Full Time/ Part Time Day Release

Rother Valley College of Further Education
Doe Quarry Lane, Dinnington, Sheffield, South Yorkshire S31 7NH
(Tel: 0909 550550)

C&G 555 Furniture Craft Subjects: Part I — Day Release

Sandwell College of Further & Higher Education
Woden Road South, Wednesbury, West Midlands WS10 0PE
(Tel: 021-556 6000)

C&G 555 Furniture Craft Subjects: Part I — Full Time/ Day Release/ Evening

C&G 555 Furniture Craft Subjects: Part II Timber Preparation — Day Release/ Evening

C&G 555 Furniture Craft Subjects: Part II — Full Time

C&G 555 Furniture Advanced Studies: Advanced Crafts in Furniture — Evening

Short Courses in Cabinet Making, Polishing and Upholstery

Shrewsbury College of Art & Technology
London Road, Shrewsbury, Shropshire SY2 6PR
(Tel: 0743 231544)

C&G 555 Furniture Craft Subjects: Part I — Full Time

C&G 555 Furniture Craft Subjects: Part II — Full Time

C&G 555 Furniture Advanced Studies: Advanced Crafts in Furniture — Full Time

Southend College of Technology
Carnarvon Road, Southend on Sea, Essex SS2 6LS
(Tel: 0702 432205)

C&G 555 Furniture Craft Subjects: Part I — Full Time/ Day Release

C&G 555 Furniture Craft Subjects: Part II (Subject not specified) — Day Release

C&G 555 Furniture Advanced Studies: Advanced Crafts in Furniture — Day Release

FURNITURE

South Fields College of Further Education Aylestone Road, Leicester, Leicestershire LE2 7LW (Tel: 0533 541818)	C&G 555 Furniture Craft Subjects: Part I C&G 555 Furniture Craft Subjects: Part II (Subject not specified)	- Full Time/ Day Release - Full Time/ Day Release
South Kent College of Technology The Grange, Shorncliffe Road, Folkestone, Kent CT20 2NA (Tel: 0303 850061)	C&G 555 Furniture Craft Subjects: Part I	- Day Release
Suffolk College of Higher & Further Education Rope Walk, Ipswich, Suffolk IP4 1LT (Tel: 0473 55885)	C&G 555 Furniture Craft Subjects: Part I C&G 555 Furniture Craft Subjects: Part II Timber Preparation C&G 555 Furniture Craft Subjects: Part II Carcase and Wooden Frame Construction C&G 555 Furniture Craft Subjects: Part II Hand-made Furniture	- Day Release - Day Release - Day Release - Day Release
Thanet Technical College Ramsgate Road, Broadstairs, Kent CT10 1PN (Tel: 0843 65111)	Furniture Restoration	- Short Course
Thomas Court Centre 26 Handbury Lane, Dublin, Ireland (Tel: 0001 531772)	C&G 555 Furniture Craft Subjects: Part II	- Day Release
Tottenham College of Technology High Road, Tottenham, London N15 4RU (Tel: 081-802 3111)	C&G 555 Furniture Craft Subjects: Part II Timber Preparation C&G 555 Furniture Craft Subjects: Part II Carcase and Wooden Frame Construction C&G 555 Furniture Craft Subjects: Part II Modern Finishing C&G 555 Furniture Craft Subjects: Part II Hand-made Furniture Construction C&G 555 Furniture Advanced Studies: Advanced Crafts in Furniture	- Day Release - Day Release - Day Release - Day Release - Day Release
Trowbridge College College Road, Trowbridge, Wiltshire BA14 0ES (Tel: 0225 766241)	C&G 555 Furniture Craft Subjects: Part I	- Day Release

FURNITURE

West Cheshire College Handbridge Centre, Eaton Road, Handbridge, Chester, Cheshire CH4 7ER (Tel: 0244 677677)	Furniture Restoration Course	- Part Time
West Kent College of Further Education Brook Street, Tonbridge, Kent TN9 2PW (Tel: 0732 358101)	C&G 555 Furniture Craft Subjects: Part I	- Day Release
Weston Super Mare College of Further Education Knightstone Road, Weston Super Mare, Avon BS23 2AL (Tel: 0934 621301)	C&G 555 Furniture Craft Subjects: Part II Traditional Upholstery	- Day Release
Yeovil College Ilchester Road, Yeovil, Somerset BA21 3BA (Tel: 0935 23921)	C&G 555 Furniture Craft Subjects: Part I C&G 555 Furniture Craft Subjects: Part II	- Day Release - Day Release

FURNITURE AND FURNISHING

CNNA - Council for National Academic Awards
  BSC (Hons) in Furniture Manufacture and Innovation
  BSC in Furniture Production
  BA (Hons) in Furniture Design
  BA (Hons) in Three-Dimensional Design (Furniture and Related Products)

BTEC: National Certificate in Furniture
BTEC: National Diploma in Design (Furniture)
BTEC: National Diploma in Furniture
BTEC: Higher National Certificate in Furniture
BTEC: Higher National Diploma in Furniture

SCOTVEC: National Certificate Modules, Furniture Crafts
SCOTVEC: Diploma in Furniture Production and Design

College Award: Certificate in Furniture Crafts
College Award: Certificate in Furniture Reproduction and Restoration
College Award: Diploma in Furniture Crafts
College Award: Diploma in Furniture Design and Craftsmanship
College Award: Diploma in Furniture Design and Production
College Award: Diploma in Furniture Production and Management
College Award: Diploma in Furniture Reproduction and Restoration
College Award: Diploma in the Restoration of Antique Clocks
College Award: Diploma in the Restoration of Antique Furniture
College Award: Higher Diploma in Furniture Production and Design
College Based: Course in Furniture Reproduction and Restoration
College Based: Course in Furniture Design, Restoration and Cabinet Making

FURNITURE AND FURNISHING

College Based: Advanced Jig-making for the Furniture Industry
College Based: High-level Craft Course in Cabinet Making and Upholstery
College Based: Pre-apprenticeship Course in Furniture
College Based: Picture Framing

Non-vocational courses

Basford Hall College of Further Education Stockhill Lane, Nottingham, Nottinghamshire NG6 0NB (Tel: 0602 704541)	BTEC: National Diploma in Furniture	- Full Time
	BTEC: Higher National Certificate in Furniture	- Day Release/ Evening
	College Award: Certificate in Furniture Reproduction and Restoration	- Day Release
	College Award: Diploma in Furniture Reproduction and Restoration	- Full Time
	College Based: Course in Furniture Reproduction and Restoration	- Day Release/ Evening
	College Based: Advanced Jig-making for the Furniture Industry	- Day Release/ Evening
Birmingham Polytechnic Perry Barr, Birmingham, West Midlands B42 2SU (Tel: 021-331 5000)	College Based: High-level Craft Course in Cabinet Making and Upholstery	- Evening
	CNAA: BA (Hons) in Three-Dimensional Design (Furniture and Related Products)	- Full Time/ Distance Learning
Buckinghamshire College of Higher Education Queen Alexandra Road, High Wycombe, Buckinghamshire HP11 2JZ Tel: 0494 22141)	BSC in Furniture Production	- Full Time
	College Award: Diploma in Furniture Production and Management	- Full Time
	CNAA: BA (Hons) in Three-Dimensional Design (Furniture and Related Products)	- Full Time
City College Abercrombie Campus, Liverpool, Merseyside (Tel: 051-708 0423)	College Award: Diploma in Furniture Design and Craftsmanship	- Full Time
City of London Polytechnic 41-71 Commercial Road, London E1 1LA (Tel: 071-247 1953)	CNAA: BSC (Hons) in Furniture Manufacture and Innovation	- Full Time
	BTEC: National Diploma in Furniture	- Full Time
	BTEC: Higher National Diploma in Furniture	- Full Time
	College Award: Diploma in Furniture Design and Production	- Sandwich

City of London Polytechnic *Continued*	College Award: Higher Diploma in Furniture Production and Design	- Sandwich
Cornwall College of Further & **Higher Education** Redruth, Cornwall TR15 3RD (Tel: 0209 712911)	College Award: Certificate in Furniture Crafts College Award: Diploma in Furniture Crafts	- Full Time - Full Time
Fife College of Technology St Brycedale Avenue, Kirkcaldy, Fife KY1 1EX (Tel: 0592 268591/7)	SCOTVEC: Certificate in Furniture Production and Design HND: Furniture Design HNC: Furniture Design	- Full Time - Full Time - Full Time/ Day Release
Jacob Kramer College Vernon Street, Leeds, West Yorkshire LS2 8PH (Tel: 0532 439931)	BTEC: National Diploma in Design (Furniture)	- Full Time
Kingston Polytechnic Penrhyn Road, Kingston upon Thames, Surrey KT1 2EE (Tel: 081-549 1366)	CNAA: BA (Hons) in Three- Dimensional Design (Furniture and Related Products)	- Full Time
Leeds Polytechnic Calverley Street, Leeds, West Yorkshire LS1 3HE (Tel: 0532 832600)	CNAA: BA (Hons) in Three- Dimensional Design (Furniture and Related Products)	- Full Time
Leicester Polytechnic PO Box 143, Leicester, Leicestershire LE1 9BH (Tel: 0533 551551)	CNAA: BA (Hons) in Three- Dimensional Design (Furniture and Related Products)	- Full Time
Lurgan College of Further **Education** Kitchen Hill, Lurgan, County Armagh, Northern Ireland BT66 6AZ (Tel: 076 22 6135)	BTEC: First and National Diplomas in Design (Furniture)	- Full Time
Middlesex Polytechnic Trent Park, Cockfosters Road, Barnet, Hertfordshire EN4 0PT (Tel: 081-368 1299)	CNAA: BA (Hons) in Three- Dimensional Design (Furniture and Related Products)	- Full Time

DIRECTORY OF COURSES

FURNITURE AND FURNISHING

Moray College of Further Education
Hay Street, Elgin,
Morayshire IV30 2NN
(Tel: 0343 543425)

SCOTVEC: Certificate in Cabinet Making

- Evenings

Norwich City College of Further & Higher Education
Ipswich Road, Norwich,
Norfolk NR2 2LJ
(Tel: 0603 660011)

College Award: Diploma in Furniture Design and Production

- Full Time

Ravensbourne College of Design & Communication
Walden Road, Chislehurst,
Kent BR7 5SN
(Tel: 081-468 7071)

CNAA: BA (Hons) in Three-Dimensional Design (Furniture and Related Products)

- Full Time

Royal National Institute for the Blind Colleges
224 Great Portland Street,
London W1N 6AA
(Tel: 071-388 1266)

College Based: Picture Framing

- Full Time

Rycotewood College
Priest End, Thame,
Oxfordshire OX9 2AF
(Tel: 084 421 2501)

BTEC HND and HNC Diploma in Design Crafts

- Full Time

Continuing Education Certificate in Design Crafts

- Full Time

St. Helens College
Water Street, St Helens,
Merseyside WA10 1PZ
(Tel: 0744 33766)

Cabinet Making, Furniture Making, French Polishing, Furniture Restoration

- Non-vocational

Southend College of Technology
Carnarvon Road,
Southend on Sea, Essex SS2 6LS
(Tel: 0702 432205)

College Based: Pre-Apprenticeship Course in Furniture

- Day Release

Suffolk College of Higher & Further Education
Rope Walk, Ipswich,
Suffolk IP4 1LT
(Tel: 0473 55885)

Advanced Diploma in Furniture Making

- Full Time

Telford College of Further Education
Crewe Toll, Edinburgh EH4 2NZ
(Tel: 031 332 2491)

SCOTVEC: National Certificate Modules, Upholstery

- Day Release

FURNITURE AND FURNISHING

Tottenham College of Technology High Road, Tottenham, London N15 4RU (Tel: 081-802 3111)	College Certificate: Fine Hand Made Furniture	- Day Release
Trent Polytechnic Burton Street, Nottingham, Nottinghamshire NG1 4BU (Tel: 0602 418418)	CNAA: BA (Hons) in Furniture Design	- Thin Sandwich Course
West Dean College West Dean, Chichester, West Sussex PO18 0QZ (Tel: 0243 63 301)	Diploma Course in Restoration of Antique Furniture (West Dean/British Antique Dealers' Association Diploma)	- Full Time
York College of Arts & Technology Dringhouses, York, North Yorkshire YO2 1UA (Tel: 0904 704141)	College Certificate: Antique Furniture Restoration	- Full Time/ Day Release

MACHINE WOODWORKING

City and Guilds of London Institute Certificates
C&G 606 Machine Woodworking: Craft, Woodworking
C&G 606 Machine Woodworking: Craft, Sawmilling
C&G 606 Machine Woodworking: Advanced Craft, Toolroom Technology
C&G 606 Machine Woodworking: Advanced Craft, Materials Technology
C&G 606 Machine Woodworking: Advanced Craft, Construction of Machined Components
C&G 606 Machine Woodworking: Advanced Craft, Production Planning for the Machine Shop
C&G 606 Machine Woodworking: Advanced Craft, Plant Layout and Materials Handling
C&G 606 Machine Woodworking: Advanced Craft, Machine Woodworking Science
C&G 606 Machine Woodworking: Advanced Craft, (Subjects not Specified)

CIOB Certificate in Site Supervisory Studies
RDC Machine Woodworking Course

Aberdeen Technical College Gallowgate, Aberdeen, Grampian AB9 1DN (Tel: 0224 640366)	C&G 606 Machine Woodworking: Advanced Craft, Toolroom Technology	- Day Release
Astra Training Services Ltd Southampton Skillcentre, West Bay Road, Southampton, Hampshire SO9 3SH (Tel: 0703 228281)	C&G 606 Machine Woodworking: Craft, Woodworking	- Day Time
Astra Training Services Ltd Wigan Skillcentre, Swan Lane, Hindley Green, Wigan, Lancashire WN2 4HD (Tel: 0942 56123)	C&G 586 Machine Woodworking: Craft	- Day Time

MACHINE WOODWORKING

Astra Training Services Ltd
Nottingham Skillcentre,
Lilac Grove, Beeston, Nottingham,
Nottinghamshire NG9 1QY
(Tel: 0602 221112)

C&G 606 Machine Woodworking:
Craft, Woodworking

- Day Time

Astra Training Services Ltd
Lancing - West Sussex Skillcentre
Churchill Industrial Estate,
Chartwell Road, Lancing,
West Sussex BN15 8UB
(Tel: 0903 764331)

Woodmachining Regulations
Appreciation

- Day Time

Astra Training Services Ltd
Tyneside Skillcentre, Green Lane,
Felling, Gateshead,
Tyne and Wear NE10 0LA
(Tel: 091-469 4314)

Woodworking Machine
Regulations

- Day Time

Astra Training Services Ltd
Leeds Skillcentre, Parkside Lane,
Leeds, West Yorkshire LS11 5SZ
(Tel: 0532 704661)

C&G 606 Machine Woodworking:
Craft, Woodworking

- Day Time

Aylesbury College
Oxford Road, Aylesbury,
Buckinghamshire HP21 8PD
(Tel: 0296 34111)

C&G 606 Machine Woodworking:
Craft

- Day Release/
Block Release

Ballymena Technical College
Farm Lodge Avenue, Ballymena,
County Antrim,
Northern Ireland BT43 7DJ
(Tel: 0266 652871)

C&G 606 Machine Woodworking:
Craft, Woodworking
C&G 586 Machine Woodworking:
Advanced Craft

- Full Time

- Day Release

Ballynahinch College
Church Road, Ballynahinch,
County Down,
Northern Ireland BT24 8LP
(Tel: 023 856 2369)

C&G 606 Machine Woodworking:
Craft, Woodworking

C&G 606 Machine Woodworking:
Advanced Craft, Toolroom
Technology
C&G 606 Machine Woodworking:
Advanced Craft, Materials
Technology

- Full Time/
Day Release/
Evening
- Day Release/
Evening

- Day Release/
Evening

Barking College of Technology
Dagenham Road, Romford,
Essex RM7 OXU
(Tel: 0708 766841)

C&G 606 Machine Woodworking:
Craft, Woodworking
C&G 606 Machine Woodworking:
Advanced Craft, (Subjects not
Specified)

- Day Release

- Day Release

Barnsley College of Technology
Church Street, Barnsley,
South Yorkshire S70 2AX
(Tel: 0226 730191)

C&G 606 Machine Woodworking:
Craft, Woodworking

- Day Release

MACHINE WOODWORKING

Basford Hall College of Further Education
Stockhill Lane, Nottingham,
Nottinghamshire NG6 0NB
(Tel: 0602 704541)

C&G 606 Machine Woodworking: Craft, Woodworking	- Day Release
C&G 606 Machine Woodworking: Advanced Craft, Toolroom Technology	- Day Release
C&G 606 Machine Woodworking: Advanced Craft, Materials Technology	- Day Release
C&G 606 Machine Woodworking: Advanced Craft, Construction of Machined Components	- Day Release
C&G 606 Machine Woodworking: Advanced Craft, Production Planning for the Machine Shop	- Day Release
C&G 606 Machine Woodworking: Advanced Craft, Plant Layout and Materials Handling	- Day Release
C&G 606 Machine Woodworking: Advanced Craft, Machine Woodworking Science	- Day Release

Bedford College of Higher Education
Cauldwell Street, Bedford,
Bedfordshire MK42 9AH
(Tel: 0234 45151)

Machine Woodworking Safety	- Block Release/ Day Release/ Evening

Belfast College of Technology
College Square East, Belfast,
Northern Ireland BT1 6DJ
(Tel: 0232 327244)

C&G 606 Machine Woodworking: Craft, Woodworking	- Day Release
C&G 606 Machine Woodworking: Advanced Craft, Toolroom Technology	- Day Release

Bilston Community College
Westfield Road, Bilston,
Wolverhampton,
West Midlands, WV14 6ER
(Tel: 0902 42871)

C&G 586 Machine Woodworking: Craft, Woodworking	- Day Release
C&G 586 Machine Woodworking: Advanced Craft, (Toolroom Technology, CNC option)	- Day Release

Blackburn College
Feilden Street, Blackburn,
Lancashire BB2 1LH
(Tel: 0254 55144)

C&G 606 Machine Woodworking: Craft, Woodworking	- Day Release
C&G 606 Machine Woodworking: Advanced Craft, Toolroom Technology	- Day Release

Bolton Metropolitan College
Manchester Road, Bolton,
Lancashire BL2 1ER
(Tel: 0204 31411)

C&G 606 Machine Woodworking: Craft, Woodworking	- Block Release/ Day Release
C&G 606 Machine Woodworking: Advanced Craft, Toolroom Technology	- Day Release

Bournemouth & Poole College of Further Education
North Road, Poole,
Dorset BH14 0LS
(Tel: 0202 747600)

C&G 606 Machine Woodworking: Craft, Woodworking	- Block Release/ Day Release/ Evening
C&G 606 Machine Woodworking: Advanced Craft, Toolroom Technology	- Day Release

MACHINE WOODWORKING

Bridgend College of Technology
Cowbridge Road, Bridgend,
Mid-Glamorgan CF31 3DF
(Tel: 0656 55588)

C&G 586/606 Machine Woodworking: Craft, Woodworking — Day Release

Bridgwater College
Bath Road, Bridgwater,
Somerset TA6 4PZ
(Tel: 0278 455464)

C&G 606 Machine Woodworking: Craft, Woodworking — Day Release

**Brooklyn Technical College
(Great Barr)**
Aldridge Road, Great Barr,
Birmingham,
West Midlands B44 8NE
(Tel: 021-360 3543)

C&G 606 Machine Woodworking: Craft, Woodworking — Block Release/ Day Release

C&G 606 Machine Woodworking: Advanced Craft, Toolroom Technology — Block Release/ Day Release

Brunel Technical College
Ashley Down, Bristol,
Avon BS7 9BU
(Tel: 0272 241241)

C&G 606 Machine Woodworking: Craft, Woodworking — Block Release/ Day Release

C&G 606 Machine Woodworking: Advanced Craft, Toolroom Technology — Block Release

C&G 606 Machine Woodworking: Advanced Craft, Materials Technology — Block Release

**Buckinghamshire College of
Higher Education**
Queen Alexandra Road,
High Wycombe,
Buckinghamshire HP11 2JZ
(Tel: 0494 22141)

C&G 606 Machine Woodworking: Craft, Woodworking — Block Release

C&G 606 Machine Woodworking: Advanced Craft, Materials Technology — Block Release

**Burton Upon Trent Technical
College**
Lichfield Street,
Burton Upon Trent,
Staffordshire DE14 3RL
(Tel: 0283 45401)

C&G 606 Machine Woodworking: Craft, Woodworking — Block Release/ Day Release

C&G 606 Machine Woodworking: Advanced Craft, Toolroom Technology — Day Release

C&G 606 Machine Woodworking: Advanced Craft (including CNC machining) — Evening

Cambridge Regional College
Newmarket Road, Cambridge,
Cambridgeshire CB5 8EG
(Tel: 0223 357545)

C&G 586/606 Machine Woodworking: Craft — Day Release/ Evening

C&G 586/606 Machine Woodworking: Advanced Craft — Day Release

Carlisle College
Victoria Place, Carlisle,
Cumbria CA1 1HS
(Tel: 0228 24464)

C&G 586 Machine Woodworking: Craft — Day Release

Central Manchester College
Lower Hardman Street,
Manchester,
Gt Manchester M3 3ER
(Tel: 061-831 7791)

C&G 606 Machine Woodworking: Craft, Woodworking — Block Release/ Day Release

C&G 606 Machine Woodworking: Advanced Craft, Toolroom Technology — Day Release

Central Manchester College *Continued*	C&G 606 Machine Woodworking: Advanced Craft, (Subjects not Specified)	- Day Release
City College Abercrombie Campus, Clarence Street, Liverpool, Merseyside L1 4DB (Tel: 051-708 0423)	C&G 606 Machine Woodworking: Craft, Woodworking C&G 606 Machine Woodworking: Advanced Craft (Subjects not Specified)	- Day Release - Day Release
City of London Polytechnic 41-71 Commercial Road, London E1 1LA (Tel: 071-247 1953)	C&G 606 Machine Woodworking: Craft, Woodworking C&G 606 Machine Woodworking: Craft, Sawmilling C&G 606 Machine Woodworking: Advanced Craft, Toolroom Technology	- Full Time/ Day Release/ Evening - Full Time/ Day Release/ Evening - Day Release/ Evening
Cleveland Technical College Corporation Road, Redcar, Cleveland TS10 1EZ (Tel: 0642 473132)	C&G 606 Machine Woodworking: Craft, Woodworking	- Block Release/ Day Release
Colchester Institute Sheepen Road, Colchester, Essex CO3 3LL (Tel: 0206 570271)	C&G 606 Machine Woodworking: Craft, Woodworking C&G 606 Machine Woodworking: Advanced Craft, Toolroom Technology	- Day Release - Day Release
Coventry Technical College Butts, Coventry, West Midlands CV1 3GD (Tel: 0203 57221)	C&G 606 Machine Woodworking: Craft, Woodworking C&G 606 Machine Woodworking: Advanced Craft, Toolroom Technology C&G 606 Machine Woodworking: Advanced Craft, Materials Technology C&G 606 Machine Woodworking: Advanced Craft, Construction of Machined Components C&G 606 Machine Woodworking: Advanced Craft, Machine Woodworking Science Machine Woodworking Regulations 1974 No. 903 Abrasive Wheels Regulations 1970	- Day Release/ Evening - Day Release/ Evening - Evening - Day Release - Day Release - Day Time - Day Time
Crawley College College Road, Crawley, West Sussex RH10 1NR (Tel: 0293 612686)	C&G 586 Machine Woodworking: Craft C&G 586 Machine Woodworking: Advanced Craft, Toolroom Technology	- Day Release - Day Release

MACHINE WOODWORKING

Croydon College
Fairfield, Croydon,
Surrey CR9 1DX
(Tel: 081-686 5700)

C&G 606 Machine Woodworking: Craft, Woodworking — Day Release

Darlington College of Technology
Cleveland Avenue, Darlington,
County Durham DL3 7BB
(Tel: 0325 467651)

C&G 606 Machine Woodworking: Craft, Woodworking — Block Release/ Day Release

C&G 606 Machine Woodworking: Advanced Craft, Toolroom Technology — Day Release/ Evening

Doncaster College
Construction & Minerals
Engineering Division, School of
Construction, Ellers Road,
Bessacarr, Doncaster, DN4 7BA
(Tel: 0302 539446)

C&G 606 Machine Woodworking: Craft, Woodworking — Block Release/ Day Release

C&G 606 Machine Woodworking: Advanced Craft, Toolroom Technology — Day Release

C&G 606 Machine Woodworking: Advanced Craft, Materials Technology — Day Release

C&G 606 Machine Woodworking: Advanced Craft, Construction of Machined Components — Day Release

C&G 606 Machine Woodworking: Advanced Craft, Machine Woodworking Science — Day Release

Down College of Further Education
Downpatrick, County Down,
Northern Ireland BT30 6ND
(Tel: 0396 615815)

C&G 606 Machine Woodworking: Craft, Woodworking — Day Release

C&G 606 Machine Woodworking: Advanced Craft, (Subjects not Specified) — Day Release

Dublin College of Technology
Bolton Street, Dublin, Ireland
(Tel: 0001 727177)

C&G 606 Machine Woodworking: Craft, Woodworking — Day Release

Dundee College of Further Education
Old Glamis Road,
Dundee DD3 8LE
(Tel: 0382 819021)

C&G 606 Machine Woodworking: Advanced Craft, (Subjects not Specified) — Day Release

East Yorkshire College of Further Education
St Mary's Walk, Bridlington,
North Humberside YO16 5JW
(Tel: 0262 672676)

C&G 606 Machine Woodworking: Craft, Woodworking — Day Release

Erith College of Technology
Tower Road, Belvedere,
Kent DA17 6JA
(Tel: 032 24 42331)

C&G 606 Machine Woodworking: Craft, Woodworking — Day Release/ Evening

C&G 606 Machine Woodworking: Advanced Craft, Toolroom Technology — Day Release/ Evening

Exeter College
Hele Road, Exeter,
Devon EX4 4JS
(Tel: 0392 53514)

C&G 606 Machine Woodworking: Craft, Woodworking — Short Course

C&G Woodmachining and Abrasive Wheel — Short Course

MACHINE WOODWORKING

Falkirk College of Technology
Grangemouth Road, Falkirk,
Central Region FK2 9AD
(Tel: 0324 24981)

C&G 586 Machine Woodworking: — Day Release
Advanced Craft, Construction
of Machined Components

Fermanagh College of Further Education
Fairview Avenue, Enniskillen,
County Fermanagh,
Northern Ireland BT74 6AE
(Tel: 0365 22431)

C&G 606 Machine Woodworking: — Day Release
Craft, Woodworking

Glasgow College of Building and Printing
60 North Hanover Street,
Glasgow G1 2BP
(Tel: 041-332 9969)

C&G 606 Machine Woodworking: — Block Release
Craft, Woodworking
C&G 606 Machine Woodworking: — Block Release
Advanced Craft, Toolroom
Technology

Gloucestershire College of Art and Technology
Brunswick Campus,
Brunswick Road, Gloucester,
Gloucestershire GL1 1HU
(Tel: 0452 426500)

C&G 606 Machine Woodworking: — Block Release/
Craft, Woodworking   Day Release
C&G 606 Machine Woodworking: — Day Release
Advanced Craft, Toolroom
Technology

Guildford College of Technology
Stoke Park, Guildford,
Surrey GU1 1EZ
(Tel: 0483 31251)

C&G 606 Machine Woodworking: — Day Release
Craft, Woodworking
C&G 606 Machine Woodworking: — Day Release
Advanced Craft, Toolroom
Technology

Halton College of Further Education
Kingsway, Widnes,
Cheshire WA8 7QQ
(Tel: 051-423 1391)

C&G 606 Machine Woodworking: — Full Time/
Craft, Woodworking   Day Release

Hartlepool College of Further Education
Stockton Street, Hartlepool,
Cleveland TS25 7NT
(Tel: 0429 275453)

C&G 586/606 Machine Wood- — Day Release
working: Craft, Woodworking
C&G 586/606 Machine Wood- — Block Release
working: Advanced Craft,
Toolroom Technology
C&G 586/606 Machine Wood- — Day Release
working: Advanced Craft,
Toolroom Technology

Hastings College of Art & Technology
Archery Road,
St Leonards on Sea,
East Sussex TN38 0HX
(Tel: 0424 423847)

C&G 606 Machine Woodworking: — Full Time/
Craft, Woodworking   Day Release
C&G 606 Machine Woodworking: — Day Release
Advanced Craft, Materials
Technology
C&G 606 Machine Woodworking: — Day Release
Advanced Craft, Construction
of Machined Components
C&G 606 Machine Woodworking: — Day Release
Advanced Craft, Production
Planning for the Machine Shop

MACHINE WOODWORKING

Hastings College of Art & Technology
Continued

C&G 606 Machine Woodworking: Advanced Craft, Plant Layout and Materials Handling — Day Release

C&G 606 Machine Woodworking: Advanced Craft, Machine Woodworking Science — Day Release

Herefordshire Technical College
Folly Lane, Hereford, HR1 1LS
(Tel: 0432 352235)

C&G 606 Machine Woodworking: Craft — Day Release/ Evening

C&G 606 Machine Woodworking: Advanced Craft — Day Release

Hertfordshire Centre for Building Studies
St Peter's Road, St Albans, Hertfordshire AL1 3RX
(Tel: 0727 47074)

C&G 606 Machine Woodworking: Craft, Woodworking — Day Release

C&G 606 Machine Woodworking: Advanced Craft, Toolroom Technology — Day Release

C&G 606 Machine Woodworking: Advanced Craft, Materials Technology — Day Release

Highbury College of Technology
Dovercourt Road, Cosham, Portsmouth, Hampshire PO6 2SA
(Tel: 0705 383131)

C&G 606 Machine Woodworking: Craft, Woodworking — Full Time/ Block Release/ Day Release

C&G 606 Machine Woodworking: Advanced Craft, Toolroom Technology — Block Release

Highlands College
PO Box 142, St Saviour, Jersey
(Tel: 0534 71800)

C&G 606 Machine Woodworking: Craft, Woodworking — Day Release

Huddersfield Technical College
New North Road, Huddersfield, West Yorkshire HD1 5NN
(Tel: 0484 36521)

C&G 606 Machine Woodworking: Craft, Woodworking — Day Release/ Evening

C&G 606 Machine Woodworking: Advanced Craft, Toolroom Technology — Day Release

C&G 606 Machine Woodworking: Advanced Craft, Materials Technology — Day Release

C&G 606 Machine Woodworking: Advanced Craft, Construction of Machined Components — Day Release

C&G 606 Machine Woodworking: Advanced Craft, Production Planning for the Machine Shop — Day Release

C&G 606 Machine Woodworking: Advanced Craft, Plant Layout and Materials Handling — Day Release

C&G 606 Machine Woodworking: Advanced Craft, Machine Woodworking Science — Day Release

MACHINE WOODWORKING

Hull College of Further Education Queen's Gardens, Hull, North Humberside HU1 3DG (Tel: 0482 29943)	C&G 606 Machine Woodworking: Craft, Woodworking	- Block Release/ Day Release
	C&G 606 Machine Woodworking: Advanced Craft, Toolroom Technology	- Day Release
Huntingdonshire College California Road, Huntingdon, Cambridgeshire PE18 7BL (Tel: 0480 52346)	C&G 586/606 Machine Woodworking: Craft, Woodworking	- Day Release
	C&G 586/606 Machine Woodworking: Advanced Craft, Toolroom Technology	- Day Release
	C&G 586/606 Machine Woodworking: Advanced Craft, Materials Technology	- Day Release
	C&G 586/606 RDC Machine Woodworking	- Block Release
Keighley College Cavendish Street, Keighley, West Yorkshire BD21 3DF (Tel: 0274 758555)	C&G 606 Machine Woodworking: Craft, Woodworking	- Block Release/ Day Release
Knowsley Community College Cherryfield Drive, Kirkby, Merseyside L32 8SF (Tel: 051-443 4324)	C&G 606 Machine Woodworking: Craft, Woodworking	- Day Release/ Evening
Leeds College of Building North Street, Leeds, West Yorkshire LS2 7QT (Tel: 0532 430765)	C&G 606 Machine Woodworking: Craft, Woodworking	- Day Release
	C&G 606 Machine Woodworking: Advanced Craft, Toolroom Technology	- Day Release
	CITB Machine Woodworking Craft	- Block Release
Luton College of Higher Education Park Square, Luton, Bedfordshire LU1 3JU (Tel: 0582 34111)	C&G 606 Machine Woodworking: Craft, Woodworking	- Day Release
Mid-Cheshire College of Further Education Hartford Campus, Northwich, Cheshire CW8 1LJ (Tel: 0606 75281/74344/74842)	C&G 606 Machine Woodworking: Craft, Woodworking	- Day Release
Mid-Kent College of Higher & Further Education Horsted, Maidstone Road, Chatham, Kent ME5 9UQ (Tel: 0634 44470)	C&G 606 Machine Woodworking: Craft, Woodworking	- Day Release
	C&G 606 Machine Woodworking: Advanced Craft, Toolroom Technology	- Day Release
Mid-Warwickshire College of Further Education Warwick New Road, Leamington Spa, Warwickshire CV32 5JE (Tel: 0926 311711)	C&G 586 Machine Woodworking: Craft, Woodworking	- Block Release/ Day Release
	C&G 586 Machine Woodworking: Craft (Int)	- Block Release/ Day Release
	C&G 586 Machine Woodworking: Advanced Craft	- Block Release/ Day Release

MACHINE WOODWORKING

Neath College
Dwr Y Felin Road, Neath,
West Glamorgan SA10 7RF
(Tel: 0639 634271)

C&G 606 Machine Woodworking: - Day Release
Craft, Woodworking

Nene College
Moulton Park, Northampton,
Northamptonshire NN2 7AL
(Tel: 0604 715000)

C&G 606 Machine Woodworking: - Day Release
Craft, Woodworking

C&G 606 Machine Woodworking: - Day Release
Advanced Craft, Toolroom
Technology

C&G 606 Machine Woodworking: - Day Release
Advanced Craft, Materials
Technology

Newcastle College
Maple Terrace,
Newcastle upon Tyne,
Tyne & Wear NE4 7SA
(Tel: 091-273 8866)

C&G 606 Machine Woodworking: - Day Release
Craft, Woodworking

**Newport College of Further
Education**
Nash Road, Newport,
Gwent NP6 2BR
(Tel: 0633 274861)

C&G 606 Machine Woodworking: - Day Release
Craft, Woodworking

**Norfolk College of Art &
Technology**
Tennyson Avenue, King's Lynn,
Norfolk PE30 2QW
(Tel: 0553 761144)

Woodworking Machine - Short Course
Regulations and Safe Practice

North Devon College
Old Sticklepath Hill, Barnstaple,
Devon EX31 2BQ
(Tel: 0271 45291)

C&G 606 Machine Woodworking: - Day Release
Craft, Woodworking

**North East Wales Institute of
Higher Education**
Deeside, Connah's Quay,
Clwyd CH5 4BR
(Tel: 0244 817531)

C&G 606 Machine Woodworking: - Day Release/
Craft, Woodworking   Evening

C&G 606 Machine Woodworking: - Day Release/
Advanced Craft, Machine
Woodworking Science

North Lincolnshire College
Lincoln Site, Cathedral Street,
Lincoln, Lincolnshire LN2 5HQ
(Tel: 0522 510530)

C&G 606 Machine Woodworking: - Day Release
Craft, Woodworking

**North West College of
Technology**
Strand Road, Londonderry,
Northern Ireland BT48 7BY
(Tel: 0504 266711)

C&G 606 Machine Woodworking: - Day Release
Craft, Woodworking

**Norwich City College of Further
& Higher Education**
Ipswich Road, Norwich,
Norfolk NR2 2LJ
(Tel: 0603 660011)

C&G 586 Machine Woodworking: - Day Release/
Craft, Woodworking   Evening

C&G 586 Machine Woodworking: - Day Release/
Advanced Craft   Evening

YTS Machine Woodworking - Block Release
Craft

MACHINE WOODWORKING

Oldham College of Technology
Rochdale Road, Oldham,
Lancashire OL9 6AA
(Tel: 061-624 5214)

C&G 606 Machine Woodworking: - Day Release
    Craft, Woodworking

Oxford College of
Further Education
Oxpens Road, Oxford,
Oxfordshire OX1 1SA
(Tel: 0865 245871)

C&G 606 Machine Woodworking: - Day Release
    Craft, Woodworking

Parkwood College
Shirecliffe Road, Sheffield,
South Yorkshire S5 8XZ
(Tel: 0742 768301)

C&G 606 Machine Woodworking: - Block Release/
    Craft, Woodworking   Day Release
C&G 606 Machine Woodworking: - Block Release/
    Advanced Craft   Day Release
C&G 606 Machine Woodworking: - Block Release
    Advanced Craft, Toolroom
    Technology
C&G Machine Woodworking &   - Block Release/
    Safety Courses College   Part Time Day Re-
    Diploma   lease
C&G Machine Woodworking
    CNC Course   - Day Release/
      Evening

Percival Whitley College of
Further Education
Francis Street, Halifax,
West Yorkshire HX1 3UZ
(Tel: 0422 358221)

C&G 606 Machine Woodworking: - Evening
    Craft, Woodworking

Plymouth College of Further
Education
King's Road, Plymouth,
Devon PL1 5QG
(Tel: 0752 264786)

C&G 586 Machine Woodworking: - Block Release/
    Craft, Woodworking   Day Release/
      Evening
C&G 586 Machine Woodworking: - Block Release/
    Advanced Craft, Toolroom   Day Release/
    Technology   Evening

Pontypool College
Blaendare Road, Pontypool,
Gwent NP4 5YE
(Tel: 049 55 55141)

C&G 606 Machine Woodworking: - Day Release
    Craft, Woodworking

Reading College of Technology
Crescent Road, Reading,
Berkshire RG1 5RQ
(Tel: 0734 583501)

C&G 606 Machine Woodworking: - Block Release/
    Craft, Woodworking   Day Release
C&G 606 Machine Woodworking: - Day Release
    Advanced Craft, Toolroom
    Technology
C&G 606 Machine Woodworking: - Day Release
    Advanced Craft, Materials
    Technology
C&G 606 Machine Woodworking: - Day Release
    Advanced Craft, Production
    Planning for the Machine Shop

Rycotewood College
Priest End, Thame,
Oxfordshire OX9 2AF
(Tel: 084 421 2501)

Wood Machining   - Short Course

MACHINE WOODWORKING

St. Helens College Water Street, St Helens, Merseyside WA10 1PZ (Tel: 0744 33766)	C&G 606 Machine Woodworking: Craft, Woodworking	- Day Release
Salisbury College of Technology Southampton Road, Salisbury, Wiltshire SP1 2LW (Tel: 0722 23711)	C&G 606 Machine Woodworking: Craft, Woodworking	- Day Release
Southall College of Technology Beaconsfield Road, Southall, Middlesex UB1 1DP (Tel: 081-574 3448)	C&G 606 Machine Woodworking: Craft, Woodworking C&G 606 Machine Woodworking: Advanced Craft, Materials Technology	- Day Release/ Evening - Day Release/ Evening
Southampton Technical College St Mary Street, Southampton, Hampshire SO9 4WX (Tel: 0703 635222)	C&G 606 Machine Woodworking: Craft, Woodworking C&G 586 Machine Woodworking: Advanced Craft, (Subjects not Specified)	- Block Release/ Day Release/ Evening - Day Release
Southend College of Technology Carnarvon Road, Southend on Sea, Essex SS2 6LS (Tel: 0702 432205)	C&G 606 Machine Woodworking: Craft, Woodworking C&G 606 Machine Woodworking: Advanced Craft, Toolroom Technology C&G 606 Machine Woodworking: Advanced Craft, Machine Woodworking Science	- Day Release - Day Release - Day Release
South Fields College of Further Education Aylestone Road, Leicester, Leicestershire LE2 7LW (Tel: 0533 541818)	C&G 606 Machine Woodworking: Craft, Woodworking C&G 606 Machine Woodworking: Advanced Craft, Toolroom Technology	- Day Release - Day Release
South Glamorgan Institute of Higher Education Western Avenue, Llandaff, Cardiff, South Glamorgan CF5 2YB (Tel: 0222 551111)	C&G 606 Machine Woodworking: Craft, Woodworking C&G 606 Machine Woodworking: Advanced Craft, Materials Technology C&G 606 Machine Woodworking: Advanced Craft, Construction of Machined Components	- Day Release - Day Release - Day Release
South Kent College of Technology The Grange, Shorncliffe Road, Folkestone, Kent CT20 2NA (Tel: 0303 850061)	C&G 606 Machine Woodworking: Craft, Woodworking C&G 606 Machine Woodworking: Advanced Craft, Machine Woodworking Science	- Block Release/ Day Release - Day Release
South Tyneside College St George's Avenue, South Shields, Tyne and Wear NE34 6ET (Tel: 091-456 0403)	C&G 606 Machine Woodworking: Craft, Woodworking C&G 606 Machine Woodworking: Advanced Craft, Toolroom Technology	- Day Release - Day Release

MACHINE WOODWORKING

Stockport College of Further & Higher Education
Wellington Road South, Stockport,
Cheshire SK1 3UQ
(Tel: 061-480 7331)

C&G 606 Machine Woodworking: Craft, Woodworking	- Evening

Stoke-on-Trent College
Stoke Road, Shelton,
Stoke on Trent,
Staffordshire ST4 2DG
(Tel: 0782 208208)

C&G 606 Machine Woodworking: Craft, Woodworking	- Full Time/ Day Release/ Evening
C&G 606 Machine Woodworking: Advanced Craft, Toolroom Technology and all Options	- Day Release/ Evening

Suffolk College of Higher & Further Education
Rope Walk, Ipswich,
Suffolk IP4 1LT
(Tel: 0473 55885)

C&G 606 Machine Woodworking: Craft, Woodworking	- Day Release

Swindon College
Regent Circus, Swindon,
Wiltshire SN1 1PT
(Tel: 0793 491591)

C&G 606 Machine Woodworking: Craft, Woodworking	- Day Release
C&G 606 Machine Woodworking: Advanced Craft, Toolroom Technology	- Day Release
C&G 606 Machine Woodworking: Advanced Craft, Construction of Machined Components	- Day Release

Thanet Technical College
Ramsgate Road, Broadstairs,
Kent CT10 1PN
(Tel: 0843 65111)

Wood Machining	- Short Course

Thurrock Technical College
Woodview, Grays,
Essex RM16 4YR
(Tel: (0375 391199)

C&G 606 Machine Woodworking: Craft, Woodworking	- Day Release

Tottenham College of Technology
High Road, Tottenham,
London N15 4RU
(Tel: 081-802 3111)

C&G 606 Machine Woodworking: Craft, Woodworking	- Day Release

Vauxhall College of Building & Further Education
Belmore Street,
London SW8 2JY
(Tel: 071-498 1234)

C&G 606 Machine Woodworking: Craft, Woodworking	- Day Release
C&G 606 Machine Woodworking: Advanced Craft, Toolroom Technology	- Day Release
C&G 606 Machine Woodworking: Advanced Craft, Materials Technology	- Day Release
C&G 606 Machine Woodworking: Advanced Craft, Construction of Machined Components	- Day Release
C&G 606 Machine Woodworking: Advanced Craft, Production Planning for the Machine Shop	- Day Release

MACHINE WOODWORKING

Vauxhall College of Building & Further Education *Continued*	C&G 606 Machine Woodworking: Advanced Craft, Plant Layout and Materials Handling	- Day Release
	C&G 606 Machine Woodworking: Advanced Craft, Machine Woodworking Science	- Day Release
Waltham Forest College Forest Road, London E17 4JB (Tel: 081-527 2311)	C&G 606 Machine Woodworking: Craft, Woodworking	- Day Release
West Glamorgan Institute of Higher Education Mount Pleasant, Swansea, West Glamorgan SA1 6ED (Tel: 0792 469004)	C&G 606 Machine Woodworking: Craft, (Options Building Industry, Furniture and Timber Industries)	- Day Release
Wigan College of Technology Parsons Walk, Wigan, Lancashire WN1 1RR (Tel: 0942 494911)	C&G 606 Machine Woodworking: Craft, Woodworking	- Day Release
Willesden College of Technology Denzil Road, London NW10 2XD (Tel: 081-451 3411)	C&G 606 Machine Woodworking: Craft, Woodworking	- Day Release
	C&G 606 Machine Woodworking: Advanced Craft, Toolroom Technology	- Day Release
Worcester Technical College Deansway, Worcester, Hereford and Worcester WR1 2JF (Tel: 0905 723383)	C&G 606 Machine Woodworking: Craft, Woodworking	- Day Release
Ystrad Mynach College of Further Education Twyn Road, Ystrad Mynach, Hengoed, Mid-Glamorgan CF8 7XR (Tel: 0443 816888)	C&G 606 Machine Woodworking: Craft, Woodworking	- Day Release

MUSICAL INSTRUMENT MAKING

C&G 563 Stringed Keyboard Instrument Manufacture Part I
C&G 563 Stringed Keyboard Instrument Manufacture Part II
C&G 563 Advanced Certificate in Musical Instrument Repair
C&G 563 Higher Award in Musical Instrument Repair

Cambridge Regional College Newmarket Road, Cambridge, Cambridgeshire CB5 8EG (Tel: 0223 357545)	Classical Spanish Guitar making	- Evening
City of London Polytechnic 41-71 Commercial Road, London E1 1LA (Tel: 071-247 1953)	C&G 563 Stringed Keyboard Instrument Manufacture Part I	- Full Time
	C&G 563 Stringed Keyboard Instrument Manufacture Part II	- Full Time

MUSICAL INSTRUMENT MAKING

Merton College Morden Park, London Road, Morden, Surrey SM4 5QX (Tel: 081-640 3001)	C&G 563 Advanced Certificate in Musical Instrument Repair	- Full Time
	C&G 563 Higher Award in Musical Instrument Repair	- Full Time
	Advanced College Diploma in Musical Instrument Repair	- Full Time
	Repair of Brass, Woodwind, Guitar and Violin	- Day Release
Moray College of Further Education Hay Street, Elgin, Morayshire IV30 2NN (Tel: 0343 543425)	Non-vocational Musical Instrument Making	- Evening
Newark Technical College Chauntry Park, Newark, Nottinghamshire NG24 1BP (Tel: 0636 705921)	C&G 563 Stringed Keyboard Instrument Manufacture Part I	- Full Time
	C&G 563 Stringed Keyboard Instrument Manufacture Part II	- Full Time
Royal National College for Visually Handicapped College Road, Hereford, Herefordshire HR1 1EB (Tel: 0432 265725)	C&G 563 Stringed Keyboard Instrument Manufacture Part I	- Full Time
	C&G 563 Stringed Keyboard Instrument Manufacture Part II	- Full Time
West Dean College West Dean, Chichester, West Sussex PO18 0QZ (Tel: 0243 63 301 Fax: 0243 63 342)	Making of Early Musical Instruments	- Full Time

SHOPFITTING

City and Guilds London Institute Certificates:
C&G 587 Shopfitting: Craft
C&G 587 Shopfitting: Advanced Craft

Bournemouth & Poole College of Further Education North Road, Poole, Dorset BH14 0LS (Tel: 0202 747600)	C&G 587 Shopfitting: Craft C&G 587 Shopfitting: Advanced Craft	- Block Release - Block Release
Brooklyn Technical College (Great Barr) Aldridge Road, Great Barr, Birmingham, West Midlands B44 8NE (Tel: 021-360 3543)	C&G 587 Shopfitting: Craft C&G 587 Shopfitting: Advanced Craft	- Block Release/ Day Release - Day Release
Building Crafts Training School 153 Great Titchfield Street, London W1P 7FR (Tel: 071-636 0480)	C&G 587 Shopfitting: Craft C&G 587 Shopfitting: Advanced Craft	- Block Release - Block Release

DIRECTORY OF COURSES

SHOPFITTING

Doncaster College
Construction & Minerals
Engineering Division,
School of Construction,
Ellers Road, Bessacarr,
Doncaster DN4 7BA
(Tel: 0302 539446)

C&G 587 Shopfitting: Craft
C&G 587 Shopfitting: Advanced
    Craft

- Block Release
- Day Release

Hackney College
Keltan House, 89-115 Mare Street,
London E8 4RG
(Tel: 081-985 8484)

C&G 587 Shopfitting: Craft

- Full Time

**Hammersmith & West London
College**
40 Lime Grove, London W12
(Tel: 081-743 3321)

C&G 587 Shopfitting: Craft
C&G 587 Shopfitting: Advanced
    Craft

- Day Release
- Day Release

**Hull College of Further
Education**
Queen's Gardens, Hull,
North Humberside HU1 3DG
(Tel: 0482 29943)

C&G 587 Shopfitting: Craft

- Day Release

Leeds College of Building
North Street, Leeds,
West Yorkshire LS2 7QT
(Tel: 0532 430765)

C&G 587 Shopfitting: Craft

C&G 587 Shopfitting: Advanced
    Craft

- Block Release/
  Day Release
- Day Release

Lewes Tertiary College
Mountfield Road, Lewes,
East Sussex BN7 2XH
(Tel: 0273 483188)

C&G 587 Shopfitting: Craft
C&G 587 Shopfitting: Advanced
    Craft

- Block Release
- Block Release

**Newport College of Further
Education**
Nash Road, Newport,
Gwent NP6 2BR
(Tel: 0633 274861)

C&G 587 Shopfitting: Craft

C&G 587 Shopfitting: Advanced
    Craft

- Day Release/
  Block Release
- Day Release

**Salford College of Further
Education**
The Crescent Campus,
Windsor Building,
Withington Street, Salford,
Lancashire M6 5BG
(Tel: 061-745 8520)

C&G 587 Shopfitting: Craft
C&G 587 Shopfitting: Advanced
    Craft

- Day Release
- Day Release

**South Devon College of Arts &
Technology**
Newton Road, Torquay,
Devon TQ2 5BY
Tel: (0803 213242/217512)

C&G 587 Shopfitting: Craft
C&G 587 Shopfitting: Advanced
    Craft

- Block Release
- Block Release

Southend College of Technology
Carnarvon Road,
Southend on Sea,
Essex SS2 6LS
(Tel: 0702 432205)

C&G 587 Shopfitting: Craft -
    CITB/YTS

- Block Release

South Fields College of Further Education
Aylestone Road, Leicester,
Leicestershire LE2 7LW
(Tel: 0533 541818)

C&G 587 Shopfitting: Craft — Block Release
C&G 587 Shopfitting: Advanced Craft — Block Release

Tottenham College of Technology
High Road, Tottenham,
London N15 4RU
(Tel: 081-802 3111)

C&G 587 Shopfitting: Craft — Day Release
C&G 587 Shopfitting: Advanced Craft — Block Release/ Day Release

Wearside College of Further Education
Sea View Road West,
Grangetown, Sunderland,
Tyne and Wear SR2 9LH
(Tel: 091 5670794)

C&G 587 Shopfitting: Craft — Day Release

YACHT AND BOAT BUILDING

City and Guilds of London Institute Certificates
C&G 245 Yacht and Boat Building and Ship Joinery Craft Studies: Part I
C&G 245 Yacht and Boat Building and Ship Joinery Craft Studies: Part II
        Ship Joinery
C&G 245 Yacht and Boat Building and Ship Joinery Craft Studies: Part II
        Yacht and Boat Building
C&G 245 Yacht and Boat Building and Ship Joinery Craft Studies: Part III
British Marine Industry Federation - Skillbuild

Anniesland College
Hatfield Drive,
Glasgow G12 0YE
(Tel: 041-357 3969)

C&G 245 Yacht and Boat Building and Ship Joinery Craft Studies: Part II Ship Joinery — Day Release
C&G 245 Yacht and Boat Building and Ship Joinery Craft Studies: Part III — Day Release

Arnold & Carlton College of Further Education
Digby Avenue, Mapperley,
Nottingham,
Nottinghamshire NG3 6DR
(Tel: 0602 876503)

C&G 245 Yacht and Boat Building and Ship Joinery Craft Studies: Part I — Day Release
C&G 245 Yacht and Boat Building and Ship Joinery Craft Studies: Part II — Day Release
C&G 245 Yacht and Boat Building and Ship Joinery Craft Studies: Part III — Day Release

Bournemouth & Poole College of Further Education
North Road, Poole,
Dorset BH14 0LS
(Tel: 0202 747600)

C&G 245 Yacht and Boat Building and Ship Joinery Craft Studies: Part I — Day Release

Cilestel Training Services
The Old Vicarage, School Lane,
Heckingham, Norwich,
Norfolk NR14 6QP
(Tel: 0508 46289)

Boatbuilding - Skillbuild — Full Time

YACHT AND BOAT BUILDING

Cornwall College
School of Yacht & Boat Building,
Falmouth Marine Centre,
Killigrew Street, Falmouth,
Cornwall TR11 3QS
(Tel: 0326 313326)

C&G 245 Yacht and Boat Building and Ship Joinery Craft Studies: Part I — Full Time/ Block Release

C&G 245 Yacht and Boat Building and Ship Joinery Craft Studies: Part II, Ship Joinery — Full Time/ Block Release

C&G 245 Yacht and Boat Building and Ship Joinery Craft Studies: Part II, Yacht and Boat Building — Full Time/ Block Release

C&G 245 Yacht and Boat Building and Ship Joinery Craft Studies: Part III — Block Release

Guernsey College of Further Education
Route des Coutanchez,
St Peter Port, Guernsey
(0481 727121)

C&G 245 Yacht and Boat Building and Ship Joinery Craft Studies: Part I — Day Release

Isle of Wight College of Art & Technology
Medina Way, Newport,
Isle of Wight PO30 5TA
(Tel: 0983 526631)

C&G 245 Yacht and Boat Building and Ship Joinery Craft Studies: Part II, Yacht and Boat Building — Day Release

C&G 245 Yacht and Boat Building and Ship Joinery Craft Studies: Part III — Day Release

Isle of Wight Industrial Group Training Scheme
6 Dodnor Lane,
Dodnor Industrial Estate,
Newport,
Isle of Wight PO30 5XA
(Tel: 0983 525583)

Boat Building - Skillbuild — Block Release

Kidderminster College of Further Education
Hoo Road, Kidderminster,
Worcestershire DY10 1LX
(Tel: 0562 820811)

C&G 245 Yacht and Boat Building and Ship Joinery Craft Studies: Part I — Block Release

C&G 245 Yacht and Boat Building and Ship Joinery Craft Studies: Part II, Yacht and Boat Building — Block Release

C&G 245 Yacht and Boat Building and Ship Joinery Craft Studies: Part III — Block Release

Skillbuild and other associated courses — Block Release

Kingston College of Further Education
Richmond Road,
Kingston-upon-Thames,
Surrey KT2 5BP
(Tel: 081-546 4626)

Marine Engineering - YTS, C&G, Skillbuild — Block Release

YACHT AND BOAT BUILDING

Lowestoft College
St Peter's Street, Lowestoft,
Suffolk NR32 2NB
(Tel: 0502 583521)

C&G 245 Yacht and Boat Building and Ship Joinery Craft Studies: Part I — Day Release

C&G 245 Yacht and Boat Building and Ship Joinery Craft Studies: Part II, Ship Joinery — Day Release

C&G 245 Yacht and Boat Building and Ship Joinery Craft Studies: Part III — Day Release

Marine & Commercial Training
Marine Training House,
Harbour Road, Oulton Broad,
Lowestoft, Suffolk NR32 3LZ
(Tel: 0502 569663)

YTS Training in Boatbuilding — Full Time
Skillbuild — Full Time

Marine Builders Training Trust
Hazel Road, Woolston,
Southampton,
Hampshire SO2 7GB
(Tel: 0703 446824)

C&G 245 Yacht and Boat Building and Ship Joinery Craft Studies — Full Time
BMIF Skillbuild — Full Time
YTS Boat Building — Full Time

Marine Training & Development
International Boatbuilding
Training Centre,
Harbour Road, Oulton Broad,
Lowestoft, Suffolk NR32 3LZ
(Tel: 0502 569663)

Boat building and additional short courses (electrics, plumbing, outfitting) Skillbuild — 1 Year

NACRO
Hutchinson Street,
Stockton-on-Tees, Cleveland
(Tel: 0642 615554)

Boat Building - Skillbuild

Plymouth Community Boatyard
3 Richmond Walk, Plymouth,
Devon PL1 4LL
(Tel: 0752 509738)

Boat building skills - Adult training and re-training ET and Skillbuild — Full Time

Southampton Technical College
St Mary Street, Southampton,
Hampshire SO9 4WX
(Tel: 0703 635222)

C&G 245 Yacht and Boat Building and Ship Joinery Craft Studies: Part I — Day Release/ Full Time

C&G 245 Yacht and Boat Building and Ship Joinery Craft Studies: Part II, Ship Joinery — Day Release

C&G 245 Yacht and Boat Building and Ship Joinery Craft Studies: Part II, Yacht and Boat Building — Day Release

C&G 245 Yacht and Boat Building and Ship Joinery Craft Studies: Part III — Day Release

YACHT AND BOAT BUILDING

South Bristol College
Technology Division,
Marksbury Centre, Bedminster,
Bristol BS3 5JL
(Tel: 0272 661105)

Marine Engineering - City &
Guilds and Skillbuild

- 3 Year Course

South Tyneside College
St George's Avenue,
South Shields,
Tyne and Wear NE34 6ET
(Tel: 091- 456 0403)

C&G 245 Yacht and Boat Building
and Ship Joinery Craft Studies:
Part I

- Day Release

C&G 245 Yacht and Boat Building
and Ship Joinery Craft Studies:
Part II, Ship Joinery

- Day Release

C&G 245 Yacht and Boat Building
and Ship Joinery Craft Studies:
Part III

- Day Release

Wirral Metropolitan College
Borough Road, Birkenhead,
Wirral L42 9QD
(Tel: 051-653 5555)

C&G 245 Yacht and Boat Building
and Ship Joinery Craft Studies:
Part I

- Day Release

YACHT AND BOAT BUILDING

Other Courses:

SCOTVEC: National Certificate Modules, Yacht and Boat Building

College Award: Diploma in Yacht and Boatbuilding
College Award: Diploma in Yacht and Boat Design

Anniesland College
Hatfield Drive,
Glasgow G12 0YE
(Tel: 041-357 3969)

SCOTVEC: National Certificate
Modules, Yacht and Boat
Building

- Day Release

Autotech Marine Training Ltd
Dominion Road, Wallisdown,
Bournemouth, Dorset BH11 8LH
(Tel: 0202 570341)

Training in basic Boat Building
and Marine Engineering

- Day Release

BIYTE
14 Frederick Place, Bristol,
Avon BS8 1AS
(Tel: 0272 737281/736323)

Basic Boat Building Training
using selected Skillbuild
Modules

- Day Release

Cornwall College
School of Yacht & Boat Building,
Falmouth Centre, Killigrew Street,
Falmouth, Cornwall TR11 3QS
(Tel: 0326 313326)

College Award: Diploma in Yacht
and Boatbuilding

- Full Time

BOATEC
Certificate in Boatbuilding and
Fitting out

- 2 Years

**Isle of Wight Industrial Group
Training Scheme**
6 Dodnor Lane,
Dodnor Industrial Estate,
Newport,
Isle of Wight PO30 5XA
(Tel: 0983 525583)

Training Placement Co-ordinators

YACHT AND BOAT BUILDING

James Watt College Finnart Street, Greenock, Renfrewshire PA16 8HF (Tel: 0475 24433)	SCOTVEC: National Certificate Modules, Yacht and Boat Building	- Day Release
Southampton College of Higher Education East Park Terrace, Southampton, Hampshire SO9 4WW (Tel: 0703 229381)	Diploma in Yacht & Boat Yard Management Diploma in Yacht & Boat Design New Design B. Eng.	- 3 Years - 3 Years
Southampton Technical College St Mary Street, Southampton, Hampshire SO9 4WX (Tel: 0703 635222)	College Award: Diploma in Yacht and Boat Design	- Full Time
Tile Hill College Tile Hill Lane, Tile Hill, Coventry, West Midlands CV4 9SU (Tel: 0203 694200)	Inland Waterways - Boating Enterprises Skills Training Scheme (BEST)	

CONSTRUCTION CRAFTS: SUPPLEMENTARY CRAFTS

City and Guilds of London Institute Certificates
C&G 600 Construction Crafts: Supplementary Studies
C&G 600 Craft Supervision
C&G 600 Construction Craft Supervision

College Based Building Craft Studies
College Based Building Craft Course in 4 Trades

Aberdeen Technical College Gallowgate, Aberdeen, Grampian AB9 1DN (Tel: 0224 640366)	C&G 600 Construction Crafts: Supplementary Studies	- Day Release
Angus Technical College Keptie Road, Arbroath, Angus DD11 3EA (Tel: 0241 72056)	C&G 600 Construction Crafts: Supplementary Studies	- Day Release/ Evening
Ballymena Technical College Farm Lodge Avenue, Ballymena, County Antrim, Northern Ireland BT43 7DJ (Tel: 0266 652871)	C&G 600 Construction Crafts: Supplementary Studies	- Evening
Ballynahinch College Church Road, Ballynahinch, County Down, Northern Ireland BT24 8LP (Tel: 023 856 2369)	C&G 600 Craft Supervision	- Day Release/ Evening
Banff & Buchan College of Further Education Argyll Road, Fraserburgh, Aberdeenshire AB4 5RF (Tel: 03465 5777)	College Based Building Craft Studies	- Block Release

SUPPLEMENTARY STUDIES

Barrow College of Further Education
Howard Street, Barrow in Furness,
Cumbria LA14 1NB
(Tel: 0229 825017)

C&G 600 Construction Crafts:
Supplementary Studies

- Evening

Barry College of Further Education
Colcot Road, Barry,
South Glamorgan CF6 8YJ
(Tel: 0446 733251)

C&G 600 Construction Crafts:
Supplementary Studies

- Evening

Basford Hall College of Further Education
Stockhill Lane, Nottingham,
Nottinghamshire NG6 0NB
(Tel: 0602 704541)

C&G 600 Construction Crafts:
Supplementary Studies

- Day Release/
Evening

Bedford College of Higher Education
Cauldwell Street, Bedford,
Bedfordshire MK42 9AH
(Tel: 0234 45151)

C&G 600 Construction Crafts:
Supplementary Studies

- Day Release/
Evening

Belfast College of Technology
College Square East, Belfast,
Northern Ireland BT1 6DJ
(Tel: 0232 327244)

C&G 600 Construction Crafts:
Supplementary Studies

- Day Release/
Evening

Bishop Auckland Technical College
Woodhouse Lane,
Bishop Auckland,
Co Durham DL14 6JZ
(Tel: (0388 603052)

C&G 600 Construction Crafts:
Supplementary Studies

- Day Release/
Evening

Blackburn College
Feilden Street, Blackburn,
Lancashire BB2 1LH
(Tel: 0254 55144)

C&G 600 Construction Crafts:
Supplementary Studies
CIOB Certificate in Site
Supervisory Studies

- Day Release/
Evening
- Evening

Blackpool & The Fylde College
Palatine Road, Blackpool,
Lancashire FY2 0HB
(Tel: 0253 52352)

C&G 600 Construction Crafts:
Supplementary Studies

- Evening

Bolton Metropolitan College
Manchester Road, Bolton,
Lancashire BL2 1ER
(Tel: 0204 31411)

C&G 600 Construction Crafts:
Supplementary Studies

- Day Release/
Evening

Boston College of Further Education
Rowley Road, Boston,
Lincolnshire PE21 6JF
(Tel: 0205 365701)

C&G 600 Construction Crafts:
Supplementary Studies

- Day Release/
Evening

Bournemouth & Poole College of Further Education North Road, Poole, Dorset BH14 0LS (Tel: 0202 747600)	C&G 600 Construction Crafts: Supplementary Studies	- Day Release
Bridgwater College Bath Road, Bridgwater, Somerset TA6 4PZ (Tel: 0278 455464)	C&G 600 Construction Crafts: Supplementary Studies	- Evening
Brooklyn Technical College (Great Barr) Aldridge Road, Great Barr, Birmingham, West Midlands B44 8NE (Tel: 021-360 3453)	C&G 600 Construction Crafts: Supplementary Studies	- Day Release
Brunel Technical College Ashley Down, Bristol, Avon BS7 9BU (Tel: 0272 241241)	C&G 600 Construction Crafts: Supplementary Studies	- Day Release/ Evening
Burnley College Shorey Bank, Ormerod Road, Burnley, Lancashire BB11 2RX (Tel: 0282 36111)	C&G 600 Construction Crafts: Supplementary Studies	- Full Time/ Day Release/ Evening
Burton Upon Trent Technical College Lichfield Street, Burton Upon Trent, Staffordshire DE14 3RL (Tel: 0283 45401)	C&G 600 Construction Crafts: Supplementary Studies	- Evening
Cambuslang College Hamilton Road, Cambuslang, Glasgow G72 7NY (Tel: 041-641 6600)	C&G 600 Construction Crafts: Supplementary Studies	- Day Release
Canterbury College New Dover Road, Canterbury, Kent CT1 3AJ (Tel: 0227 66081)	C&G 600 Construction Crafts: Supplementary Studies	- Day Release
Carlisle College Victoria Place, Carlisle, Cumbria CA1 1HS (Tel: 0228 24464)	C&G 600 Construction Crafts: Supplementary Studies	- Evening
Carmarthenshire College of Technology & Art Ammanford Campus, Tir-y-dail, Ammanford, Dyfed SA18 3TA (Tel: 0269 591978)	C&G 600 Construction Crafts: Supplementary Studies	- Day Release

SUPPLEMENTARY STUDIES

Castlereagh College of Further Education Montgomery Road, Belfast, Northern Ireland BT6 9JD (Tel: 0232 797144)	C&G 600 Construction Crafts: Supplementary Studies	- Day Release/ Evening
Central Manchester College Lower Hardman Street, Manchester, Gt Manchester M3 3ER (Tel: 061-831 7791)	C&G 600 Construction Crafts: Supplementary Studies	- Day Release/ Evening
Ceredigion College of Further Education Llanbadarn Campus, Llanbadarn Fawr, Dyfed SY23 2BP (Tel: 0970 4511)	C&G 600 Construction Crafts: Supplementary Studies	- Day Release
Chelmsford College of Further Education Upper Moulsham Street, Chelmsford, Essex CM2 0JQ (Tel: 0245 265611)	C&G 600 Construction Crafts: Supplementary Studies	- Day Release/ Evening
Chichester College of Technology Westgate Fields, Chichester, West Sussex PO19 1SB (Tel: 0243 786321)	C&G 600 Construction Crafts: Supplementary Studies	- Day Release
Cleveland Technical College Corporation Road, Redcar, Cleveland TS10 1EZ (Tel: 0642 473132)	C&G 600 Construction Crafts: Supplementary Studies	- Day Release/ Evening
Clydebank College Kilbowie Road, Clydebank, Dunbartonshire G81 2AA (Tel: 041-952 7771)	C&G 600 Construction Crafts: Supplementary Studies	- Day Release
Coalville Technical College Bridge Road, Coalville, Leicester, Leicestershire LE6 2QR (Tel: 0530 36136)	C&G 600 Construction Crafts: Supplementary Studies	- Evening
Coleg Powys Coleg Howell Harris, Penlan, Brecon, Powys LD3 9SR (Tel: 0874 5252)	C&G 600 Construction Crafts: Supplementary Studies	- Day Release/ Evening
Coleraine Technical College Union Street, Coleraine, Northern Ireland BT52 1QA (Tel: 0265 54717/8)	C&G 600 Construction Crafts: Supplementary Studies	- Day Release/ Evening

Cornwall College of Further & Higher Education Redruth, Cornwall TR15 3RD (Tel: 0209 712911)	C&G 600 Construction Crafts: Supplementary Studies	- Day Release
Coventry Technical College Butts, Coventry, West Midlands CV1 3GD (Tel: 0203 57221)	C&G 600 Construction Crafts: Supplementary Studies	- Day Release
Darlington College of Technology Cleveland Avenue, Darlington, Co. Durham DL3 7BB (Tel: 0325 467651)	C&G 600 Construction Crafts: Supplementary Studies	- Evening
Down College of Further Education Downpatrick, County Down, Northern Ireland BT30 6ND (Tel: 0396 615815)	C&G 600 Construction Crafts: Supplementary Studies	- Evening
Dumfries & Galloway College of Technology Heathhall, Dumfries DG1 3QZ (Tel: 0387 61261/ Fax: 0387 50006)	C&G 600 Construction Crafts: Supplementary Studies	- Day Release/ Evening
Dungannon Further Education College Circular Road, Dungannon, County Tyrone, Northern Ireland BT71 6BQ (Tel: 086 87 22323)	C&G 600 Construction Crafts: Supplementary Studies	- Open Learning
East Yorkshire College of Further Education St Mary's Walk, Bridlington, North Humberside YO16 5JW (Tel: 0262 672676)	C&G 600 Construction Crafts: Supplementary Studies	- Evening
Erith College of Technology Tower Road, Belvedere, Kent DA17 6JA (Tel: 032 24 42331)	C&G 600 Construction Crafts: Supplementary Studies	- Day Release
Fermanagh College of Further Education Fairview Avenue, Enniskillen, County Fermanagh, Northern Ireland BT74 6AE (Tel: 0365 322431)	C&G 600 Construction Crafts: Supplementary Studies	- Evening
Glasgow College of Building & Printing 60 North Hanover Street, Glasgow G1 2BP (Tel: 041-332 9969)	C&G 600 Construction Crafts: Supplementary Studies	- Day Release/ Evening

SUPPLEMENTARY STUDIES

Gloucestershire College of Art & Technology Brunswick Campus, Brunswick Road, Gloucester, Gloucestershire GL1 1HU (Tel: 0452 426500)	C&G 600 Construction Crafts: Supplementary Studies	- Day Release/ Evening
Grantham College of Further Education Stonebridge Road, Grantham, Lincolnshire NG31 9AP (Tel: 0476 63141)	C&G 600 Construction Crafts: Supplementary Studies	- Evening
Gt. Yarmouth College of Further Education Southtown, Great Yarmouth, Norfolk NR31 0ED (Tel: 0493 655261)	C&G 600 Construction Crafts: Supplementary Studies	- Evening
Guernsey College of Further Education Route des Coutanchez, St Peter Port, Guernsey (Tel: 0481 727121)	C&G 600 Construction Crafts: Supplementary Studies	- Day Release
Guildford College of Technology Stoke Park, Guildford, Surrey GU1 1EZ (Tel: 0483 31251)	C&G 600 Construction Crafts: Supplementary Studies	- Day Release
Hackney College Keltan House, 89-115 Mare Street, London E8 4RG (Tel: 081-985 8484)	C&G 600 Construction Crafts: Supplementary Studies	- Day Release
Hall Green College Cole Bank Road, Birmingham, West Midlands B28 8ES (Tel: 021-778 2311)	C&G 600 Construction Crafts: Supplementary Studies	- Day Release
Hammersmith & West London College 40 Lime Grove, London W12 (Tel: 081-743 3321)	C&G 600 Construction Crafts: Supplementary Studies	- Day Release
Hartlepool College of Further Education Stockton Street, Hartlepool, Cleveland TS25 7NT (Tel: 0429 275453)	C&G 600 Construction Crafts: Supplementary Studies	- Day Release/ Evening
Herefordshire Technical College Folly Lane, Hereford HR1 1LS (Tel: 0432 352235)	C&G 600 Construction Crafts: Supplementary Studies	- Evening

Hertfordshire Centre for Building Studies St Peter's Road, St Albans, Hertfordshire AL1 3RX (Tel: 0727 47074)	C&G 600 Construction Crafts: Supplementary Studies	- Day Release/ Evening
Highbury College of Technology Dovercourt Road, Cosham, Portsmouth, Hampshire PO6 2SA (Tel: 0705 383131)	C&G 600 Construction Crafts: Supplementary Studies	- Day Release
Highlands College PO Box 142, St Saviour, Jersey (Tel: 0534 71800)	C&G 600 Construction Crafts: Supplementary Studies	- Day Release
Huddersfield Technical College New North Road, Huddersfield, West Yorkshire HD1 5NN (Tel: 0484 36521)	C&G 600 Construction Crafts: Supplementary Studies	- Day Release/ Evening
Hull College of Further Education Queen's Gardens, Hull, North Humberside HU1 3DG (Tel: 0482 29943)	C&G 600 Construction Crafts: Supplementary Studies	- Day Release/ Evening
Huntingdonshire College California Road, Huntingdon, Cambridgeshire PE18 7BL (Tel: 0480 52346)	C&G 600 Construction Crafts: Supplementary Studies	- Evening
Inverness College of Further & Higher Education 3 Longman Road, Inverness IV1 1SA (Tel: 0463 236681)	C&G 600 Construction Crafts: Supplementary Studies	- Block Release
Isle College Ramnoth Road, Wisbech, Cambridgeshire PE13 2JE (Tel: 0945 582561)	C&G 600 Construction Crafts: Supplementary Studies	- Evening
Isle of Man College of Further Education Homefield Road, Douglas, Isle of Man (Tel: 0624 23113)	C&G 600 Construction Crafts: Supplementary Studies	- Evening
Keighley College Cavendish Street, Keighley, West Yorkshire BD21 3DF (Tel: 0274 758555)	C&G 600 Construction Crafts: Supplementary Studies	- Day Release
Lancaster & Morecambe College Morecambe Road, Lancaster, Lancashire LA1 2TY (Tel: 0524 66215 Fax: 0524 843078)	C&G 600 Construction Crafts: Supplementary Studies	- Evening

SUPPLEMENTARY STUDIES

Langley College
Station Road, Langley,
Slough, Berkshire SL3 8BY
(Tel: 0753 49222)

C&G 600 Construction Crafts: Supplementary Studies — Day Release

Lauder Technical College
Halbeath, Dunfermline,
Fife KY11 5DY
(Tel: 0383 726201)

C&G 600 Construction Crafts: Supplementary Studies — Day Release

Leeds College of Building
North Street, Leeds,
West Yorkshire LS2 7QT
(Tel: 0532 430765)

C&G 600 Construction Crafts: Supplementary Studies — Day Release/ Evening

Lewisham College
Worsley Bridge Road,
Lower Sydenham,
London SE26 5BD
(Tel: 081-650 8227)

C&G 600 Construction Crafts: Supplementary Studies — Day Release/ Evening

Limavady Technical College
Limavady, County Londonderry,
Northern Ireland BT49 0EX
(Tel: 050 47 62334)

C&G 600 Construction Crafts: Supplementary Studies — Day Release

Lisburn College of Further Education
Castle Street, Lisburn,
County Antrim,
Northern Ireland BT27 4SU
(Tel: 084 6677225)

C&G 600 Construction Crafts: Supplementary Studies — Day Release/ Evening

Loughborough College
Radmoor, Loughborough,
Leicestershire LE11 3BT
(Tel: 0509 215831)

C&G 600 Construction Crafts: Supplementary Studies — Day Release

Lowestoft College
St Peter's Street, Lowestoft,
Suffolk NR32 2NB
(Tel: 0502 583521)

C&G 600 Construction Crafts: Supplementary Studies — Evening

Merthyr Tydfil Technical College
Ynsfach, Merthyr Tydfil,
Mid-Glamorgan CF48 1AR
(Tel: 0685 723663)

C&G 600 Construction Crafts: Supplementary Studies — Day Release
C&G 600 Craft Supervision — Evening

Mid-Cornwall College
Palace Road, St Austell,
Cornwall PL25 4BW
(Tel: 0726 67911)

C&G 600 Construction Crafts: Supplementary Studies — Evening

Mid-Kent College of Higher & Further Education
Horsted, Maidstone Road,
Chatham, Kent ME5 9UQ
(Tel: 0634 44470)

C&G 600 Construction Crafts: Supplementary Studies — Day Release

Neath College Dwr Y Felin Road, Neath, West Glamorgan SA10 7RF (Tel: 0639 634271)	C&G 600 Construction Crafts: Supplementary Studies	- Day Release/ Evening
Nene College Moulton Park, Northampton, Northamptonshire NN2 7AL Tel: 0604 715000)	C&G 600 Construction Crafts: Supplementary Studies	- Day Release
Newcastle College Maple Terrace, Newcastle upon Tyne, Tyne & Wear NE4 7SA Tel: 091-273 8866)	C&G 600 Construction Crafts: Supplementary Studies	- Day Release/ Evening
Newcastle College of Further Education Donard Street, Newcastle, County Down, Northern Ireland BT33 0AP Tel: 039 67 22451)	C&G 600 Construction Crafts: Supplementary Studies	- Day Release/ Evening
New College Framwellgate Moor, Durham, Co Durham DH1 5ES Tel: 091 386 2421)	C&G 600 Construction Crafts: Supplementary Studies	- Day Release/ Evening
Newry Technical College Patrick Street, Newry, County Down, Northern Ireland BT35 8DN Tel: 0693 61071)	C&G 600 Construction Crafts: Supplementary Studies	- Evening
Newtownabbey Technical College Shore Road, Newtownabbey, County Antrim, Northern Ireland BT37 9RS Tel: 0232 864331)	C&G 600 Construction Crafts: Supplementary Studies	- Day Release
Norfolk College of Art & Technology Tennyson Avenue, King's Lynn, Norfolk PE30 2QW Tel: 0553 761144)	C&G 600 Construction Crafts: Supplementary Studies	- Evening
North Down & Ards College of Further Education Castle Park Road, Bangor, County Down, Northern Ireland BT20 4TF Tel: 0247 271254/5)	C&G 600 Construction Crafts: Supplementary Studies	- Day Release/ Evening
North East Surrey College of Technology Reigate Road, Ewell, Surrey KT17 3DS Tel: 081-394 1731)	C&G 600 Construction Crafts: Supplementary Studies	- Day Release/ Evening

SUPPLEMENTARY STUDIES

**North East Wales Institute of
Higher Education**
Deeside, Connah's Quay,
Clwyd CH5 4BR
(Tel: 0244 817531)

C&G 600 Construction Crafts:
Supplementary Studies

- Day Release

**North Nottinghamshire College
of Further Education**
Carlton Road, Worksop,
Nottinghamshire S81 7HP
(Tel: 0909 473561)

C&G 600 Construction Crafts:
Supplementary Studies

- Day Release/
Evening

**Northumberland College of Art
& Technology**
College Road, Ashington,
Northumberland NE26 9RG
(Tel: 0670 813248)

C&G 600 Construction Crafts:
Supplementary Studies

- Day Release

**North West College of
Technology**
Strand Road, Londonderry,
Northern Ireland BT48 7BY
(Tel: 0504 266711)

C&G 600 Construction Crafts:
Supplementary Studies

- Evening

**Norwich City College of Further
& Higher Education**
Ipswich Road, Norwich,
Norfolk NR2 2LJ
(Tel: 0603 660011)

C&G 600 Construction Crafts:
Supplementary Studies

- Day Release

Oldham College of Technology
Rochdale Road, Oldham,
Lancashire OL9 6AA
(Tel: 061-624 5214)

C&G 600 Construction Crafts:
Supplementary Studies

- Day Release

**Omagh College of Further
Education**
Omagh, County Tyrone,
Northern Ireland BT79 7AH
(Tel: 0662 45433)

C&G 600 Construction Crafts:
Supplementary Studies

- Evening

**Oxford College of Further
Education**
Oxpens Road, Oxford,
Oxfordshire OX1 1SA
(Tel: 0865 245871)

C&G 600 Construction Crafts:
Supplementary Studies

- Day Release/
Evening

Parkwood College
Shirecliffe Road, Sheffield,
South Yorkshire S5 8XZ
(Tel: 0742 768301)

C&G 600 Construction Crafts:
Supplementary Studies

- Day Release/
Evening

**Percival Whitley College of
Further Education**
Francis Street, Halifax,
West Yorkshire HX1 3UZ
(Tel: 0422 358221)

C&G 600 Construction Crafts:
Supplementary Studies

- Evening

Perth College of Further Education Brahan Estate, Creiff Road, Perth PH1 2NX (Tel: 0738 21171)	C&G 600 Construction Crafts: Supplementary Studies	- Day Release/ Evening/ Distance Learning
Peterborough Regional College Park Crescent, Peterborough, Cambridgeshire PE1 4DZ (Tel: 0733 67366)	C&G 600 Construction Crafts: Supplementary Studies	- Evening
Plymouth College of Further Education King's Road, Plymouth, Devon PL1 5QG (Tel: 0752 264786)	C&G 600 Construction Crafts: Supplementary Studies	- Day Release
Reading College of Technology Crescent Road, Reading, Berkshire RG1 5RQ (Tel: 0734 583501)	C&G 600 Construction Crafts: Supplementary Studies	- Day Release
Reid Kerr College Renfrew Road, Paisley, Renfrewshire PA3 4DR (Tel: 041-889 4225)	C&G 600 Craft Supervision	- Day Release
Rochdale Technical College St Mary's Gate, Rochdale, Lancashire OL12 6RY (Tel: 0706 345346)	C&G 600 Construction Crafts: Supplementary Studies	- Day Release/ Evening
Rotherham College of Art & Technology Eastwood Lane, Rotherham, South Yorkshire S65 1EG (Tel: 0709 362111)	C&G 600 Construction Crafts: Supplementary Studies	- Evening
St. Helens College Water Street, St Helens, Merseyside WA10 1PZ (Tel: 0744 33766)	C&G 600 Construction Crafts: Supplementary Studies	- Day Release/ Evening
Salisbury College of Technology Southampton Road, Salisbury, Wiltshire SP1 2LW (Tel: 0722 23711)	C&G 600 Construction Crafts: Supplementary Studies	- Evening
Scarborough Technical College Lady Edith's Drive, Scarborough, North Yorkshire YO12 5RN (Tel: 0723 372105)	C&G 600 Construction Crafts: Supplementary Studies	- Evening
Shrewsbury College of Art and Technology London Road, Shrewsbury, Shropshire SY2 6PR (Tel: 0743 231544)	C&G 600 Construction Crafts: Supplementary Studies	- Evening

DIRECTORY OF COURSES

SUPPLEMENTARY STUDIES

Somerset College of Art and Technology
Wellington Road, Taunton,
Somerset TA1 5AX
(Tel: 0823 83403)

C&G 600 Construction Crafts:
Supplementary Studies

- Evening

Southampton Technical College
St Mary Street, Southampton,
Hampshire SO9 4WX
(Tel: 0703 635222)

C&G 600 Construction Crafts:
Supervision (Special)

- Full Time

South Devon College of Arts & Technology
Newton Road, Torquay,
Devon TQ2 5BY
Tel: (0803 213242/217512)

C&G 600 Construction Crafts:
Supplementary Studies

- Day Release

South East Derbyshire College
Field Road, Ilkeston,
Derbyshire DE7 5RS
(Tel: 0602 324212)

C&G 600 Construction Crafts:
Supplementary Studies

- Day Release/
Evening

Southend College of Technology
Carnarvon Road,
Southend on Sea, Essex SS2 6LS
(Tel: 0702 432205)

C&G 600 Construction Crafts:
Supplementary Studies

- Day Release/
Evening

South Fields College of Further Education
Aylestone Road, Leicester,
Leicestershire LE2 7LW
(Tel: 0533 541818)

C&G 600 Construction Crafts:
Supplementary Studies

- Day Release/
Evening

South Glamorgan Institute of Higher Education
Western Avenue, Llandaff,
Cardiff,
South Glamorgan CF5 2YB
(Tel: 0222 551111)

C&G 600 Construction Crafts:
Supplementary Studies

- Day Release

South Mersey College
Riversdale Road, Liverpool,
Merseyside L19 3QR
(Tel: 051-427 1227)

C&G 600 Construction Crafts:
Supplementary Studies

- Day Release

Southport College of Art & Technology
Mornington Road, Southport,
Merseyside PR9 0TT
(Tel: 0704 542411)

C&G 600 Construction Crafts:
Supplementary Studies

- Evening

Stockport College of Further & Higher Education
Wellington Road South, Stockport,
Cheshire SK1 3UQ
(Tel: 061-480 7331)

C&G 600 Construction Crafts:
Supplementary Studies
C&G 600 Craft Supervision

- Day Release/
Evening
- Day Release/
Evening

Stoke-on-Trent College Stoke Road, Shelton, Stoke on Trent Staffordshire ST4 2DG (Tel: 0782 208208)	C&G 600 Construction Crafts: Supplementary Studies	- Day Release/ Evening
Stourbridge College of Technology and Art Hagley Road, Stourbridge, West Midlands DY8 1LY (Tel: 038 43 78531)	C&G 600 Construction Crafts: Supplementary Studies	- Evening
Stroud College Stratford Road, Stroud, Gloucestershire GL5 4AH (Tel: 0453 763424)	C&G 600 Construction Crafts: Supplementary Studies College Based Building Craft Course in 4 Trades	- Evening - Full Time
Swindon College Regent Circus, Swindon, Wiltshire SN1 1PT (Tel: 0793 491591)	C&G 600 Construction Crafts: Supplementary Studies	- Evening
Telford College of Further Education Crewe Toll, Edinburgh, Scotland EH4 2NZ (Tel: 031-332 2491)	C&G 600 Construction Crafts: Supplementary Studies	- Day Release
Tottenham College of Technology High Road, Tottenham, London N15 4RU (Tel: 081-802 3111)	C&G 600 Construction Crafts: Supplementary Studies	- Day Release
Tresham College St Mary's Road, Kettering, Northamptonshire NN15 7BS (Tel: 0536 85353)	C&G 600 Construction Crafts: Supplementary Studies	- Evening
Trowbridge College College Road, Trowbridge, Wiltshire BA14 0ES (Tel: 0225 766241)	C&G 600 Construction Crafts: Supplementary Studies	- Day Release
Vauxhall College of Building & Further Education Belmore Street, London SW8 2JY (Tel: 071-498 1234)	C&G 600 Construction Crafts: Supplementary Studies	- Day Release/ Evening
Waltham Forest College Forest Road, London E17 4JB (Tel: 081-527 2311)	C&G 600 Construction Crafts: Supplementary Studies	- Evening
West Cheshire College Handbridge Centre, Eaton Road, Handbridge, Chester, Cheshire CH4 7ER (Tel: 0244 677677)	C&G 600 Construction Crafts: Supplementary Studies	- Day Release

SUPPLEMENTARY STUDIES

West Cumbria College
Park Lane, Workington,
Cumbria CA14 2RW
(Tel: 0900 64331)

C&G 600 Construction Crafts:
Supplementary Studies

- Day Release/
Evening

**West Glamorgan Institute of
Higher Education**
Mount Pleasant, Swansea,
West Glamorgan SA1 6ED
(Tel: 0792 469004)

C&G 600 Construction Crafts:
Supplementary Studies

- Day Release

**West Nottinghamshire College
of Further Education**
Derby Road, Mansfield,
Nottinghamshire NG18 5BH
(Tel: 0623 27191)

C&G 600 Construction Crafts:
Supplementary Studies

- Day Release

**West Suffolk College of Further
Education**
Out Risbygate, Bury St Edmunds,
Suffolk IP33 3RL
(Tel: 0284 701301)

C&G 600 Construction Crafts:
Supplementary Studies

- Evening

Weymouth College
Cranford Avenue, Weymouth,
Dorset DT4 7LQ
(Tel: 030 57 761100)

C&G 600 Construction Crafts:
Supplementary Studies

- Day Release

Wigan College of Technology
Parsons Walk, Wigan,
Lancashire WN1 1RR
(Tel: 0942 494911)

C&G 600 Construction Crafts:
Supplementary Studies

- Day Release/
Evening

Worcester Technical College
Deansway, Worcester,
Hereford and Worcester
WR1 2JF
(Tel: 0905 723383)

C&G 600 Construction Crafts:
Supplementary Studies

- Day Release

W R Tuson College
St Vincent's Road, Fulwood,
Preston, Lancashire PR2 4UR
(Tel: 0772 53558)

C&G 600 Construction Crafts:
Supplementary Studies

- Day Release/
Evening

**Ystrad Mynach College of
Further Education**
Twyn Road, Ystrad Mynach,
Hengoed,
Mid-Glamorgan CF8 7XR
(Tel: 0443 816888)

C&G 600 Construction Crafts:
Supplementary Studies

- Day Release/
Evening

Listed in this chapter are the courses offered by private colleges. Some offer courses towards examinations such as City & Guilds and some offer courses with their own certificates at the end of them.

BUCKINGHAMSHIRE COLLEGE OF HIGHER EDUCATION

Queen Alexandra Road, High Wycombe, Buckinghamshire HP11 2JZ (Tel: 0494 22141)

In April 1989 Buckinghamshire College stepped away from the control of Bucks County Council and became a Higher Education Corporation and one of the 89 UK polytechnics and colleges funded by the new Polytechnics and Colleges Funding Council (PCFC).

Now, with a student population of 6,500 of whom 2,500 are on full-time courses, the Buckinghamshire College seeks to develop and expand its range of courses at all levels, but particularly, at advanced level. With a dozen or so new degree and Higher National Diploma courses currently in the pipeline, as well as a growing portfolio of postgraduate courses, including a unique MBA for Europe, the Buckinghamshire College is well placed to meet the challenges of the 1990s and beyond.

On becoming one of the UK's 89 PCFC colleges in 1989, the Buckinghamshire College restructured its existing seven teaching schools into three new faculties: the Faculty of Design, Informatics and Technology: the Faculty of International Management and Applied Social Sciences; and the Faculty of Business, Science and Humanities.

The Faculty of Design, Informatics and Technology was formed by a merger of three schools: the School of Art and Design, Furniture and Timber; the School of Informatics and Technology and Engineering; and the School of Building.

Based entirely at the High Wycombe site, the Faculty runs a wide range of well-respected courses from apprenticeships to master degrees in art and design, furniture, timber, building, engineering, electronics and all forms of informatics.

Furniture and Timber

As the foremost training establishment for two major industries, furniture and timber, the Faculty provides a qualification scaffolding in those areas taking students from craft technician to technologist and from honours degree to masters degree. The Faculty boasts a wide range of well-equipped studios and workshops, as well as new purpose-built premises for building courses.

BSc in Furniture Production

High Wycombe is famed throughout the world for its furniture and timber industries. The College is the only UK educational establishment to offer education and training to Masters Degree level.

The College currently runs the multi-disciplined BSc in Furniture Production. The four year full-time course is aimed at students with an interest in the design and manufacture of furniture and who wish to pursue a management career in the furniture and timber industries.

The first two years of the course concentrate on production technology, production management, materials technology and related sciences, history of design and industry, and computer aided design and manufacture (DAC/CAM). The course is balanced equally between theory and practical work.

Projects involving materials testing, furniture design and furniture production are carried out in the College's laboratories and workshops. Students also pay regular visits to furniture manufacturers throughout the course.

In year three, students are placed by the College in a furniture company and work there for one full year. They are paid a salary and have the opportunity to work on the factory floor and in administration.

The students complete two major projects in the final year and carry out an in-company project. The first project involves the production of manufacturing drawings and specifications (of a production of a piece of furniture) and the manufacture by each student of a prototype in the workshop. The second is the planning of a manufacturing unit in which the product could, in theory, be made in commercially viable quantities.

Entry requirements for the BSc Furniture Production are normally three passes at GCSE (A, B or C grade) plus two passes at A level; or an ONC, OND or BTEC Diploma in a relevant subject; or four GCSE passes (A, B or C grade) and two passes in City & Guilds Advanced Furniture subjects. Candidates over the age of 21 may be admitted subject to relevant industrial experience.

Timber Technology

Although wood-based industries play a key role in the UK economy, Buckinghamshire College is the only UK college to offer education and training in Timber Technology to degree level.

Such is the industry's commitment to degree-level training, leading timber company, Manson Timber Ltd, offer to sponsor a Buckinghamshire College degree student to the value of £1,000 per annum. The sponsorship will also include work experience, work placement and assistance with research projects.

The BSc Timber Technology, just one of the specialist courses run by the Department of Timber, Materials and Construction Technology, offers an excellent route for entry into the wood-based industries, while at the same time being intellectually stimulating and relevant to the challenges of both the developing and developed worlds.

The overall aim of the course is to provide an integrated technological, scientific and commercial understanding of wood and the wood-processing industries. Graduates will be able to practice the business and management functions required within an industry employing modern technologies.

The three year full-time course concentrates on wood as a material, wood processing, wood science, wood protection/preservation, wood engineering and business/management studies. An overseas visit is usually made during the second year to study the international context of wood technology.

The BSc Timber Technology offers a stimulating study of man's leading renewable raw material, an advanced qualification directly related to the wide range of wood-based industries worldwide and

relevant management experience of growth-potential industries in the UK, EEC and overseas.

Course applicants should hold five GCSE passes (one of which should be a Science or Technology), including two at A level, or equivalent qualifications. The College's policy is to interview all UK applicants.

Enquiries

A prospectus covering the range of courses available at the College can be obtained on request.

Enquiries, giving details of the course or courses of interest, should be made to the Assistant Registrar (Admissions), The Buckinghamshire College, Newland Park, Gorelands Lane, Chalfont St. Giles, Bucks HP8 4AD (Tel: 02407 4441).

Admission

Applications for entry to full-time and sandwich first Higher National Diploma and Degree courses are made through the Polytechnics Central Admissions System (PCAS), PO Box 67, Cheltenham, Gloucestershire GL50 3AP. Applications should reach PCAS between 1st September and 15th December of the year prior to entry to the course.

Students taking courses leading to a first degree or other equivalent qualification are eligible for a Major Award. Awards for other courses are at the discretion of the Local Education Authority.

CITY & GUILDS OF LONDON ART SCHOOL

124 Kennington Park Road, London SE11 4DJ
(Tel: 071-735 2306)
This is a school whose students have become famous for their technical skill and design ability. They learn from those who are still primarily

involved in their arts and who, generally, teach part time. There are some 70 artists and craftspeople who variously teach at the school.

A unique collection of craft courses in restoration, conservation, carving, gilding, lettering and the decorative arts are taught. Students learn to carve in wood and stone and the arts of gilding, lacquering, verre eglomise, faux marbre and so on. Many former students of this school are responsible for the conservation of the country's heritage in stately homes, churches, cathedrals, museums and other important buildings.

Students are taught in the tradition of working from life. They are taught to think in three dimensions. Their courses include the restoration of historical pieces lent to the school for the purpose. They often need re-gilding, and repairing may involve precise matching of wood carving.

Although the school shares the name of the examination Institute, these days the school is quite separate. It was established, in 1879, by the City & Guilds Institute as its first foundation.

At that time there were stone yards and wood carving studios around that area of South London and the City & Guilds School was established to teach apprentices in those crafts. That remains the function of the school now, although it separated from the City & Guilds Institute in 1971 to be run by an independent charitable trust.

CITY OF LONDON POLYTECHNIC
SIR JOHN CASS FACULTY OF ARTS, DESIGN AND MANUFACTURE

(Incorporating the LONDON COLLEGE OF FURNITURE) 41 Commercial Road, London E1 1LA

(Tel: 071-247 1953)

This new Faculty is an amalgamation of the London College of Furniture and the Sir John Cass Departments of Fine and Applied Art and Silversmithing and Jewellery.

Birth and Growth

The London College of Furniture began in 1899 as an establishment to teach craft skills. Ninety years later, considerable growth has taken place, so

that the name belies its many activities. At its six-storey premises at Aldgate, there are 700 full-time and 1500 part-time students, and the college now provides education, at all levels, for designers, design craftsmen, design managers, production managers and production technicians, as well as for craftsmen in a variety of specialisms.

The merger with Sir John Cass Departments brings a further 550 full-time and 1500 part-time students, working from Central House, another Aldgate Building.

Courses are available at all levels, from school leavers to post graduates, and the ages of students range from 16-70.

The original Department of Furniture is concerned with the materials, design, making and production technology of furniture and related products, including equipment for disability.

It was a logical extension for the Department of Furnishing & Interior Design to grow out of this department and, here, courses are provided in interior design, contract furnishing, upholstery, soft furnishing and textiles, screen-printing, basketry and cane-work, toys and play equipment.

An Unexpected Child

It might not seem quite so logical to find a Department of Music Technology. This began because craft skills in wood were required for pianos and violins as well as for tables and chairs. But, today, nearly 300 students follow courses in this Department. These include piano design and construction, and studies in the making of violins, harpsichords, early woodwind, early fretted and modern fretted instruments.

Alongside the revival in renaissance music (which has led to an increased demand for lutes, mandolins and sackbutts), there has also been an enormous interest in electronic music and electronic equipment. The work of the Music Technology Department reflects this interest, and streams of students, working on traditional, or renaissance, or electronic musical instruments, flow gently side by side and, at many points, flow together as students discover that they have much to learn from each other's disciplines. So the lute-maker may feel that he has little in common with the physicist who is

working on acoustics, or computerised electronic technology, until the day he realises that he can test the pitch and tone of his hand made instrument on the synthesiser constructed by his colleague.

The New Additions

The Department of Fine & Applied Art offers opportunities to study art and design from basic and introductory to advanced courses in painting and drawing, printmaking, photography, graphic design, computer graphics, ceramics and sculpture. The Department of silversmithing and jewellery offers a number of courses on design, technology and industrial production methods, as well as the established craft traditions of the trade.

Many Industries Served

Apart from the Department of Fine & Applied Art and because of strong vocational links, the tradition of the Faculty demands that craft pieces should be functional. Consequently, carving tends to be for frames or mirrors rather than for representational or abstract sculpture. Or marquetry decorates

tables, or guitars, rather than becoming a substitute for painting.

At the same time, the need for experiment, creativity and investigation into the world of art is not summarily dismissed. On the contrary, this is considered so vital that a Visual Research Section teaches across all disciplines, and students are encouraged to stretch their imaginations visually.

The Complete Craftsman

The realisation that man cannot live by craft alone, but has to ally craft skills to others, leads to a widening of traditional apprenticeship systems. The full-time craft student cannot solely concentrate on developing manual skills.

A thinking process has to take place before any artifact is made or restored and, for this process to be effective, it is necessary that the student should be aware of the history of his craft and the work of past eras of craftsmen. It is reasonable that this should be supplemented by at least a rudimentary knowledge of the history of other arts and crafts in their social milieu.

A communication process has to take place, sometimes between craftsman and patron, sometimes between craftsman and a wide public and, for this process to be effective, it is reasonable that the craftsman should be able to indicate his proposals, or intentions, clearly and unambiguously. This entails verbal and visual skills, which need to be strengthened alongside craft skills. So drawing is considered important and, besides technical drawing, students are encouraged to keep sketch-books for personal, as well as for communication purposes.

A marketing process has to take place in order that the product, or service, offered actually reaches the customer. Consequently, a Management Studies Section provides a range of subjects, across all departments, so that students can be more aware of the commercial world in which they are going to make their livings, and to help them with the basic understanding for running a business.

Machinery and Equipment

Most craftsmen accept the use of machinery up to a certain stage. Few craftsmen in wood cut down their own trees, or saw trunks into planks, or kiln dry, but are prepared to acquire their timber at a more advanced stage. Many will accept that the machine has a place in taking some of the drudgery out of preliminary work, allowing them to concentrate on their own hand skills. The Faculty does not try to make decisions for the craft student about the particular stage of acceptance but it does want to introduce all students to a wide range of machinery and equipment so that, when that decision is made, it is with full awareness of what is possible.

The Faculty has invested in sophisticated machinery, both for manufacture and for Information Technology. There are numerically controlled machines in workshops and a computer-aided design and draughting/computer-aided manufacture (CADD/CAM) suite which gives students hands-on experience and the chance to come to terms with the rapidly changing commercial world.

Further information about courses can be obtained from the Registrar at the above address.

ANSELM FRASER SCHOOL OF ANTIQUE FURNITURE RESTORATION

The Carthouse, Crauchie, by East Linton,
East Lothian EH40 3EB (Tel: 0620 860067)

The Anselm Fraser School of Antique Furniture Restoration holds courses for students that teaches the whole range of restoration skills. The course is also intended to impart to students everything he or she will need to know to have the confidence to set up their own restoration business.

The course duration is 46 weeks commencing mid-September and consists of three terms. Emphasis is placed on individual tuition.

Students need not necessarily have any previous woodworking experience, nor artistic flair as the restorer is mainly concerned with creating a faithful copy, rather than creating an original piece. Basic requirements are a steady hand and a willingness to learn.

Throughout the course the principles of restoring furniture ethically will be taught, using recognised techniques. Ethical restoration is the art of restoring a piece as near as possible to its original value. Principles of ethical restoration includes:

Cabinet constructions, gesso mouldings, timber recognition, grain simulation, veneering, metal repairs, wood turning, french polishing, wood carving, simple upholstery, boulle work, antique furniture recognition, marquetry, brass inlays, gilding, office and workshop organisation, running a business.

During the second half of the course, students are encouraged to practise their newly acquired skills by restoring furniture for their family and friends. Keen students are able to supplement their income substantially in this way.

Accommodation is provided throughout the course and comprises a fully furnished 3-4 bedroomed cottage next to the workshops, which is shared by students on a self-catering basis. The cottage, converted from stables, has colour television and recreation such as snooker, badminton and croquet is provided. Details of rent, electricity and telephone costs are available on application.

HOOKE PARK COLLEGE (run by The Parnham Trust) Hooke, Near Beaminster, Dorset DT8 3PH (Tel: 0308 863130)

Hooke Park College, opened by The Parnham Trust in 1989, offers a challenging training to potential entrepreneurs keen to make intelligent use of Britain's neglected timber resource. Over two years, twelve mature students benefit from a unique combination of inter-disciplinary tuition in Forest Management, Timber Technology, Product Design and Development, Computer-integrated Manufacture, Marketing and Enterprise Development.

The emphasis in the first year of the course is on learning the practical skills of marketing, design, production and business practice. In the following year, students research markets, clarify business objectives and develop the product range in relation to a specific timber resource. Assistance is given in choosing a suitable location, preparing business plans and identifying suitable sources of venture capital for the future business.

Students will be taught to make use of small dimension timber, in plentiful supply from Britain's woodlands, to make furniture, domestic products and building components. The college buildings are an innovative example of the potential of using small dimension timber in construction.

The course is open to English-speaking applicants of either sex from all parts of the world. Applicants should have a relevant degree or practical experience in subjects such as design, engineering, forestry management, timber technology, marketing, business or land management.

Short courses of six weeks duration teaching a part of the syllabus offered by the two-year course began in 1990 especially for those already in design or timber-related activities.

For further details and application forms, contact the Administrator at Hooke Park College.

INTERNATIONAL BOATBUILDING TRAINING CENTRE

Harbour Road, Oulton Broad, Lowestoft, Suffolk NR32 3LZ (Tel: 0502 569663)

This is one of two boat building training establishments to have received the recognition of the British Marine Industries Federation (the other is the Marine Builders Training Trust, mentioned later in this chapter).

Probably uniquely among training centres it also has the accreditation of the British Accreditation Council for Independent schools.

The centre accepts 55 students a year on its main 47 week course. Some local authorities will make grants available for students.

The course is intensive. During it students will sit their City & Guilds in yacht and boat building crafts, which usually takes two years. Assuming they complete the course successfully, students will leave the centre with its diploma.

Teachers at the centre are all time-served craftsmen and while it is necessary for students to learn the theory of what they are doing, this is very much a practical course with plenty of hands-on experience of boat building and fitting out.

The centre is run by John Elliot, who was taken on by local boatbuilders many years ago to train their apprentices. Eventually he bought the training company from the boat yards and set up the centre as an international training establishment.

THE JOHN MAKEPEACE SCHOOL FOR CRAFTSMEN IN WOOD

The Parnham Trust, Beaminster, Dorset DT8 3NA (Tel: 0308 862204/Fax: 0308 863494)

An intensive two-year, fully residential course is offered by The Parnham Trust to those of either sex with commitment, entrepreneurial energy and practical aptitude to train in craftsmanship, design, management and marketing, in preparation for setting up their own furniture-making businesses as self-employed designers and makers at the end of the course.

Emphasis in the first year of the course is given to learning the theory and techniques of hand and machine woodworking, sketching, draughtsmanship and design, photography, book-keeping, accountancy and management.

During the second year, students are required to develop their design abilities and personal direction, their productivity and their income through a series

of commissions obtained individually, to design and make objects, and through these to explore the fundamental principles learned in the first year.

At the end of the two years, the student's work is assessed and awarded a graded "Certificate of Craftsmanship in Wood" as a record of performance during the course.

This course is open to English-speaking applicants from all parts of the world aged between 18 and 40 years old. Application forms are available on request from The Secretary of The Parnham Trust.

For information, the course has been grant-aided at the discretion of a number of local education authorities. Applicants should contact the Education Officer of their own local authority.

There is also the Ellen Cooper-Dean Bursary of £250 per annum available to a successful applicant living in the County of Dorset.

MARINE BUILDERS' TRAINING TRUST

Hazel Road, Woolston, Southampton SO2 7GB (Tel: 0703 446824)

The traditional skills of building boats in timber by the clinker construction and carvel methods are still being taught and the number of people eager to learn these skills is increasing each year.

One of the leading centres for training in this type of work is the Marine Builders' Training Trust. It has a purpose-built training centre in Southampton with its own moorings on the river Itchen.

The staff at the Trust continue to teach traditional high class boat building skills not only to young apprentices, but also to adults who wish to change their career direction and, in middle age, are turning to learning the skills of making objects with their hands.

Trainees undertake a 48 week off-the-job training course at the Training Centre or, if they are training under Youth Training arrangements, 20 weeks off-the-job training at the Centre spread over two years with the balance of training on-the-job.

All courses at the MBTT Training Centre are devised to allow students to earn their NVQ at Level

II or III in addition to the necessary City & Guilds certificates. The boat building training is conducted in accordance with the British Marine Industries Federation (BMIF) Skillbuild Training Programme and each course is written to a modular format which quickly indentifies the essential units and elements of competence being sought.

As well as building boats there are mock-ups of ships/boats cabins so that those wishing to be boat outfitters can learn how to outfit cabins, galleys, heads and all accommodation. Furniture is produced to outfit these cabins. It is all hardwood, freestanding and some built-in.

There are no entry qualifications to obtain a place on the Centre's training courses, but all would-be trainees undergo an aptitude test to ensure they are suitable for training in the skills taught at the Centre.

Courses normally start in January and September of each year.

The chief Executive of the Trust is at the Training Centre and is always happy to show visitors around so they can see for themselves the standard of work being achieved by the trainees.

ARTHUR MOORE

The Old Booking Hall, Hove Park Villas, Hove, East Sussex BN3 6HP (Tel: 0273 25380)

This is a one-year intensive course (40 weeks) on the restoration of antique furniture, with special attention paid to English barometers and clocks. Students work at the workbench throughout the course on every type of antique furniture and notes are taken on every piece at each stage of its progress through the workshop - from discussion with the client, repair, staining, polishing, cabinet fittings and preparation of customers accounts.

This is not a course for those unsure of their interest and dedication to restoration, but in lighter moments visits are made to Museums, Antique Fairs, Auctions, specialist suppliers and workshops.

Only one pupil, of either sex, is taken each year and after the course every assistance is given in placing them in other workshops to gain further experience according to abilities.

A more detailed description of the course and application forms are available after Easter each year for the course starting in September.

NATIONAL HISTORIC BUILDING CRAFTS INSTITUTE

Witham Park, Stamp End, Waterside South, Lincoln LN5 7JL (Tel: 0522 534750)

Britain has a wealth of historical buildings, but not enough people with the skills to be able to maintain and repair them. The National Historical Building Crafts Institute aims to correct that.

The Institute was set up by Paul Hodgkinson, chairman of the Simons Group, which built, among other properties, the home of the Duke and Duchess of York.

The chairman's late father, Peter Hodgkinson, wanted to establish a school to train craftsmen in traditional skills. When he died he asked that some of his estate be used to establish the Institute. A fellow director, Albert Roberts, left the Simons Group to carry out Peter Hodgkinson's wishes.

In 1989 the first 24 pupils entered the Institute on its one year foundation course. They may continue their studies at Witham Park for anything up to five years.

Students are not required to have sat examinations previously in order to enter NHBCI. Some have GCSES, some do not. They are however required to sit and pass two entry examinations – one for the Construction Industry Training Board which gives a lot of support to the Institute, and one for the Institute itself.

There is plenty of hands-on experience organised by the Institute – for example, students have recently been working with English Heritage and Heritage Lincolnshire on Tupholme Abbey. There are opportunities to go abroad to study and work as well.

Training at the Institute includes formal education not only on building technology, but also on archaeology and the history of architecture so that students can appreciate the development of buildings and restore them in styles sympathetic to the period in which they were built.

After the foundation course, education includes self-development and business management instruction.

THE QUEEN ELIZABETH'S TRAINING COLLEGE

Leatherhead Court, Leatherhead, Surrey KT22 0BN
(Tel: 037 284 2204)

This College is a residential and day College for DISABLED men and women from the age of 18.

Training is offered in bench joinery, besides other courses such as technical, clerical and practical courses, and students are admitted throughout the year as vacancies arise, thus allowing the instructor to give individual instruction. The instructor's close link with the student, together with a system of tests throughout the course, ensures that the best possible results are achieved. Whenever practicable, all courses will lead to appropriate National Vocational Qualifications.

The courses are sponsored by the Training Agency (RTC Unit) of the Department of Employment and application should in the first place be made through the Disablement Resettlement Officer where the applicant resides.

WEST DEAN COLLEGE (The Edward James Foundation) West Dean, Chichester, West Sussex PO18 0QZ (Tel: 0243 63301)

This College provides various courses for the professional and amateur woodworker and accommodation is available if required.

Professional courses are held for one and two years in the conservation and restoration of antique furniture, antique clocks, ceramics and porcelain and are held in conjunction with the British Antique Dealers' Association. There is a three year course in The Care of Books and Bookbinding and a three year apprenticeship scheme in the Making of Early Musical Instruments. Also a one year course in Tapestry Weaving and commencing September a one year course in Conservation and Restoration of Fine Metals.

Short courses are from weekend to ten days duration and are open to anyone over school age with no qualifications. The courses available are as follows:

The West Dean BADA One-Year Professional Course in the Restoration of Antique Furniture

The course is open to anyone over the age of 18 who can show that they are skilled with their hands in woodwork, are keenly interested in antiques and who have the necessary dedication and patience. Applicants with a high standard of training in cabinet-making will be especially well qualified for the course. It is not envisaged that this one-year course will make students master-craftsmen in furniture restoration and all students after leaving the College will be expected to gain further experience by working for at least two years with an experienced furniture restorer. Students who work well during the year and pass the final examination will be given a Diploma at the end of the course.

Syllabus for the Course

The main emphasis of the course is training at the bench whereby skills in the restoration of antique furniture are acquired on antique period pieces. The course will also attempt to cover the following :

a) History of Furniture. With special emphasis on the periods of the carpenters, cabinet makers and designers in relation to oak, walnut, mahogany and satinwood etc.

b) Science and Properties. The study of brasswork – locks, hinges and handles – and the various metals used. Timber – the growth and distribution in various parts of the world. Fungal and insect attacks and the remedies. Veneers – the study of the different types, including inlays and bandings, etc.

c) Workshop Technology. The use of machines to save energy and not to produce a finished product. The repairs of all types of period furniture including the laying of veneers, inlay, marquetry and inlaid brass, together with glass cutting and table lining in cloth or leather, etc. The correct selection of timber in repairs, adhesives and their uses, and joining of all types will also be covered.

d) Wood Finishing. The preparation and use of all stains and bleaches, fillers, stoppings and polishes. Strict attention will be paid to the correct matching of colours and finishes, both high and waxed.

e) Estimating. The preparation of estimates, costing, materials, labour insurance, VAT etc.

f) General. During the course reference will be made to gilding, oriental lacquer work and painted furniture.

g) Lectures. During the year weekly lectures will be given on the history of furniture by members of BADA with specialist knowledge.

The course is supervised and examinations and assessment of practical work organised by an Advisory Committee.

Further information and application form can be obtained from the Principal of the College.

Apprenticeships in Musical Instrument Making

This scheme is designed to fill the need for a highly specialised apprenticeship in musical instrument making, enabling apprentices to attain a professional level of skill by working alongside practising professional makers who have their workshops within the College.

The three-year training covers all aspects of plucked fretted instruments.

Applicants should be over 18 with previous woodworking experience, preferably in musical instrument making. There are no formal academic requirements but there will be a practical test before entry to the course.

Each apprentice will be expected to finish at least 15 instruments during their three-year stay. These will be representative of the peak of instrument making in Europe between 1550 and 1750 mainly in Germany and Italy, and will include lutes and guitars after such makers as Martino Presbyther, Hans Frei, Laux Maler, Magno Tieffenbrucker, Antonio Stradivari, Vendelio Venere and Matteo Sellas, Sebastian Schelle, J. C. Hoffman and M. Hoffman.

Attention will be given to the following aspects of method, style and function; proceeding in the correct order, cleanliness and repetition; correct choice of materials and tools, preparation for harsh climates; edges, corners and planes, "grounds" and varnish, national characteristics such as the Italian Linear style, the German and French ornamental or introspective style and their relationship to their music; the perfect peg and action, scaling and voicing, the effects of barring and thicknessing on tone and focus; building for repertoire. Further benefits from training in a workshop will be the opportunity of dealing with customers and understanding the financial aspects of running a business.

Making Musical Instruments

This is an extended nine-day course for teachers in Primary, Middle and Upper Schools for those interested in craft and music, making a wide range of musical instruments, especially the types that could be made and used in schools.

Other applicants will also be accepted from those interested in making musical instruments for themselves. Some ability with tools and materials is desirable, but lack of skill need not be a deterrent for anyone wishing to apply.

SHORT COURSES

Making Cottage Furniture (Stage I) – For experienced Woodworkers or Beginners.

The aim is to design and make items of furniture such as stools, chairs, tables and the like appropriate to present-day needs, but broadly based on traditional cottage furniture such as the Windsor chair.

Cottage or stick furniture is in the main built up from members which are round in section; the joints are made by fitting the ends of the members into round sockets bored to size.

The shaping and jointing is through the use of traditional tools known as rotary planes. These tools have been modified so as to be more dependable in their accuracy for jointing and in the surface finish. Accurate jointing is ensured even when done for the first time by beginners.

Week course.

Cottage Furniture (Stage II) – For experienced workers in wood

This course covers chair planning – design and making of equipment and the general content of the course is as follows:

1. Selection of materials
2. Drawing, solid geometry, setting out
3. Chair design – anthropometrics

4. Drilling aids – hand and machine
5. Steam bending – equipment
    Design and making of formers etc.
    Five day course.

Woodcarving – For beginners and advanced students.

This course is expressly planned for students interested in learning the important techniques of wood carving. For example, how to sharpen the many different shaped tools used in the craft; how to use the right tool for a particular situation, whether it is bas-relief or in the round; how to set out a design using the wood to its best advantage and all important, the correct way to sharpen tools. Letter cutting in wood will also be included.

Weekend course; five-day, seven-day course, or one day a week for six weeks course.

Woodcarving – working towards an object in shallow relief.

This course is designed to enable the student to produce an object using shallow relief carving techniques. The course will begin with a simple cut out form which will then be carved to its various planes to give the impression of a real life object.

This will be followed by another related classic shape – the flower – to familiarise the student with "setting in" and the use of tool outline in determining shape.

After this the more complex "ribbon" ornament will be dealt with, finally leading up to the interpretation and application of a pattern in order to make a frame, box top or object of the student's choice.

Students having attended the introductory weekend course will obviously concentrate mostly on this stage of the programme and its more advanced techniques.

Five-day course. Introductory weekend course.

Woodcarving – A Course in Ornamental Shallow Relief

This course aims at introducing techniques and design concepts in approaching shallow relief woodcarving.

The course begins with a simple cut out form which will then be carved to its various planes to give the impression of a real life object. This will be followed by another related classic shape – the flower – to familiarise the student with "setting in" and the use of tool outline in determining shape.

Finally, the more complex "ribbon" ornament will be dealt with, with its natural development towards the object in the round.

The importance of "approach", "break down" and "setting up" will all be incorporated, along with how colour, finish and position will influence execution and design.

According to progress, time will be available for each student to design and carve a piece of his or her own.

Weekend course.

Wood Engraving

A course provided for those with some drawing ability.

Weekend course or seven-day course.

Upholstery for Beginners
Stage I – Weekend course.

Upholstery for those with little experience
Stage II – Seven-day course (six days tuition).

Upholstery for those with experience
Stage III – Five-day course.

Apprenticeships in Musical Instrument Making

This scheme is designed to fill the need for a highly specialised apprenticeship in musical instrument making, enabling apprentices to attain a professional level of skill by working alongside practising professional makers who have their workshops within the College.

The three-year training covers all aspects of plucked fretted instruments.

Applicants should be over 18 with previous woodworking experience, preferably in musical instrument making. There are no formal academic requirements but there will be a practical test before entry to the course.

Each apprentice will be expected to finish at least 15 instruments during their three-year stay. These will be representative of the peak of instrument making in Europe between 1550 and 1750 mainly in Germany and Italy, and will include lutes and guitars after such makers as Martino Presbyther, Hans Frei, Laux Maler, Magno Tieffenbrucker, Antonio Stradivari, Vendelio Venere and Matteo Sellas, Sebastian Schelle, J. C. Hoffman and M. Hoffman.

Attention will be given to the following aspects of method, style and function; proceeding in the correct order, cleanliness and repetition; correct choice of materials and tools, preparation for harsh climates; edges, corners and planes, "grounds" and varnish, national characteristics such as the Italian Linear style, the German and French ornamental or introspective style and their relationship to their music; the perfect peg and action, scaling and

voicing, the effects of barring and thicknessing on tone and focus; building for repertoire. Further benefits from training in a workshop will be the opportunity of dealing with customers and understanding the financial aspects of running a business.

Making Musical Instruments

This is an extended nine-day course for teachers in Primary, Middle and Upper Schools for those interested in craft and music, making a wide range of musical instruments, especially the types that could be made and used in schools.

Other applicants will also be accepted from those interested in making musical instruments for themselves. Some ability with tools and materials is desireable, but lack of skill need not be a deterrent for anyone wishing to apply.

Introduces to you the skills and pleasures of making your own fine furniture

At Wiston, we offer a range of courses which take you through the various skills required to make fine furniture, from the marking out and cutting of joints, through the assembly, veneering and marquetry to the final finishing coat of polish.

Choose from *Corner Cupboard, Drum Table, Edwardian Style Mahogany Inlaid Display Cabinet, Card Table, Classical Grandfather Clock, Rocking Horse, Welsh Dresser* or *Settle.*

**WISTON PROJECT SCHOOL   THE OLD SCHOOL HOUSE
Nr HAVERFORDWEST, DYFED, WEST WALES SA62 4PS
TEL: (0437) 731579 & 731544**

PRIVATE TUITION, LEISURE AND HOLIDAY COURSES

Various courses by craftsmen are held throughout the country for both beginners and advanced students. The courses are usually of short duration with accommodation available if required.

A selection of courses available are shown here. Similar courses are advertised regularly in woodworking magazines and full details can be obtained direct from the craftsman offering the course. If you wish to study locally and cannot find a suitable course, seek out local craftsmen and see if you can persuade them to start a course, or give you individual tuition. Older craftsmen are often keen to pass on their skills and your enthusiasm may be just the incentive they need.

AVON

Gordon Stokes
202 The Hollow, Bath, Avon BA2 1NG
(Tel: 0225 422617)
Intensive two/three day courses in **woodturning** for beginners. Personal instruction.

BEDFORDSHIRE

Hagen Restorations
The Stables, Wakes End Farm, Eversholt, Bedfordshire (Tel: 052 528 505)
Courses in **furniture restoration.**

BUCKINGHAMSHIRE

Theo Fossel
4 Shot Ltd, Freepost, 119 Station Road, Beaconsfield, Buckinghamshire HP9 1DR
(Tel: 0494 672349)
Courses on all aspects of **stick making** and **stick handle carving** by international authority on the subject, Theo Fossel.

Missenden Summer School
Missenden Abbey, Great Missenden, Buckinghamshire HP16 0BD (Tel: 0494 890295)
The following 1 week residential courses are available during the summer months: **the pleasure of working with wood; wildfowl carving; wood and stone carving; picture framing; create your own picture in exotic wood; restoration of antique furniture; calligraphy for beginners** – a foundation course; **introducing puppetry; Restoration of Upholstery** – modern and antique furniture; **gilding** – a practical introduction.
Weekend courses: **Early Stringed Instrument;**

Learn How to Carve series; **gold finishing, picture framing; upholstery; calligraphy.**

CHESHIRE

Leslie Syson BA, DLC (Hons), MCCEd
Church House, Eaton, Congleton, Cheshire CW12 2NH (Tel: 0260 274331)
Residential or day courses, from two to five days or more for beginners and advanced students in **cabinet-making, furniture restoration** or **woodturning.**
Accommodation available in 16th century timber-framed farmhouse with workshops in old farm buildings.

Alan Waterhouse and Philippa Barstow
22 Willow Court, Abbey Road, Upton, Macclesfield, Cheshire SK10 3PD (Tel: 0625 616737)
A series of 2 and 4 day **polishing** courses throughout the year.

CLEVELAND

D Bolton
44 Church Lane, Acklam, Middlesbrough, Cleveland TS5 7EB (Tel: 0642 817097)
Harpsichord making – 7 day course.

CORNWALL

Graham Usher
Fairhope Venture, 5 Rose Terrace, Mitchell, Newquay, Cornwall TR8 5AU (Tel: 0872 510551)
3½ day intensive, 5 day intensive and 6 morning holiday courses in **antique furniture restoration** and **french polishing. Marquetry** and **parquetry, veneering** and **inlay.**

Jeremy Williams
Sycamore Cottage, Trabae, St. Martin, Helston, Cornwall TR12 6EA (Tel: 032-623 609)
Short courses ideal for beginners in **woodcarving.**

CO DURHAM
Beamish Hall Residential College
Beamish, Stanley, Co Durham
(Tel: 0207 233147/238212)
Courses in **woodcarving.**

CUMBRIA
International School of French Polishing
Colin Campbell, 48 Broad Street, Carlisle, Cumbria CA1 2AQ (Tel: 0228 49183)
Extensive four-day residential courses in **french polishing** and **re-finishing.**

DERBYSHIRE
Craft Supplies
The Mill, Miller's Dale, Buxton, Derbyshire SK17 8SN (Tel: 0298 871636)
Two-day intensive courses in **woodturning** and **woodcarving.**

Melbourne Hall Workshops
Melbourne, Derbyshire DE7 1EN
(Tel: 0332 701463)
Woodturning courses for beginners/improvers in well equipped workshop.

Reg Slack
Saracens Head Coaching House Yard, Brailsford, Derbyshire DE6 3AS
(Tel: 0335 60829/0332 591563 evenings)
1-3 day **woodturning** courses and **woodturning supplies.** (Closed Thursdays and Fridays).

DEVON
Campions Crafts
Fred and Sheila Ward, Campions, Buzzacott Lane, Combe Martin, North Devon EX34 0NL
(Tel: 0271 882626)
Two day course in **woodturning.**

David Charlesworth
Harton Manor, Hartland, Bideford, Devon EX39 6BL (Tel: 0237 441 288)
Intensive individual tuition in **hand** and **machine skills.** Professional workshop producing "one-off"

commissions, in beautiful coastal surroundings. Maximum 3 students. Individual programmes with flexible start and duration. Introductory weeks available. Send SAE or ring for details.

Christopher Faulkner
Ashbridge Workshops, Tigley, Nr Totnes, South Devon TQ9 6EW (Tel: 0803 862861)
Short or full time courses in **fine cabinet making** in long established professional workshop. Introductory courses available.

Oliver Plant
Hartford Barton, Gittisham, Honiton, Devon EX14 0AW (Tel: 0404 44155)
Two day residential **woodturning** courses for beginners.

Dave Regester
Millstream Cottage, Higher Town, Sampford Peverell, Tiverton, Devon EX16 7BR
(Tel: 0884 820109)
Weekend or hourly tuition courses in **woodturning** by experienced professional tutor. Well equipped workshop.

John Sainsbury
1 Lichfield Drive, Brixham, Devon TQ5 8DL
(Tel: 08045 6204)
Woodturning, woodcarving, basic **cabinet making, creative woodcraft, tool sharpening** and **router** courses. Two days and upwards. Courses arranged to suit the individual – beginners and advanced students.

David Savage
21 Westcombe, Bideford, Devon EX39 3JQ
(Tel: 0237 479202)
Full time courses of one or two years duration in **cabinet making.**

Malcolm Wood Harps Workshop
121 Plymouth Road, Buckfastleigh, Dartmoor, Devon TQ11 0DA (Tel: 0364 43020)
One-month course leading to the completion of a **Celtic harp,** including detailed instruction and supervision of the assembly from raw materials to the finished article. Tools are provided and prospective students must have some aptitude for carpentry and joinery.

One-week course in the assembly of a **harp kit.** Weekend introductory courses available to would-be players and makers of this instrument. Accommodation available.

DORSET

Ted Payne

Dorset Craft Guild, Walford Mill Craft Centre, Stone Lane, Wimborne, Dorset BH21 1NL (Tel: 0202 841400)

All levels of **woodturning.**

ESSEX

Peter Child

The Old Hyde, Little Yeldham, Essex CO9 4QT (Tel: 0787 237291)

Woodturning – 2 day courses twice a week. Suitable for any level, beginners very welcome.

Roy Hems

29 Burstead Drive, Billericay, Essex CM11 2QP (Tel: 0277 622028)

1, 2 or 3 day courses in **woodturning** in fully equipped workshops.

GLOUCESTERSHIRE

Paul Spriggs

The Croft, Silver Street, South Cerney, Cirencester, Gloucestershire. (Tel: 0285 86029)

Two day courses on **cane** and **rushwork.** Students to bring their own chair frames; all materials and tools provided. A maximum of four students can be taken at a time.

HAMPSHIRE

Robin Maddock

25 Chessel Avenue, Bitterne, Southampton, Hampshire SO2 4DY (Tel: 0703 433569)

Beginners and advanced **woodturning** courses, individual tuition by professional tutor. Evenings and weekends.

HEREFORDSHIRE

B R Honeyborne

The Whyle Cottage, Pudleston, Leominster, Herefordshire (Tel: 056 887 250)

5-day **antique restoration** course of your chosen item or piece of furniture provided by professional tutor.

3-day **polishing** course.

HERTFORDSHIRE

Mr Harding

12d Paramount Industrial Estate, Sandown Road, Watford, Hertfordshire WD2 4XA (Tel: 0923 816209/081-863 3585)

1 day intensive training in **woodmachining,** covering all aspects of timber preparation with spindle moulding and router work. The course involves hands on working and individual tuition is offered, if required.

KENT

Charles Cliffe

3 South Close, Bexley Heath, Kent DA6 8HH (Tel: 081-301 5318)

Two day **french polishing** course with personal instruction. Beginners welcome.

Advanced tutorials can be arranged. Consultations available to advise on particular difficulties.

Bruce Luckhurst

Little Surrenden Workshop, Bethersden, Kent TN26 3BG (Tel: 023 382 589)

One-year course on **conserving** and **restoring antique furniture.** Previous cabinet making and polishing experience not essential.

Roy Sutton

14 St Georges Avenue, Herne Bay, Kent CT6 8JU (Tel: 0227 273297/272136 evenings)

Two-day **wood machining** course to learn the basics of machine woodworking, including **spindle moulding** and **routing.**

Richard Weaver

26 Stonecroft, Vigo Village, Meopham, Kent DA13 0ST (Tel: 0732 822197)

Individual **woodturning** courses by master wood-turner.

LINCOLNSHIRE

Horncastle Residential College

Mareham Road, Horncastle, Lincolnshire LN9 6BW (Tel: 0507 522449)

Weekend courses in **woodcarving.**

LONDON

Barkes Restoration and Decorative Courses

Garden Flat, 74 Harwood Road, London SW6 4PZ (Tel: 071-731 1356)

Short courses for practical people. Subjects include: **furniture, gilding, china mending** and **painting, upholstery, picture framing** and **restoration. Tapestry, upholstery, oil painting, clocks** and **rug conservation.**

Peter and Frances Binnington
65 St John's Hill, London SW11 1SX
(Tel: 071-223 9192)
Intensive short courses in **gilding.** Application of gold leaf to furniture, frames, carving, glass etc; interior and exterior ornament.

Ben Hill Woodturners
Stratford Workshops, Unit 050, Stratford, East London (Tel: 081-534 0275)
Courses in **centre lathe turning, face plate turning** and **small bowl turning.**

MERSEYSIDE

The Balluster
102 High Street, Wavertree, Liverpool, Merseyside (Tel: 051 420 3379)
Lathe tuition in your own home.

MIDDLESEX

Zachary Taylor
13 Churchfield Close, North Harrow, Middlesex HA2 6BD (Tel: 081-427 3005)
1-5 day courses in **musical instrument** making for all levels of abilities.

NORFOLK

Aubrey Hammond
Southview Cottage, 33 Lynch Green, Hethersett, Norwich (Tel: 0603 810571)
Woodturning – professional tuition in fully equipped workshop.

Tony Waddilove
Unit A Hill Farm Workshops, Great Dunham, Kings Lynn, Norfolk PE32 2LP
(Tel: 0760 755674)
1 and 2 day **woodturning** courses for all levels by professional instructor in fully equipped workshops. Also weekend workshops for the experienced woodturner.

Pauline McGowan
Old Hall Farm, Scole, Diss, Norfolk
(Tel: 0379 740911)
Carving courses available, specialising in decorative duck decoy carving.

Wensum Lodge
King Street, Norwich, Norfolk NR1 1QW
(Tel: 0603 666021)
Courses in **upholstery** and **woodcarving.**

NOTTINGHAMSHIRE

Midland School of French Polishing
A.V. Fry DLC; LCG, 18a Mansfield Road, Eastwood, Nottinghamshire NG16 3AQ
(Tel: 0773 531157/715911 evenings)
Traditional hand-work courses in **french polishing** taught throughout the year.

Keith Rowley
68 Moorgreen, Newthorpe, Nottinghamshire NG16 2FB (Tel: 0773 716903)
One and two day **woodturning** courses, to suit beginners and advanced students.

OXFORDSHIRE

Rycotewood College
Department of Fine Craftsmanship and Design, Priest End, Thame, Oxfordshire OX9 2AF
(Tel: 084421 2501)
Residential summer courses available – **woodturning, wood machining** for furniture makers, **cabinet making, furniture repair** and **restoration, hand finishing, woodcarving, book binding** and **guitar making.**

SOMERSET

Decoy Art Studio
Kingshill, Chewton Mendip, Nr. Bath, Somerset BA3 4PD. (Tel: 0761 21357)
The Decoy Gallery offers 2, 3 and 5 day courses in **decorative decoy carving.** The five day course, Monday-Friday, takes the Carver through the various stages of carving, feather texturing and painting. Each student completes the course with a finished duck. Various visiting American carvers also instruct at The Gallery.

Dillington House
Ilminster, Somerset TA19 9DT (Tel: 04605 2427)
One week residential courses in **calligraphy, marquetry** and **picture framing** – non-residents welcome. Also one-day courses provided in **furniture restoration** and **calligraphy**.

Zoë Gertner
Deans Cottage, Bagley, Wedmore, Somerset
BS28 4TD (Tel: 0934 712679)
Woodcarving courses suitable for beginners or more experienced students are held in pleasant well equipped studio. All types of carving are taught, each course being tailored according to the specific interest of the individual, whether it be carving in relief or in the round, lettering or decoration. Courses are limited to five students, ensuring individual attention.

John & Jan Sanders
Potters Cottage, Northay, Chard, Somerset
TA20 3DN (Tel: 046034 534)
Two day, residential and non-residential **woodturning** courses.

SUFFOLK

Ernie Ives
Belstead House, Sprites Lane, Ipswich, Suffolk
IP8 3NA (Tel: 0473 686321)
Weekend and residential summer courses in **marquetry**; basic techniques.

Smithies Woodcrafts
Stephen Gumbrell, Smithies Cottage, Troston, Bury St Edmunds, Suffolk IP31 1ER (Tel: 0359 269268)
Two-four day **furniture making** course covering skills and techniques through making an item of furniture in a well equipped workshop.

SUSSEX (EAST)

A Moore
The Old Booking Hall, Hove Park Villas, Hove, East Sussex BN3 6HP (Tel: 0273 25380)
Six-month or one-year courses in the **restoration** of antiques in well established workshops specialising in **furniture, clocks** and **barometers.**

Gillian Reeve
Longshaw Farm, Waldron, East Sussex TN21 0PN
(Tel: 04353 2296)

Woodcarving courses in peaceful Sussex farmhouse, professional tuition, fully equipped studio, full board.

SUSSEX (WEST)

Earnley Concourse
Nr Chichester, West Sussex PO20 7JL
(Tel: 0243 670392/Fax: 0243 670832)
Two-day courses in **care** and **restoration** of **antique furniture.** Two-day courses in **woodcarving** and **whittling.** Two-day courses in **mounting** and **framing pictures**.

The Old Rectory
Fittleworth, Pulborough, West Sussex RH20 1HU
(Tel: 079 882 306)
Short courses in **antique furniture restoration, furniture finishes, woodcarving** and **picture framing.** Residential adult education college.

John Storrs
Hunston, Chichester, West Sussex PO20 6NR
(Tel: 0243 776263)
Fourteen-day residential **instrument making** courses (keyboard instruments only), making early keyboard instruments.

West Dean College
West Dean, Nr. Chichester PO18 0QZ
(Tel: 024363 301)
Courses in making **cottage furniture, woodcarving, wood engraving, woodturning miniatures, making miniature furniture, making musical instruments, cabinet making, hand finishing techniques, picture framing, green woodturning.**
Weekend, five and seven day courses.

WARWICKSHIRE

Ronald F Storr
2 Gerrard Street, Warwick, Warwickshire
CV34 4HD (Tel: 0926 497300)
Half-day (sampler), one-day and two-day **woodturning** courses.

WILTSHIRE

Cricklade Craft Workshop
Den Hatchard, Gas Lane, Cricklade, Wiltshire
SN6 6BY (Tel: 0285 861049 after 4pm)
One-day courses: **veneering, French polishing,**

working with machines, manufactured board-
ing. 5 day intensive courses in basic **woodworking**
skills for beginners. Other specialist courses available covering most aspects of woodworking –
**woodturning, marquetry, woodcarving,
pyrography, design.**

Ramon Weston Craftworkshops

Finnygook, Days Lane, Kington Langley, Wiltshire
SN15 5PA (Tel: 0249 75272)
Individualised, intensive, short courses, (residential
or day), in fine **furniture making** for students of
all ages and abilities emphasising hand skills, use
of modern wood machines, power tools and jigs.
Ramon Weston is an apprentice trained practising
Craftsman, qualified teacher, and Leigh Dovetail
Jig expert (all courses M.O.D. approved).

YORKSHIRE (NORTH)

Allan Batty

20 Low Mill Estate, Ripon, North Yorkshire
HG4 1NP (Tel: 0765 690340)
One and two day courses in **woodturning** in fully
equipped studios.

John Boddy's Fine Wood & Tool Store Ltd

Riverside Sawmills, Boroughbridge,
North Yorkshire YO5 9LJ (Tel: 0423 322370)
Courses held in custom built school rooms: **woodcarving, woodturning** (basic and refresher) **bowl
turning, woodfinishing, veneering, chairmaking,
stickmaking, marquetry, signmaking, pyrography, decoy duck carving, lace bobbin making,
furniture restoration, french polishing.**

Peter Hibbard

Old School Arts Workshop, Middleham, Leyburn,
North Yorkshire DL8 4QG (Tel: 0969 23056)
Creative sculpture, woodcarving and **woodturn-
ing** courses.

W Thompson

Chapel Fold, Grassington, Skipton,
North Yorkshire BD23 5NH (Tel: 0756 752463)
Residential **antique furniture** courses in practical
workshop.

David Tippey

Victoria Lodge, Kirkham Malham, Skipton,
North Yorkshire BD23 4BS (Tel: 0729 3547)

Carving courses, particularly in **bird sculpture** and
decorative decoy ducks.

YORKSHIRE (SOUTH)

Ron Butterfield

205 Shirebrook Road, Sheffield, South Yorkshire
S8 9RF (Tel: 0742 554834)
Private tuition in **woodcarving** for beginners and
semi-experienced. All types of carving taught by
church craftsman and designer and sculptor and
carver of wood or stone.

YORKSHIRE (WEST)

Rawdon Machine Sales Ltd

6 Acorn Park, Charlestown, Shipley,
West Yorkshire BD17 7SW (Tel: 0274 597826)
Wood finishing, wood machining and **copy turn-
ing** courses available.

H. Middleton

Studio 7 Holroyd Watermill, Beck Road,
Micklethwaite, Bingley, West Yorkshire
(Tel: 0274 581311)
Woodturning and **carving** courses available either
short course, by the hour, weekend evenings
possible. Beginners welcome.

SCOTLAND

CAITHNESS

Michael O'Donnell

The Croft, Brough, Thurso, Caithness, Scotland
KW14 8YE (Tel: 084 785 605)
5 day **woodturning** courses available for all
abilities: **Exploration into Woodturning; Turning Green**; a 7-day **Instructor Training Course**
and a course on *"The Woodturning Business"* for
people wishing to become self-employed woodturners, which is a 4-week course.

ROSS-SHIRE

Parkin Loy

"Tigh an Fhraoich", Hartmount, Tain, Ross-shire
IV19 1NQ (Tel: 086 284 2511)
One-five day courses in **woodturning/cabinet
making** techniques based in the Scottish Highlands
throughout the year.

WALES

DYFED

Derek Krelle
The Carver's Workshop, Tower View, Marloes, Haverfordwest, Dyfed SA62 3BA
(Tel: 0646 636 361)
Project based courses in **woodcarving, turning** and **construction** by highly experienced professional tutors.

Wiston Projects School
The Old School, Wiston, Haverfordwest, Dyfed SA62 4PS (Tel: 043782 579)
One and two week courses during which students will complete the construction of a piece of furniture – even if they have no previous woodworking experience.

Craft, design and technology (CDT) is a subject of growing importance in schools. It is also one of the subject areas in which there is a shortage of qualified teachers in middle and secondary schools, so that the CDT teacher has a much better chance of finding a post than do many other newly qualified teachers. And the number of posts is likely to increase as the significance of CDT becomes more widely recognised.

The term CDT, introduced in 1975, includes the former "handicraft" element and reflects the shift in emphasis that has taken place in our schools. No longer are pupils solely concerned with learning to use the basic materials of wood and metal. Greater importance is attached to design and the technology involved. However, the experience of using wood and metal is still retained in the "making" element.

If you are thinking of only teaching wood as a career the possibilities in state schools are limited. Yes, wood still features in the guidelines laid down for the teaching of Technology in the new National Curriculum, but you will be one of a team of CDT teachers involved in an individual school. The new curriculum envisages a much wider use of materials and an ever increasing technological content. The materials include textiles, paint, paper, photographs, clay, wood, metal, plastic and food. The teaching of technology is envisaged throughout the school years of 5-16 and the use of the suggested materials commences from about 7 onwards.

Whether you are a school leaver, a graduate or have work experience outside teaching, there is a training course to suit you. If you are leaving school you can obtain a Bachelor of Education degree at a polytechnic or institute or college of higher education. Two universities award BSc or BA Honours degrees which also give Qualified Teacher Status.

If you are a graduate and your degree is in a relevant subject you can go on a one-year post-graduate teacher training course. There is no upper limit on the age of admission to these courses.

If you are already experienced in the world of technology and hold technical qualifications such as HND or CGLI, you can take a short course to train to teach your subject. Qualified teachers in other subjects, too, may be interested in the prospects in CDT, and, for them, one-year retraining courses are available.

Initial training to teach CDT

To teach in a maintained school you must first become a qualified teacher. This means that you will need to obtain from a recognised institution a Bachelor's Degree or a Certificate in Education.

You can gain these qualifications by taking:

- A course leading to a BEd degree. This is a four-year honours course (Honours degree graduates start teaching at a higher point on the pay scale and may have better career prospects). Holders of HND or similar technical qualifications may, at the discretion of the colleges, gain remission from the first year course.

- A degree course other than BEd, normally three years, followed by a one-year postgraduate course for a teaching certificate (the training of graduates in engineering and design is specially relevant to a later career in CDT teaching).

Qualifying for teacher training

Degree in Education (BEd)

Normal minimum entry requirements to a BEd course (as for a degree course in other subjects or for a DipHE course) are five different GCE/GCSE subjects at grade C, which must include Mathematics and English, and at least two at advanced level.

Students in colleges of further education should note that an OND in technology may be considered by some colleges as an adequate entry qualification.

Holders of the DipHE may qualify for a shortened (one or two-year) BEd course.

Those who hold a non-graduate teaching certificate may after teaching experience, qualify for a one-year BEd degree course. Qualified teachers may also obtain a place on a one-year retraining course to specialise in teaching CDT.

Applying for a training course to teach CDT

Training courses leading to qualification as a teacher are held at all the institutions shown in this

CRAFT, DESIGN & TECHNOLOGY

chapter. They provide specialist courses in CDT. The institutions themselves are responsible for their own entry requirements and for the selection of candidates.

The first step in applying for a place on a degree or certificate course at a college or polytechnic is to write to the college of your choice for its application forms: you should then send the enquiry card returned with them to the Central Register & Clearing House Ltd, 3 Crawford Place, London W1H 2BN. You should complete the forms they provide and send both sets of forms to the institute of your choice with the required registration fee. The fee covers the cost of passing on the application to other colleges if it is not accepted by the college of your first choice.

If you are applying for a first degree place at a UK university (see Brunel and Loughborough in the list of institutions) you should apply through the Universities Central Council on Admissions (UCCA). Write for an application form to UCCA, PO Box 28, Cheltenham, Glos GL50 1HY, and return the completed form with the appropriate fee. UCCA's handbook and form are available from the July preceding the proposed year of entry to a course.

If you are a graduate and wish to apply for a postgraduate teacher training course a similar clearing-house system is available through the Graduate Teacher Training Registry, 3 Crawford Place, London W1H 2BN. If you write to them, they will send you a leaflet which lists all the colleges and departments offering postgraduate

Certificate in Education courses, details the courses available and includes application forms. You should complete the forms and return them to the Graduate Teacher Training Registry with the registration fee.

Candidates are recommended to apply to a college even if they try at the same time for a place on a specialist degree course at a university or polytechnic as a first step on the road to a teaching career. Procedures for admission to teacher training courses take such dual applications into account – it is common for some applications for BEd places to be withdrawn following acceptance on subject degree courses. Candidates will probably be called for an interview and, if accepted, are expected to pass a medical test. The decision to offer a place or not rests with the institution.

CRAFT, DESIGN & TECHNOLOGY TEACHING COURSES

The Colleges shown offer one or more of the teacher training options listed above. The majority of the training institutions are the responsibility of the local education authorities, but some of them are run by religious denominations or by independent bodies. Nearly all the colleges have some living accommodation for students in halls of residence or college houses. The colleges also welcome students who prefer to live at home and attend college during the day.

The institutions listed below offer courses leading to qualification as a Craft, Design & Technology teacher.

Bristol Polytechnic
Coldharbour Lane, Frenchay,
Bristol,
Avon BS16 1QY
(Tel: 0272 656261)

Bachelor of Education (this initial teacher training programme consists of a four-year sandwich course in design and technology with education)
One-year retraining course

Brunel University
Runnymede Campus, Faculty
of Education and Design,
Egham,
Surrey TW20 0JZ
(Tel: 0784 431341)

Batchelor of Science (Hons) 4-year course
Batchelor of Arts (Hons) 3-year course
One-year non-graduate Certificate in Education
Postgraduate Certificate in Education
One-year retraining course

218

College of Ripon and York St. John
Lord Mayor's Walk, York,
North Yorkshire YO3 7EX
(Tel: 0904 656771)

Bachelor of Education (this initial teacher training programme consists of a four-year sandwich course in design and technology with education)
One-year retraining course
Bachelor of Arts

College St Mark & St John College (Plymouth)
Derriford Road, Plymouth,
Devon PL6 8BH
(Tel: 0752 777188)

Bachelor of Education (this initial teacher training programme consists of a four-year sandwich course in design and technology with education)

Crewe and Alsager College of Higher Education
Crewe Road, Crewe,
Cheshire CW1 1DU
(Tel: 0270 500661)

Bachelor Arts
One-year non-graduate Certificate in Education
Postgraduate Certificate in Education
One-year retraining course

Edge Hill College of Higher Education
St Helens Road, Ormskirk,
Lancashire L39 4QP
(Tel: 0695 75171)

One-year retraining course

Gwent College of Higher Education
Allt-yr-yn Avenue, Newport,
Gwent NP9 5XA
(Tel: 0633 51525)

Bachelor of Education (this initial teacher training programme consists of a four-year sandwich course in design and technology with education)
One-year non-graduate Certificate in Education
Diploma in Higher Education
One-year retraining course
Bachelor of Arts

King Alfred's College
Sparkford Road, Winchester,
Hampshire SO22 4NR
(Tel: 0962 841515)

Bachelor of Education (this initial teacher training programme consists of a four-year sandwich course in design and technology with education)
One-year retraining course

Leeds Polytechnic
Calverley Street, Leeds,
West Yorkshire LS1 3HE
(Tel: 0532 462971)

Bachelor of Education (this initial teacher training programme consists of a four-year sandwich course in design and technology with education)
One-year non-graduate Certificate in Education
Postgraduate Certificate in Education

Liverpool Polytechnic
Rodney House,
70 Mount Pleasant, Liverpool,
Merseyside L3 5UX
(Tel: 051-207 3581)

Bachelor of Education (this initial teacher training programme consists of a four-year sandwich course in design and technology with education)
One-year non-graduate Certificate in Education

Loughborough University
Ashby Road, Loughborough,
Leicestershire LE11 3TU
(Tel: 0509 263171)

Bachelor of Arts
One-year non-graduate Certificate in Education
Postgraduate Certificate in Education (Craft, Design and Technology)

Middlesex Polytechnic
Trent Park,
Cockfosters Road, Barnet,
Hertfordshire EN4 0PT
(Tel: 081-368 1299)

Bachelor of Education (this initial teacher training programme consists of a four-year sandwich course in design and technology with education)
One-year retraining course
One-year non-graduate Certificate in Education

Newcastle Polytechnic
Ellison Building,
Ellison Place,
Newcastle-upon-Tyne,
Tyne and Wear NE1 8ST
(Tel: 091-232 6002)

Bachelor of Arts
One-year non-graduate Certificate in Education
Postgraduate Certificate in Education
One-year retraining course

Nottingham Polytechnic
Burton Street, Nottingham,
Nottinghamshire NG1 4BU
(Tel: 0602 418248)

Bachelor of Education (this initial teacher training programme consists of a four-year sandwich course in design and technology with education)
One-year non-graduate Certificate in Education
Postgraduate Certificate in Education (Technology)
One-year retraining course

Sheffield City Polytechnic
Pond Street, Sheffield,
South Yorkshire S1 1WB
(Tel: 0742 720911)

Bachelor of Education (this initial teacher training programme consists of a four-year sandwich course in design and technology with education)
One-year non-graduate Certificate in Education

Sunderland Polytechnic
Langham Tower,
Ryhope Road, Sunderland,
Tyne and Wear SR2 7EE
(Tel: 091-567 6231)

One-year non-graduate Certificate in Education (Technology)

Thames Polytechnic
Wellington Street,
London SE18 6PF
(Tel: 081-854 0081)

Bachelor of Education (this initial teacher training programme consists of a four-year sandwich course in design and technology with education)
One-year non-graduate Certificate in Education

**University of London
Goldsmiths' College**
Lewisham Way, New Cross,
London SE14 6NW
(Tel: 081-692 7171)

Bachelor of Education (this initial teacher training programme consists of a four-year sandwich course in design and technology with education)
Postgraduate Certificate in Education
One-year retraining course.

**Wolverhampton
Polytechnic**
Molineux Street,
Wolverhampton,
West Midlands WV1 1SB
(Tel: 0902 31300)

Bachelor of Education (this initial teacher training programme consists of a four-year sandwich course in design and technology with education)
One-year non-graduate Certificate in Education
One-year retraining course

LONDON BOROUGHS

Barking

A. P. Larbalestier, M.A.
Chief Education Officer
Town Hall
Barking
Essex IG11 7LU

081-594 3880

Barnet

N. M. Gill, M.A.
Director of Educational Services
and Chief Education Officer
Town Hall
Frien Barnet
London N11 3DL

081-368 1255

Bexley

G. Hall, BA, D.M.
Director of Education
Hillview
Hillview Drive
Welling
Kent DA16 3RY

081-303 7777

Brent

G. F. Benham, BA, M.Phil, Dip.Ed,
M.A, FRSA, FBIM
Director of Education
London Borough of Brent
Education Department
Chesterfield House
9 Park Lane
Wembley
Middlesex HA9 7RW

081-904 1244

Bromley

G. Grainge
Director of Education
London Borough of Bromley
The Town Hall
Widmore Road
Bromley
Kent BR1 1SB

081-464 3333

Croydon

P. Benians, BSc (Econ)
Director of Education
Taberner House
Park Lane
Croydon
Surrey CR9 1TP

081-760 5555

Ealing

Mrs U. Barlow
Director of Education
Hadley House
79-81 Uxbridge Road
Ealing
London W5 5SU

081-579 2424

Enfield

G. Hutchinson, BA
Director of Education
Education Department
PO Box 56
Civic Centre
Silver Street
Enfield
Middlesex EN1 3XQ

081-366 6565

Haringey

R. L. Jones
Director of Educational Services
Haringey Council Education Offices
48 Station Road
London N22 4TY

081-579 9700

Harrow

H. Fielding, M.A, M.Ed
Director of Education
PO Box 22, Civic Centre
Harrow
Middlesex HA1 2UW

081-863 5611

Havering

B. H. Laister, M.A.
Director of Educational Services
London Borough of Havering
Education Department
Mercury House
Mercury Gardens
Romford
Essex RM1 3DR

0708 766999

Hillingdon

T. M. Hinds
Director of Education
London Borough of Hillingdon
Civic Centre
Uxbridge
Middlesex UB8 1UW

0895 50111

Hounslow

J. Trickett
Director of Education
Civic Centre
Lampton Road
Hounslow
Middlesex TW3 4DN

081-570 7728

Kingston upon Thames

W. E. Dickinson, BA(Hons), ADipEd
Director of Education
London Borough of Kingston upon Thames
Guildhall
High Street
Kingston upon Thames
Surrey KT1 1UE

081-546 2121

Merton

R. Davies BA
Director of Education
London Borough of Merton
Station House
London Road
Morden
Surrey SM4 5DR

081-543 2222

Newham

S. Lawless
Director of Education
London Borough of Newham
Education Office
Broadway House
322 High Street
Stratford
London E15 1AJ

081-555 5552

Redbridge

K. G. M. Ratcliffe, M.A, M.Ed
Director of Educational Services
London Borough of Redbridge
Lynton House
255-259 High Road
Ilford
Essex IG1 1NN

081-478 3020

Richmond upon Thames

G. A. Alexander, BA
Director of Education
London Borough of Richmond upon Thames
Education Offices
Regal House
London Road
Twickenham TW1 3QB

081-891 1411

Sutton

C. Blurton, BA
Director of Education
London Borough of Sutton
The Grove
Carshalton
Surrey SM5 3AL

081-770 6500

Waltham Forest

M. Shepherd
Chief Education Officer
London Borough of Waltham Forest
Municipal Offices
High Road
Leyton
London E10 5QJ

081-527 5544

METROPOLITAN COUNTY OF GREATER MANCHESTER

Bolton

B. Hughes, BSc
Director of Education
PO Box 53
Paderborn House
Civic Centre
Bolton
Lancashire BL1 1JW

0204 22311

Bury	M. Gray, BA, M.Ed Director of Education Education Department Athenaeum House Market Street Bury Lancashire BL9 0BN	061-705 5000
Manchester	R. Jobson Chief Education Officer Education Offices Crown Square Manchester M60 3BB	061-234 7001
Oldham	Dr W. R. Kneen, M.A Director of Education Old Town Hall Middleton Road Chadderton Oldham Lancashire OL9 6PP	061-624 0505
Rochdale	A. N. Naylor, BA Chief Education Officer PO Box 70 Municipal Offices Smith Street Rochdale Lancashire OL16 1YD	0706 47474
Salford	A. Lockhart, M.A, D.M.S. Chief Education Officer Education Office Chapel Street Salford M3 5LT	061-832 9751
Stockport	J. E. Hendy, BA Director of Education Education Division Stopford House Town Hall Stockport Lancashire SK1 3XE	061-480 4949
Tameside	A. Webster, BA Director of Education Tameside Metropolitan Borough Council Education Department Council Offices Wellington Road Ashton-U-Lyne OL6 6DL	061-330 8355
Trafford	C. J. Radley, BA Chief Education Officer PO Box 19 Town Hall Tatton Road Sale Trafford M33 1YR	061-872 2101

Wigan	J. K. Hampson, M.A Director of Education Education Offices Gateway House Standishgate Wigan WN1 1AE	0942 828891

METROPOLITAN COUNTY OF MERSEYSIDE

Knowsley	A. Culley Director of Education Knowsley Borough Council Education Office Huyton Hey Road Huyton Liverpool L36 5YH	051-480 5111
Liverpool	M. F. Cogley Director of Education 14 Sir Thomas Street Liverpool L1 6BJ	051-227 3911
St. Helens	N. D. Nelson, BA Director of Education Education Department Century House Hardshaw Street St. Helens Merseyside WA10 1RN	0744 24061
Sefton	J. A. Marsden, BA Director of Education Education Department Town Hall Oriel Road Bootle Merseyside L20 7AE	051-922 4040
Wirral	D. Rigby Director of Education Hamilton Centre Conway Street Birkenhead Merseyside	051-666 2121

METROPOLITAN COUNTY OF WEST MIDLANDS

Birmingham	D. Hammond Chief Education Officer Education Department Margaret Street Birmingham West Midlands B3 3BU	021-235 9944
Coventry	C. Farmer, M.A. Director of Education Education Offices Earl Street Coventry West Midlands CV1 5RS	0203 831511

LOCAL EDUCATION AUTHORITIES

Dudley	R. K. Westerby Director of Education Westox House 1 Trinity Road Dudley West Midlands DY1 1JD	0384 456000
Sandwell	G. A. Brinsdon, M.A. Director of Education Sandwell Metropolitan Borough Council PO Box 41 Shaftesbury House 402 High Street West Bromwich West Midlands B70 8LT	021-525 7366
Solihull	M. Sweet, M.A, M.Ed Director of Education PO Box 20 Council House Solihull West Midlands B91 3QU	021-704 6000
Walsall	Mrs D. Tuck, M.A. Director of Education The Civic Centre Darwall Street Walsall Staffordshire WS1 1DQ	0922 650000
Wolverhampton	Miss C. Adams Director of Education Education Department Civic Centre St. Peter's Square Wolverhampton WV1 1RR	0902 27811

METROPOLITAN COUNTY OF TYNE AND WEAR

Gateshead	J. D. Arbon Director of Education Civic Centre Regent Street Gateshead Tyne and Wear NE8 1HH	091 4771011
Newcastle upon Tyne	W. B. Downer Director of Education Civic Centre Newcastle upon Tyne Tyne and Wear NE1 8PU	091 2328520
Sunderland	J. Hall, BA, BSc(Econ) Director of Education Education Department Town Hall & Civic Centre Sunderland Tyne and Wear SR2 7DN	091 5676161

Tyneside (North)   J. F. Partington   091 2576621
Director of Education
North Tyneside Metropolitan Borough Council
Education Offices
The Chase
North Shields
Tyne and Wear NE29 0HW

Tyneside (South)   Director of Education   091 4271717
Borough Council of South Tyneside
Education Department
Town Hall & Civic Offices
Westoe Road
South Shields
Tyne and Wear NE33 2RL

METROPOLITAN COUNTY OF NORTH YORKSHIRE

Harrogate   J.P. Aldridge BSc   0423 60511
Director of Education
Education Department
59 Grove Road
Harrogate
North Yorkshire HG1 5ER

Scarborough   D. Harrison BA   0723 361376
Director of Education
Education Department
Huntriss Row
Scarborough
North Yorkshire YO11 2EQ

Skipton   R.T. Billing BA   0756 792427
Director of Education
Education Department
Water Street
Skipton
North Yorkshire BD23 1PD

York   D. Hudson BA   0904 628933
Director of Education
Education Department
60 Picadilly
York
North Yorkshire YO1 1PW

METROPOLITAN COUNTY OF SOUTH YORKSHIRE

Barnsley   T. Brooks BSc   091 733252
Director of Education
Education Offices
Berneslai Close
Barnsley
South Yorkshire

Doncaster   A. M. Taylor, BA   0302 734104
Director of Education
Princegate
Doncaster
South Yorkshire DN1 3EP

LOCAL EDUCATION AUTHORITIES

Rotherham

K. Snowden, M.A.
Director of Education
Norfolk House
Walker Place
Rotherham
South Yorkshire S60 1QT

0709 382121

Sheffield

B. Walton, BA
Chief Education Officer
PO Box 67
Leopold Street
Sheffield
South Yorkshire S1 1RJ

0742 26341

METROPOLITAN COUNTY OF WEST YORKSHIRE

Bradford

W. R. Knight, CBE, M.A.
Director of Education
Provincial House
Tyrrel Street
Bradford
West Yorkshire BD1 1NP

0274 752111

Calderdale

A. Pickvance
Chief Education Officer
Metropolitan Borough of Calderdale
Education Department
PO Box 33
Northgate House
Halifax
West Yorkshire HX1 1UN

0422 357257

Kirklees

J. G. Evans
Executive Director of Education
Kirklees Metropolitan Council
Oldgate House
2 Oldgate
Huddersfield
West Yorkshire HD1 6QW

0484 422133

Leeds

R. S. Johnson, BSc
Director of Education
Merrion House
110 Merrion Centre
Leeds LS2 8JH

0532 463000

Wakefield

A. Lenney, M.A.
Chief Education Officer
Education Department
County Hall
Wakefield
West Yorkshire WF1 2QL

0924 290900

NON-METROPOLITAN COUNTIES

Avon

Dr C. Saville
Director of Education
County of Avon
PO Box 57
Avon House North
St. James Barton
Bristol BS99 7EB

0272 290777

Bedfordshire

D. G. Wadsworth, M.A.
Chief Education Officer
County Hall
Bedford MK42 9AP

0234 63222

Berkshire

S. R. Goodchild, BA, FBIM, FRSA
Director of Education
Education Department
Shire Hall
Shinfield Park
Reading RG2 9XE

0734 875444

Cambridgeshire

G. H. Morris, BA, FCP
Chief Education Officer
Shire Hall
Castle Hill
Cambridge CB3 0AP

0223 317111

Cheshire

N. J. Fitton
Group Director
Education Services
County Hall
Chester CH1 1SQ

0244 602424

Cleveland

A. H. R. Calderwood, M. A, M.Ed, FRSA
FBIM
County Education Officer
Woodlands Road
Middlesbrough
Cleveland TS1 3BN

0642 248155

Cornwall

D. W. Fryer, BSc
Secretary for Education
Cornwall County Council
County Hall
Truro TR1 3BA

0872 74282

Cumbria

Miss P. Black
Director of Education
Education Department
5 Portland Square
Carlisle CA1 1PU

0228 23456

LOCAL EDUCATION AUTHORITIES

Derbyshire

J. G. Evans, BA
Director of Education
Education Department
Science Block
Chatsworth Hall
Chesterfield Road
Matlock DE4 3FW

0629 580000

Devon

S. W. G. Jenkin
Chief Education Officer
County Hall
Exeter EX2 4QG

0392 77977

Dorset

R. P. Slade
Principal Careers Officer
Careers Service Headquarters
33 Trinity Street
Dorchester DT1 1TT

0305 3131

Durham

K. D. Grimshaw
Director of Education
Education Department
County Hall
Durham DH1 5UJ

091 3864411

Essex

R. M. Sharp, BA
County Education Officer
Education Department
PO Box 47
Threadneedle House
Market Road
Chelmsford CM1 1LD

0245 492211

Gloucestershire

K. D. Anderson, BA, DipEd, FRSA
Chief Education Officer
Shire Hall
Gloucester GL1 2TP

0452 425300

Hampshire

P. J. Coles, MSc
County Education Officer
The Castle
Winchester
Hampshire SO23 8UG

0962 841841

Hereford & Worcester

J. W. Turnbull, M.A, BSc(Econ)
County Education Officer
Castle Street
Worcester WR1 3AG

0905 763763

Hertfordshire

D. Fisher, M.A.
County Education Officer
County Hall
Hertford SG13 8DF

0992 555818

Humberside	Dr M. Garnett Director of Education County Hall Beverley North Humberside HU17 9BA	0482 867131
Isle of Man	Director of Education Education Department Government Buildings Bucks Road Douglas Isle of Man	0624 26262
Isle of Wight	Dr J. A. Williams, M.A, PhD, FRSA County Education Officer County Hall Newport Isle of Wight PO30 1UD	0983 823454
Isles of Scilly	L. W. Michell Secretary for Education Council of the Isles of Scilly Town Hall St. Mary's Isles of Scilly TR21 0LW	0720 22537
Kent	R. Pryke, BA, FRSA Director of Educational Services Education Department Springfield Maidstone Kent ME14 2LJ	0622 671411
Lancashire	A. J. Collier, M.A. Chief Education Officer PO Box 61 County Hall Preston PR1 8RJ	0772 54868
Leicestershire	K. H. Wood-Allum, BA, M.Ed, FRSA Director of Education Leicestershire County Council County Hall Glenfield Leicester LE3 8RF	0533 871313
Norfolk	M. H. Edwards, BA County Education Officer County Hall Martineau Lane Norwich NR1 2DL	0603 222300
Northamptonshire	J. R. Atkinson, M.A, DipEd Psych, DMS Director of Education and Libraries County Education Department Northampton House Northampton NN1 2HX	0604 236252

LOCAL EDUCATION AUTHORITIES

Northumberland	C. C. Tipple Director of Education Northumberland County Council County Hall Morpeth Northumberland NE61 2EF	0670 514343
Nottinghamshire	A. J. Fox, M.A. Chief Education Officer County Hall West Bridgford Nottingham NG2 7QP	0602 823823
Oxfordshire	Mrs J. Stephens, BSc Chief Education Officer Education Department Macclesfield House New Road Oxford OX1 1NA	0865 792422
Shropshire	P. Cates, BA County Education Officer The Shirehall Abbey Foregate Shrewsbury SY2 6ND	0743 222252
Somerset	Mrs. J. Wisker Chief Education Officer County Hall Taunton Somerset TA1 4DY	0823 333451
Staffordshire	Chief Education Officer Education Office Tipping Street Stafford ST16 2DH	0785 223121
Suffolk	T. R. Cornthwaite County Education Officer St. Andrew House County Hall Ipswich IP4 2LJ	0473 230000
Surrey	M. C. Pinchin, BSc, FRSA County Education Officer County Hall Penrhyn Road Kingston upon Thames Surrey KT1 2DJ	081-541 9500
Sussex (East)	County Education Officer PO Box 4 County Hall St. Anne's Crescent Lewes BN7 1SG	0273 26121

Sussex (West)	R. D. C. Bunker, M. A. Director of Education County Hall West Street Chichester PO19 1RF	0243 777100
Warwickshire	Ms Margaret Maden, BA(Hons) County Education Officer 22 Northgate Street Warwick CV34 4SR	0926 410410
Wiltshire	I. M. Slocombe Chief Education Officer County Hall Bythesea Trowbridge Wiltshire BA14 8JB	0225 753641
Yorkshire (North)	F. F. Evans, M.A, FRSA County Education Officer County Hall Northallerton North Yorkshire DL7 8AE	0609 780780
SCOTLAND	Director of Education Regional Headquarters Newtown St. Boswells Roxburghshire TD6 0SA	0835 23301
Central Region	I. Collie Director of Education Central Regional Council Hillpark Education Centre Benview Bannockburn FK7 0JY	0786 816205
Dumfries & Galloway Region	W. Fordyce Education Offices 30 Edinburgh Road Dumfries DG1 1JQ	0387 61234
Fife Region	M. More Director of Education Fife Regional Council Fife House North Street Glenrothes Fife KY7 5LT	0592 754411
Grampian Region	J. A. D. Michie, MA, M.Ed Director of Education Woodhill House Westburn Road Aberdeen AB9 2LU	0224 682222
Highland Region	Director of Education Regional Buildings Glenurquhart Road Inverness IV3 5NX	0463 234121

LOCAL EDUCATION AUTHORITIES

Lothian Region

Lothian Region Careers Service
Information Unit
27 Torphichen Street
Edinburgh EH3 8HX

031 229 9166

Strathclyde Region

Director of Education
Department of Education
Strathclyde House
20 India Street
Glasgow G2 4PF

041 204 2900

Tayside Region

A. R. Watson, M.A, M.Ed, FBIM
Director of Education
Tayside House
Crichton Street
Dundee DD1 3RJ

0382 23281

Orkney Islands Council

R. L. Henderson, M.A, M.Ed
Director of Education
Council Offices
Kirkwall
Orkney KW15 1NY

0856 3535

Shetland Islands Council

R. A. B. Barnes, M.A, DipEd
Director of Education
Education Offices
1 Harbour Street
Lerwick
Shetland ZE1 0LS

0595 3535

**Western Isles
Islands Council**

N. R. Galbraigh
Director of Education
Education Department
Stornoway
Isle of Lewis PA87 2BW

0851 3773

WALES

Clwyd

K. Evans, M.A, FRSA
Director of Education
Clwyd County Council
County Education Offices
Shire Hall
Mold
Clwyd CH7 6ND

0352 55798

Dyfed

W. J. Phillips, M.A, LLB
Director of Education
Education Headquarters
Dyfed County Council
Pibwrlwyd
Carmarthen
Dyfed SA31 2NH

0267 233333

Glamorgan (Mid)

E. Roberts, MSc
Director of Education
Mid-Glamorgan County Council
Cathays Park
Cardiff CF1 3NF

0222 820820

Glamorgan (South)

D. Orrell
Director of Education
South Glamorgan County Council
County Hall
Atlantic Wharf
Cardiff CF1 5UW

0222 872000

Glamorgan (West)

J. Beale, M.A.
Director of Education
West Glamorgan County Council
County Hall
Swansea SA1 3SN

0792 471111

Gwent

G. V. Drought
Director of Education
Gwent County Council
Cwmbran
Gwent NP4 2XG

0633 838838

Gwynedd

G. E. Humphreys
Director of Education
County Education Office
Caernarfon
Gwynedd LL55 1SH

0286 4121

Powys

R. W. Bevan, BA
Director of Education
Powys County Hall
Llandrindod Wells
Powys LD1 5LG

0597 826000

NORTHERN IRELAND

Belfast Area

Director of Education
Education Department
1 Brunswick Street
Belfast BT2 7QA

0232 229211

North Eastern Area

Director of Education
Education Department
County Hall
182 Galgorm Road
Ballymena
Co Antrim BT42 2HN

0266 653333

South Eastern Area

Director of Education
Education Department
18 Windsor Avenue
Belfast BT9 6EF

0232 661188

Southern Area

Director of Education
Education Department
3 Charlemont Place
The Mall
Armagh

0861 523811

LOCAL EDUCATION AUTHORITIES

Western Area

Director of Education
Education Department
Headquarters Office
1 Hospital Road
Omagh BT79 0AW

0662 244931

GUERNSEY

Director of Education
Education Department
PO Box No 32
La Couperderie
St Peter Port
Guernsey

0481 710821

JERSEY

Director of Education
Education Department
PO Box 142
St Saviour
Jersey

0534 71065

The organisations listed and described in this chapter are associated with woodworking or, more generally, able to offer help to the would-be woodworker, woodworking employee or employer.

Some offer scholarships, grants or awards; others are responsible for training or technical advice. All will provide further information or literature.

THE BUILDING CONSERVATION TRUST

Apartment 39, Hampton Court Palace,
East Molesey, Surrey KT8 9BS (Tel: 081-943 2277)
The Building Conservation Trust was formed in 1979 to encourage the good upkeep of ordinary houses and flats. As an independent educational charity the Trust's aim is to provide unbiased technical information on maintenance, repair and improvement.

This work is becoming increasingly important in the 90's when there are two million homes (10% of the total stock) in need of urgent repair; and there are many first-time home owners, and others newly responsible for housing, all needing advice and encouragement to prefer structural repair to cosmetic improvement.

The work of the Building Conservation Trust is based on a large permanent exhibition, "Care of Buildings' in a wing of Hampton Court Palace. This shows by life-size and realistic reconstructions how buildings are put together; what goes wrong with them, and what can be done to put things right.

The exhibition is open to the public and the Trust promotes visits by college students and school children. The Trust is also involved in the organisation of courses ranging from 2-day seminars to half-day visits built around study packages and discussion. As a result of new legislation and trends in housing there are growing numbers of housing and tenants associations and co-operatives. Larger local authorities are running their housing departments on a neighbourhood basis. The staff of all these new groups standing between householders and tenants, and builders, surveyors and architects, need the basic knowledge of the construction, maintenance and repair of houses and flats that the Building Conservation Trust can provide.

The Trust also takes its message out to the public with regular press statements and strip cartoons, and a range of advisory articles on how and why to look after your home.

There is now growing awareness of the need to care for housing, both at the national and personal level. In expanding its activities the Building Conservation Trust aims to play its part in channelling that awareness into informed action.

BUILDING EMPLOYERS CONFEDERATION

82 New Cavendish Street, London W1M 8AD
(Tel: 071-580 5588)
Construction is one of the biggest single industries in Britain with an annual output of around £40,000 million, 80 per cent of which is on the building side; this is equivalent to nearly 10 per cent of the nation's gross domestic product. The building industry also plays a crucial role in forming the economic, industrial and social make-up of British society.

An industry of such magnitude and importance requires direction and guidance.

The Building Employers Confederation is the most influential trade organisation in the building industry and has been serving the interests of building employers for over a hundred years.

At present, the BEC represents 9,500 members ranging from the smallest local builder to the largest international contractors, who together account for over 75 per cent of Britain's building output.

Although it is a national organisation, the BEC also represents the regional and local interests of its members through ten regional and 140 local associations.

The Confederation is divided into five sectors:

The **Building Contractors Federation,** together with the Confederation's National Committee for Smaller Builders.

The **National Contractors Group** comprising the 80 largest members who operate throughout the country.

The **Housebuilders Federation** representing private new housebuilders.

The **Federation of Building Specialist Contractors** including representatives of trades such as painting, scaffolding, plastering and stonemasonry.

British Woodworking Federation representing manufacturers of wood products such as windows and doors.

The BEC provides benefits, advice and guidance to its members, and represents their views and interests to Government, to relevant organisations within the construction industry, to industry and commerce, and to the public at large. It employs specialist staff dealing with political lobbying and the media; manpower matters including industrial relations, training and safety; legal and contractual; technical; management training and consultancy; pensions and insurance, and publishing.

The BEC also operates a Guarantee Scheme for small building works which can help protect innocent householders from the damage and misery caused by 'cowboy' builders.

The Builder Employers Confederation is therefore one of the major foundations of the construction industry, proving its worth and influence at both local and national levels, and providing an invaluable service not only to its members, but also to the public at large.

CARPENTERS COMPANY

Carpenters Hall, 1 Throgmorton Avenue, London EC2N 2JJ (Tel: 071-588 7001)

The Carpenters' Company founded in the 13th/early 14th century, has its own Building Crafts Training School at 153 Great Titchfield Street, London W1P 7FR.

Apprentice training courses in joinery and shopfitting are available which meet the requirements of the City and Guilds of London Institute Examination Board. In addition they meet the requirements of the Construction Industry Training Board and enable levy-paying companies to obtain grant aid.

Joinery and shopfitting students are encouraged in their third year to study in greater depth and, with guidance from their instructors, prepare for the examinations held by the Institute of Carpenters.

Apprentice craft courses comprise:

Technology:
>   Study of materials, process and usages of each craft.

Practical Work:
>   All workshop activity and practical processes.

Associated subjects:
>   History of the craft, craft calculations, craft geometry, craft science, building construction, safety.

Prizes are given to students achieving sufficiently high standards and it is hoped that scholarships and bursaries may become available to students in need.

A full time two-year fee paying course in fine woodwork is also available. This course is designed to equip students with the craft skills and expertise to enable them to set themselves up as independent small businessmen. Bursaries may be available to pay course fees for those needing assistance.

Evening courses are offered on two evenings a week on woodturning. These courses are of six weeks duration and are aimed at beginners and those wishing to improve their basic skills.

A short course is also offered on woodworking machinery. This course is a one-day Safety course for supervisors and machine operators and is designed to enable them to interpret the Woodworking Machines Regulations 1974.

Enquiries regarding the training programme and grants should be made to the Director, Building Crafts Training School, 153 Great Titchfield Street, London W1P 7FR. Telephone: 071-636 0480. A brochure setting out clearly each training programme is also available from this address.

A Scholarship to either an architect or a builder, enabling the scholar to study at his respective profession in the United States for one year is offered annually by the company and further details are obtainable from the Carpenters' Company.

In association with William Mallinson & Sons and Mallinson-Denny Ltd., the company also supports the Carpenters' Award which was founded to encourage high general standards of hardwood and softwood joinery associated with building construction in the United Kingdom.

The award is presented for an outstanding example of joinery in terms of suitability of the design for its location and purpose and of the choice of timber, and its manufacture, installation, finish and behaviour. The award is made in alternate years and covers two years completed work at each assessment. Any joinery work in or associated with any building in the United Kingdom which has been put to its intended use in the two years immediately prior to the 1st January of the year of the Award may be nominated.

Anyone may submit a nomination provided permission from the owner of the building has been obtained. All nominations should be sent on an entry form available from the Carpenters' Company, and returned to them by the required date.

Design effectiveness, craftsmanship and standard joinery are taken into consideration and assessments are made between May and August in the year of the Award.

More detailed information is available from the Clerk to the Company.

THE INSTITUTE OF CARPENTERS

PO Box 111, Aldershot, Hampshire GU11 1YW
To further a career it is possible to become a Member of the Institute of Carpenters. A training programme is offered. On passing examinations you may apply for membership of the Institute.

The examination and membership structure is as follows :

Intermediate	Affiliate Membership
Licentiate	Licentiate Membership
Member	Member
Fellow	Fellowship

Copies of the Institute of Carpenter's examination syllabus are available from the Examinations Registrar, 44 Charlcote Crescent, Wistaston, Crewe, Cheshire CW2 6UH.

Student membership may be offered to those over 16 and studying for an Institute or City & Guilds examination in carpentry and joinery, shopfitting, or cabinet making. This class of membership is for a maximum of 4 years, or on obtaining one of the above qualifications (whichever is the sooner).

Entrance by City & Guilds of London Institute examinations are also acceptable subject to grades, technical ability and at the discretion of the Council.

Applications for candidates over 35 years old can be accepted subject to educational qualifications, technical ability and at the discretion of the Council.

Membership of the Institute offers increased opportunities within the Construction Industry and members are kept informed of developments within the craft.

There is also an active social side to the Institute, particularly within Sections throughout the country. A brochure setting out the objectives and activities can be obtained from the Institute at the above address.

CONSTRUCTION INDUSTRY TRAINING BOARD

Headquarters: Bircham Newton, King's Lynn, Norfolk PE31 6RH (Tel: 0553 776677)
The CITB is a statutory body which advises firms on their training needs and assists them with the cost of training by providing a wide range of grants, designed to encourage industry to maintain an adequate skilled workforce despite fluctuations in work levels.

The Board's advisory operations in the field are backed up by a team of specialists who develop improved forms of training for all areas of the industry. A wide range of training publications are produced and research and manpower studies undertaken.

CITB staff are closely involved in giving greater emphasis to safety training at all levels of the industry, and to management training. The Board has also been made lead industry body for the introduction of National Vocational Qualifications.

The Board's Construction Careers Service is proving very successful in attracting school leavers into the industry, whether at operative level or for professional and management careers.

CITB runs by far the largest Youth Training programme in the country, and also runs the Employment Training scheme for the industry.

The Board's field areas, together with its principal field offices, are as follows :

Greater London and South East

General Manager: Jim Hughes, Radnor House,
1272 London Road, Norbury, London
SW16 4EL
(Tel: 081-679 6917)

Scotland

General Manager: Ian Wright, 4 Edison Street,
Hillington Industrial Estate, Hillington,
Glasgow G52 6XN
(Tel: 041-883 4781)

East

General Manager: Leonard Scott, Dishley House,
Bishop Meadow Road, Loughborough,
LE11 0RE
(Tel: 0509 610266)

Wales and West Midlands

General Manager: Kenneth Gunning, 1st Floor,
Shenstone House, Dudley Road, Halesowen
B63 3NT
(Tel: 021-585 5252)

South West

General Manager: David Algate, Lawrence House,
Lower Bristol Road, Bath, Avon BA2 9ET
(Tel: 0225 447914)

North West

General Manager: Mike Gee, Parade Chambers,
103 The Parade, Swinton, Manchester M27 2BJ
(Tel: 061-794 8931/3)

North East

General Manager: Jeffrey Lister, Milton House,
Queen Street, Morley, Leeds LS27 9EL
(Tel: 0532 521966)

Construction Careers Service

General Manager: Stan Robertson, Bircham
Newton Training Centre, Nr. King's Lynn,
Norfolk PE31 6RH
(Tel: 0553 776677)

THE CRAFTS COUNCIL

12 Waterloo Place, Lower Regent Street, London
SW1Y 4AU (Tel: 071-930 4811)
The Crafts Council administers an annual government grant for the support of the crafts in England
and Wales and the promotions of the work of artist
craftspeople. Facilities include a large gallery at
Waterloo place showing a changing programme of
exhibitions, an information centre, slide library, and
bookstall. The Council provides grants, loans and
bursaries, publishes the bi-monthly magazine Crafts
and a range of other books, postcards and slide
packs. There is an education section, which works
at school and college levels, and the Council also
manages the Craft Council Shop at the Victoria &
Albert Museum. Funding is given to the Welsh Arts
Council and the Regional Arts Associations for the
support of craft activities, and also to Contemporary
Applied Arts, a membership organisation for craftspeople which holds exhibitions and sells work
through its gallery in Covent Garden, London.

Scotland receives a separate government grant
which is administered by the Crafts Consultative
Committee of the Scottish Development Agency.

THE BRITISH DECOY AND WILDFOWL CARVERS ASSOCIATION

6 Pendred Road, Reading, Berkshire RG2 8QL
(Tel: 0734 311867)
This Association was formed in June 1990 to
promote and nurture the art of decoy carving in all
its aspects in the UK and to provide a forum for
the exchange of ideas and techniques. It also intends
to run an exhibition each year at which the work
of members will be judged and awarded prizes.
Membership is open to all carvers, collectors,
instructors and suppliers of materials.

FORESTRY COMMISSION

231 Corstorphine Road, Edinburgh EH12 7AT
(Tel: 031 334 0303)
At the same address is the Forestry Training Council
which comprises the representatives of 17 forestry
organisations, including the Forestry Commission.
The Commission and the Council work together on
training and have a useful booklet "Careers and
Training in Forestry" available free.

The council does not employ people directly but
will arrange training courses if there are large
enough groups involved, or will help individuals
find the sort of training they are looking for in
forestry.

The Forestry Commission directly employs 8,000 people – administration staff as well as foresters. It tends to recruit foresters from among graduates with the appropriate degree.

BRITISH FURNITURE MANUFACTURERS FEDERATION

30 Harcourt Street, London W1H 2AA
(Tel: 071-724 0854)

The BFM – a federation of regional associations interested in the training and education of woodworking students employed by or intended to be employed by furniture manufacturers. Information on career opportunities in any region can be obtained from the appropriate Association Secretary or other training contacts as specified below:

London and South East

Comprising: Greater London (including the City of London and Middlesex), Cambridgeshire, Essex, Hertfordshire, Kent, Norfolk, Suffolk, Surrey, West Sussex, East Sussex.

BFM Association: London & South Eastern Furniture Manufacturers Association (LFM), 93 Great Eastern Street, London EC2A 3JB (Tel: 071-739 7916)

Secretary: Mr D K Allen

High Wycombe and Mid-Southern Counties

Comprising: Oxfordshire, Buckinghamshire, Berkshire, Hampshire, Isle of Wight, East Dorset.

BFM Association: British Furniture Manufacturers Association (Southern), Wycombe House, 9 Amersham Hill, High Wycombe, Buckinghamshire HP13 6NR (Tel: 0494 23021)

Secretary: Mr D P Sanger
Training Officer: Mr G V P Vockins

West of England and South Wales

Comprising: Gloucestershire, Avon, Wiltshire, Somerset, West Dorset, Devonshire, Cornwall, Herefordshire, Mid-Glamorgan, West Glamorgan, South Glamorgan, Gwent, Dyfed, South of Powys.

BFM Association: West of England & South Wales Furniture Manufacturers' Association, First Floor, York House, Bond Street, Bristol, Avon BS1 3LQ (Tel: 0272 420269)

Secretary: Mr G B Tymms

Midlands and North West

Comprising: West Midlands, Staffordshire, Salop, Worcestershire, Warwickshire, Northamptonshire, North of Powys, Southern Lancashire, Merseyside, Greater Manchester with Northern FMA as indicated below – Cheshire, Clwyd, Gwyneddd, Nottinghamshire, Derbyshire, Leicestershire, Lincolnshire, South Humberside.

BFM Association: Midlands & North West Furniture Manufacturers Association, 263a Monton Road, Monton, Eccles, Manchester M30 9LF (Tel: 061-788 9018/9)

Secretary: Mr G Pitt

Associated Training Group: WEBS (Training) Association, Abbeyfield Road, Lenton Industrial Estate, Nottingham NG7 2TB (Tel: 0602 866866)

GTO: Mr B Whitaker

Northern and North East

Comprising: Durham, Northumberland, Tyne and Wear, Cleveland, North Yorkshire, West Yorkshire, South Yorkshire, North Humberside, Cumbria, Northern part of Lancashire, with the western boundary running roughly North-West from a point East of Wigan to the River Ribble West of Preston.

BFM Association: Northern Furniture Manufacturers' Association, 32 Scott Green, Gildersome, Nr Leeds, West Yorkshire (Tel: 0532 852413)

Secretary: Mr G Mellor

Associated Training Group: Northern Lancashire Training Group, 85 Whalley Road, Accrington, Lancashire BB5 1AS (Tel: 0254 36408)

Senior GTO: Mr J Harkness

Associated Training Group: North East Coast Timber Training Group, East Jarrow, Tyne and Wear, NE32 2EE (Tel: 0632 894182)

GTO: Mr M Howorth

Scotland

Comprising: the whole of Scotland

BFM Association: Scottish Furniture Manufacturers' Association, George House, 50 George Square, Glasgow G2 1RR (Tel: 041-552 4994)

Secretary: Mr A Grahame Thomson

Associated Training Group: Scottish Furniture Training Group, George House, 50 George Square, Glasgow G2 1RR (Tel: 041-552 4994).

THE WORSHIPFUL COMPANY OF FURNITURE MAKERS

30 Harcourt Street, London W1H 2AA
(Tel: 071-724 5160)

A number of valuable scholarships are offered annually by The Worshipful Company of Furniture Makers to young people engaged in, or studying to enter, the furniture industry. The intention of these scholarships is to enable the holders to improve his, or her, ability to undertake a position of responsibility in the industry and to enlarge the sum of knowledge available to the industry.

In previous years awards have been used for study tours, at home and abroad, to finance prototype construction, to buy marketing and publicity expertise, to pay for commercial training courses and to provide subsistence for a student during a work experience placement. The Company will consider any worthwhile project.

The value and scope of the scholarships is reviewed annually to keep abreast of current needs. A brochure is published in September of each year giving details of the scholarships to be awarded in the following calendar year.

Brochures and application forms can be obtained from The Clerk to The Worshipful Company of Furniture Makers at the above address.

THE GUILD OF MASTER CRAFTSMEN

166 High Street, Lewes, East Sussex BN7 1XU
(Tel: 0273 477374)

The Guild of Master Craftsmen brings together all skilled people engaged in craft, art, trade, professional or vocation.

The Guild has over 27,000 members and can provide a list of craftsmen within a certain area for any enquirer.

BRITISH MARINE INDUSTRIES FEDERATION

Boating Industry House, Vale Road, Oatlands Park, Weybridge, Surrey KT13 9NS (Tel: 0932 854511) Training under the BMIF consists of a series of skill modules developed by the Federation and collectively known as Skillbuild.

Skillbuild allows employees, or prospective employees, to learn the crafts and then build on their current skills at any time during their career for their own advancement or as company skill requirements change. The courses are presented as self-contained modules. The basic craft development module covers the first year of the Training For Skills section of the YTS.

More Skillbuild modules are being designed and at the time of publication City & Guilds accreditation is being negotiated to bring the Skillbuild qualification in to line with new government requirements. Some modules have already been fully accepted.

The British Marine Industries Federation is the central trade association of the industry with 10 regional associations and other group associations.

The BMIF has further advice and information on courses and training schemes for the industry and may be able to direct inquirers towards boat building companies in their particular areas.

THE MARQUETRY SOCIETY

The Barn House, Llanon, Nr Aberystwyth, Dyfed SY23 5LZ (Tel: 09748 581)

The Society was founded in 1952 and is recognised as a leading authority on the craft of marquetry in all its aspects. It is a non-commercial organisation which exists solely to promote, foster and encourage interest in this ancient craft.

The Society has members in all parts of the British Isles and in many places abroad.

Today the Society has a flourishing membership, growing annually, and has formed groups throughout the country where members meet to exchange ideas and further their knowledge of the craft.

Membership is from January to December and the groups are based at: Bexley, Bristol, Broadlands, Canvey Island Marquestrians, Chelmsford, Cotswolds, Croydon and East Surrey, East Dorset, Harpenden, Harrow, Humberside, Ipswich, Leeds, Leicester, Manchester, Meopham, Northwood, Redbridge, St Albans, Scotland, Thames Ditton, Thurrock, Tunbridge Wells, West Kent, West Wales, Australia and Canada.

Your nearest group will be happy to welcome you to their activities. If a group does not exist in your area, write to the Hon General Secretary, Mrs P. M. Austin, at the above address for further information.

You will benefit immediately you become a member of the Society and enjoy the following privileges:

> Free quarterly issue of the Marquetarian which contains articles, line drawings, letters relating to marquetry subjects and many other interesting items.

> Free entry to the National Exhibition held each year vin a different venue, and the right to exhibit your own work if you desire.

> Free advice on every subject related to marquetry by a panel of experts.

THE MUSEUMS ASSOCIATION

34 Bloomsbury Way, London WC1A 2SF
(Tel: 071-404 4767)

There is a variety of work within a museum, but it must be pointed out that in the current economic climate there are not many vacancies. Any posts for woodworkers technicians are advertised in the National Press and two specialised publications – the Appointments Vacant Bulletin of the International Institute for Conservation (quarterley) and the Museum Journal published monthly by the Museums Association.

The Association does not offer scholarships or funding, but qualifications in their conservation, craftsman and technical Certificates are all covered by in-service training in museums and art galleries and fees are normally met by the candidates' museum.

A good educational background is required for museum work and the minimum entry requirements for national museums are GCSE "O" level passes in English Language and at least two other subjects or equivalent or higher qualifications. For most curatorial posts, however, a good relevant degree is required. Once employment has been found, a series of qualifications can be studied for through the Museums Association – the Museum Attendants Certifcate, Craftsman, Technical and Conservation Certificates and the Museums Diploma, which is a curatorial qualification in Museum Management. Anyone interested in museum work should contact the Museums Association at the address above who will be pleased to forward information on museum and art gallery careers on receipt of stamped addressed envelope.

If you are a Curator, Keeper, Administrator, Research Assistant, Director, Designer, Conservation or Education Officer, Attendant, Volunteer, Technician, Museum Shop Manager or Information Officer you can become an individual member of the Museums Association and have an active part in your community of museums and museum professionals.

Individual members of the Museums Association receive the monthly Museums Journal containing many articles, appraisals of new developments and exhibitions and book reviews.

An annual Museums Yearbook (a directory of all Museums and Galleries in the British Isles and their staff) is also available at a reduced price to members, as are various information sheets on museum topics.

You can attend seminars, register for the appropriate professional qualifications (such as: Museums Diploma; Conservation Diploma, and Technical Craftsman Conservation and Attendants' Certificates) and meet other Members of the profession at the Association's Annual Conference, plus other benefits from the membership. To obtain an application form write to the Museums Association at the above address.

The Museums Journal may be bought as individual copies or on a yearly subscription – for details of prices, please contact the Museums Association at the above address.

THE PUPPET CENTRE

Battersea Arts Centre, Lavender Hill, London SW11 5RA (Tel: 071-228 5335)

There are a select number of puppeteers who still work in wood. The Puppet Centre has contact with these makers and can organise special courses on wood carving for the puppet theatre. It has basic workshop facilities available to anyone wishing to use them (with a request for a donation). The Centre has a well stocked Reference Library (over 1,000 titles on all aspects of puppetry) and a permanent display of all types of puppet.

RURAL DEVELOPMENT COMMISSION

141 Castle Street, Salisbury, Wiltshire SP1 3TP (Tel: 0722 336255/Fax: 0722 332769)

The Rural Development Commission Business Service is intended to help small businesses with 20 skilled employees or less in the country or in small towns with less than 10,000 inhabitants. Its training courses are available to others but subsidies are removed.

Professional advisers offer advice on business management including business start-up, accountancy. Technical advisers offer advice on building, mechanical engineering, furniture making, sawmill management, farriery, saddlery, leatherwork, including transport, tourism and leisure projects. The Commission's Productivity Centre can assist with projects and prototypes.

The Commission can provide loans for suitable business developments. However, as a first step, it will always seek to arrange funding from the private sector. Advice is also available and can include preparing business plans, marketing strategies and identifying training on a wide range of technical subjects.

Training Courses

The majority of courses are designed for those who already have experience in business or a degree of skill in their trade. The courses are intended for those who run their own businesses, are just about to set up in business, or are employed in a small rural business. The aim is to teach new skills while taking people away from their job for the minimum period. The instructor pupil ratio is seldom more than one to five and instruction may in some cases be on a one-to-one basis. Many of these courses can be adjusted to suit individual requirements.

The courses available are held at Salisbury and other suitable locations, and are as follows :

Woodworking Machinery

Short courses in woodworking machinery of one, two and three day duration covering saws, planers, morticers, tenoners, overhead routers, spindle moulders, spraying and finishing.

Wheelwrighting

One-week course covering the general and advanced techniques in wheelmaking.

Antique Furniture and Antique Furniture Restoration

These courses, held at Salisbury, are again intended for practising craftsmen with at least three years' experience or a City & Guilds Certificate, cabinet-makers and upholsterers wishing to extend their skills.

The courses include one-week tuition on furniture restoration, carving, gilding, advanced upholstery and loose covers.

Two-day courses include woodturning, veneering, colouring and polishing, upholstery.

For further information on training courses please contact The Rural Development Commission at the above address.

NATIONAL ASSOCIATION OF SHOPFITTERS

NAS House, 411 Limpsfield Road, The Green, Warlingham, Surrey CR3 9HA (Tel: 08832 4961)

Members of the Association of Shopfitters carry out work in a vast range of establishments – from banks to bars; restaurants to boardrooms; museums and libraries to hotels. In fact, the term shopfitter is a little misleading.

Today shopfitting companies employ state of the art technology and work in every kind of material, not only wood. They offer total contract management from pre-drawing and scheduling to final finishing on site.

THE TOOL & TRADES HISTORY SOCIETY

60 Swanley Lane, Swanley, Kent BR8 7JG.

An international society formed to further the knowledge and understanding of hand tools and trades. Regional meetings, annual journal and regular newsletters.

BRITISH WOOD PRESERVING AND DAMP-PROOFING ASSOCIATION

Building No 6, The Office Village,
4 Romford Road, Stratford, London E15 4EA
(Tel: 081-519 2588/Fax: 081-519 3444)

A scientific and advisory association which collects information on the preservation and fireproofing of timber and on the methods of applying preservatives and fire retardants. It sponsors scientific research into the use of preservatives and fire retardants and makes available the results of its researches to all enquirers by the publication of leaflets, a technical advisory service and specialist lectures. It is completely impartial in its outlook and in the advice it gives. Among other objects it aims at making known the advantages of using preserved timber in the interests both of the consumer and the national economy.

The Association also provides advice and assistance on matters concerning rising dampness in properties and has a technical advisory service and leaflets on this subject.

Various technical publications concerning the preservation and fireproofing of timber together with publications on rising dampness may be purchased from the Association at nominal costs.

The Association depends entirely upon subscriptions from its Members. This enables it to remain completely independent and to maintain its impartial and scientific approach to all problems. Details about subscription rates for the various categories of members will be supplied on request.

BRITISH WOODCARVERS ASSOCIATION

White Knight Gallery, 28 Painswick Road, Cheltenham, Gloucestershire GL50 2HA
(Tel: 0242 238582)

The Association produces a quarterly newsletter which helps with many aspects of woocarving, including providing inspiration by featuring the work of members.

Members can be contacted by each other for mutual help, an aspect which is extended to the national and local meetings which are held. Visits are organised to places of interest both in this country and abroad.

BRITISH WOODWORKING FEDERATION

82 New Cavendish Street, London W1M 8AD
(Tel: 071-631 3872)

The British Woodworking Federation is a sector of the Building Employers Confederation. Membership of the BWF is split into sections: architectural and general joinery; doors and windows; timber frame and engineering; kitchen furniture manufacturing.

The Federation offers technical advice as well as advice on training, safety and industrial relations to its members. It has an information service about any market developments and a newsletter which it distributes to members to keep them informed about developments. It will offer advice to anyone wishing to enter the industry in the areas it covers.

THE INSTITUTE OF WOOD SCIENCE

Stocking Lane, Hughenden Valley, High Wycombe, Buckinghamshire HP14 4NU
(Tel: 0240 24 5374)

The purpose of the Institute is to advance and encourage the scientific, technical, practical and general knowledge of timber and wood based materials.

In conjunction with a number of colleges in the UK, the Institute organises courses in wood technology and utilisation and awards appropriate qualifications. The Institute is also the examining body for allied qualifications, for example the Introductory Open Learning Course in Timber Technology, in co-operation with the Timber Research & Development Association, and the Timber Infestation Surveyors certificate on behalf of the British Wood Preserving and Damp-proofing Association.

The Institute Journal, published twice yearly, contains both scientific and technical papers.

The Institute has branches throughout the UK and in Australia. These branches organise local activities including lectures, joint meetings with other interested bodies, symposia and visits to places of interest.

Membership of the Institute of Wood Science is open to all who are interested in the science and technology of wood and in encouraging its usage in new or improved ways. The categories of membership are:

Member: This category is open to any applicant and requires no formal qualifications for entry. All members receive the Journal and are entitled to attend meetings and conferences of the Institute.

Student Member: Student members are those engaged on Institute courses or on courses which have been approved by the Institute. Since they pay a reduced subscription they do not receive individual copies of the Journal, but copies are sent to libraries of the colleges attended by the students.

Certificated and Associate Members: These are members who have taken the Institute's examination. Certificated members have a pass certificate and may use the letters CMIWSc. The Associate grade will be awarded to those who have obtained a credit mark. They may use the letters AIWSc.

Associateship may also be granted to an applicant who has either obtained equivalent qualifications from another source or, in exceptional cases, can provide proof of relevant technical expertise.

Fellow: Fellowships may be awarded to members with Associate or equivalent qualification who have made an outstanding contribution to the advancement of wood science or technology. Fellows may use the letters FIWSc.

TIMBER RESEARCH & DEVELOPMENT ASSOCIATION

Stocking Lane, Hughenden Valley, High Wycombe, Buckinghamshire HP14 4ND
(Tel: 024 3091/2771/3956)

The Timber Research & Development Association (TRADA) is the centre of excellence in timber technology – the interface between wood as a material and science.

Education is an important part of its role and the Association runs many courses catering for the needs of everyone involved in the timber trade from woodworking apprentices through to those studying for advanced academic qualifications.

Getting Started

Starting with the roots of learning, an excellent course for beginners is **Timberstart**. It is a two year programme with two basic options, although both are very flexible and can be tailored in a number of ways.

The **Foundation Scheme** uses a comprehensive range of open learning, residential and in-company training techniques to prepare young people for a career on the commercial side of the timber trade. The **Craft Scheme** is grant aided and is designed for trainees or apprentices who will be working with woodworking machinery. It provides for 16-18 year olds to have hands on experience working with a qualified wood machinist. The main off-the-job training is attendance at a local college of further education to study the City & Guilds 586/606 Wood Machining Competence Course. This is supplemented by residential courses which are optional but strongly recommended. Here students have personal effectiveness training as well as sessions on computer literacy and the health and safety regulations relevant to the timber trade.

On the Foundation Scheme, the first year's work leads to a Timber Studies Certificate, a nationally recognised qualification from the City & Guilds of London Institute. Topics covered include softwoods and hardwoods; extraction, primary sawmilling, secondary conversion and wood machining; preservation and drying; yard operations; sheet materials and adhesives. The course is aimed at giving a practical understanding with sections dealing with the origins of species, their principal features and working properties; the felling of timber and its conversion; importing, shipping and documentation procedures; merchandising and selling as well as how timber is used.

Students progress in their second year to studies providing a broader perspective with training in sales practice, commercial considerations and the operation of the timber trade. On the technical side, knowledge gained during the first year is reinforced and amplified. At the end of the second year, which includes a five day residential course, trainees will have an understanding of finance, marketing, selling, communications, trading structures and operations.

The TRADA Open Learning course taken in the second year is, on examination success, an entry into the two year Institute of Wood Science Timber

Technology course building towards a professional qualification. Product knowledge and other open learning courses run by TRADA are approved by the Institute as optional modules leading to this qualification.

TRADA Courses

TRADA itself runs workshops and many practical courses to help in the understanding of timber and its appropriate use. They are held at the Association's purpose designed training centre at its headquarters in the Chiltern Hills, at regional centres throughout the country and at companies' own premises.

Three day residential **Product Knowledge** courses are run on softwood, hardwood, panel products and the specification of timber for construction and joinery. They provide both those who are new to the timber trade and more experienced people with a practical understanding of species, properties, sources of supply, grading, measurement, drying, preservation, standards and regulations. The courses also take delegates through the further uses of timber in manufacture, joinery and construction.

The Wood Based Panel Products course unravels the mystique surrounding the great number of these materials now on the market. It is a valuable ongoing training aid to experienced personnel as well as to beginners as the range of these products, their application and the standards regulating their use and specification is constantly being up-graded.

Specific practical courses are also held covering such fields as timber drying, import procedures, visual stress grading and scaffold board grading.

The **Timber Drying** course covers not only the principles of drying timber and the operation of kilns but also includes practical work in sampling, weighing, trouble shooting and remedial action.

The **Import Procedure** course guides delegates through all the necessary procedures and documentation required to bring wood goods into the UK.

The **Visual Stress Grading** course gives in-depth practical training in the skills needed to select and supply softwoods for structural use. Delegates sit an examination managed by TRADA's subsidiary, TRADA Quality Assurance Services

Ltd, and the course – as with others run by TRADA – is recognised by the Institute of Wood Science and contributes towards the Timber Technology and Utilisation course. The ten day grading course, which is divided into two blocks of five days, is extremely popular and CITB members are eligible for a grant.

The **Scaffolding Board Grading** course is an extension of the stress grading course but is also appropriate for anyone concerned with the selection, quality control, supply and use of timber for this purpose.

Open Learning

A highly flexible route to a career in timber is via TRADA "Open Learning" courses. The Basic Timber Technology course, already mentioned in conjunction with Timberstart, is well established and a relatively new course on Panel Products is proving extremely popular.

Sheet Materials are a highly significant part of the timber market and one which is growing. The open learning package provides a broad introduction to the types, manufacture, characteristics, properties and uses of these materials. Students are provided with audio tapes and slides for home study. These are supplemented by regularly marked homework with TRADA tutors monitoring students' progress through telephone calls and correspondence. The result is a high degree of motivation from the students and a commensurately high level of passes.

In-Company Training

Increasingly, companies are perceiving the benefits of TRADA courses held at their own premises as a highly cost effective method of staff training. The timing and content can be fine-tuned to specific requirements. In addition to product related training, TRADA runs courses in timber yard management, stock control, timber frame and trussed rafter manufacture, drying, preservation and other processes. The requirements of recent legislation such as the Control of Substances Hazardous to Health and Noise at Work regulations are also covered. TRADA also helps companies fulfill the training obligations necessary for registration to BS5750 systems for quality assurance.

TRADA Services for Education

For schools and colleges, TRADA provides a range of teaching aids. Slide sets, accompanied by comprehensive notes and TRADA Wood Information Sheets, enable college lecturers to present a well illustrated and informed talk on the principal applications of wood.

TIMBER TRADE FEDERATION

Clareville House, 26/27 Oxendon Street, London SW1Y 4EL (Tel: 071-839 1891)
An organisation of companies in the timber trades.

WINSTON CHURCHILL MEMORIAL TRUST

15 Queen's Gate Terrace, London SW7 5PR
(Tel: 071-584 9315)
The Winston Churchill Memorial Trust was established as a living tribute to Sir Winston Churchill at the time of his death in 1965.

It is unique in that it allows men and women who might otherwise never have the chance to visit countries overseas to acquire knowledge and experience which will enable them to be effective in their work and in the community, and to gain a better insight into the lives and work of people in other countries.

The Churchill Fellowships are open to all UK Citizens with no age limit and in any occupation. No educational or professional qualifications are needed but candidates must be able to show that they can make effective use of the opportunity and of the information they gain.

Awards are offered in different categories each year. Applicants propose a study project related to their trade, profession or interests under an appropriate category, and if selected, they are expected to make their own plans and arrangements within the scope of the grant.

The grants cover all Fellowship expenses for up to three months and are normally given for academic studies. Return air fare, plus all travel and living expenses abroad are included.

The final selection is made by interview in London during January and successful candidates are expected to start their travels during that year.

To apply send your name and address only on a postcard between August and mid-October to the Winston Churchill Memorial Trust at the address above. You will receive an explanatory leaflet and a form to complete which should be returned before the end of October – the actual date for return will be confirmed by the Trust.

WOMEN & MANUAL TRADES

52/54 Featherstone Street, London EC1Y 8RT
(Tel: 071 251 9192)
Women & Manual Trades gives advice and information to women training and working within the woodworking trade and to careers officers. They publish a quarterly newsjournal containing interviews, news, conference reports, job and course listing; manual on where to go for trades training; posters, video, exhibition, general information on women and the skilled trades.

Also available is a listing of self-employed tradeswomen available to do work in homes and offices.

Anyone interested in woodworking as a career or hobby should read the woodworking magazines. They provide a valuable insight into the opportunities offered and will help to increase your knowledge and skills.

Articles about woodworking craftsmen, their methods and techniques and the tools and equipment they use; news of new products and developments, courses, exhibitions and shows; individual success stories; working plans and projects; test reports; book reviews; letters and queries from readers – all these features and more help you feel a part of the woodworking scene and not merely an observer. Even the advertisements can be an education, making you aware of the numerous woodworking products and services available and the catalogues, advice and information offered.

Below is listed a wide range of magazines, including some where only a proportion of the editorial is devoted to woodworking. Do-it-Yourself magazines, for instance, fall into the latter category but can be quite useful if bought judiciously from the newsagents' shelves.

Magazine Title	Frequency	Price UK	Annual Subscription UK	Name and Address of Publisher
Do-it-Yourself	Monthly	£1.30	£15.60	Link House Magazines Ltd Link House Dingwall Avenue Croydon Surrey CR9 2TA
Practical Householder	Monthly	£1.40	£16.80	Maxwell Consumer Magazines Greater London House Hampstead Road London NW1 7QQ
Practical Woodworking	Monthly	£1.65	N/A	IPC Magazines Ltd King's Reach Tower Stamford Street London SE1 9LS
Traditional Woodworking	Bi-monthly	£1.60	£ 9.60	Link House Magazines Ltd Link House Dingwall Avenue Croydon Surrey CR9 2TA
Woodworker	Monthly	£1.50	£18.00	Argus Specialist Publications Argus House Boundary Way Hemel Hempstead HP2 7ST
Woodworking Today	Bi-monthly	£1.95	£15.75	Guild of Master Craftsmen Publications Ltd 166 High Street Lewes East Sussex BN7 1XU

Woodturning	Quarterly	£2.25	£13.75	Guild of Master Craftsmen Publications Ltd 166 High Street Lewes East Sussex BN7 1XU

OVERSEAS MAGAZINES

American Woodworker	Bi-monthly	$4.00	N/A	Rodale Press Inc 33 E. Minor St., Emmaus PA 18098 USA
Australian Home Woodworker	Quarterley	SA12		Skills Book Publishing Private Mail Bag 7 Rozelle NSW 2039
Australian Woodworker	Bi-monthly	$2.95	$15.00	Skills Book Publishing Private Mail Bag 7 Rozelle NSW 2039
Fine Woodworking	Bi-monthly	$4.95 £2.95	N/A	The Taunton Press Inc Newton CT 06470
New Zealand Woodworker	Quarterly	$6	£22 for 8	Macpherson Publishing PO Box 307 Alexandra New Zealand
Popular Woodworking	Bi-monthly	$4.95	$22.00	EGW Publishing Co 1320 Galaxy Way Concord CA 94520
Wood	Bi-monthly	$3.95	$24.00	Meredith Corporation Locust at 17th Des Moines IA 50336
Woodsmith	Bi-monthly	$2.50	$12.00	Woodsmith Publishing Co 1912 Grand Avenue Des Moines Iowa 50309
Woodworker Projects and Technics	Quarterly	$3.25	$13.50	Davis Publications Inc 380 Lexington Avenue New York NY 10017

Workbench	Bi-monthly	$2.50	$11.00	Modern Handcraft Inc
				4251 Pennsylvania Avenue
				Kansas City
				Missouri 6411

PUBLISHERS

There are a small number of publishers who regularly publish books on woodworking subjects – these are shown below in alphabetical order. Most of them produce a leaflet or brochure giving details of the books they publish. You should write to the Publicity Department requesting a copy of their literature and ask to be kept up to date with any further books published.

Argus Books Ltd
Argus House
Hemel Hempstead
Herts HP2 7ST

B T Batsford
1 Bradbury Drive
Springwood Industrial Est
Rayne Road
Braintree
Essex

A & C Black
35 Bedford Row
London WC1R 4GH

Cassells PLC
Stanley House
3 Fleet Lane
Poole
Dorset BH15 3AJ

Constable/Dover
Publications
Tiptree Book Services
Church Road
Tiptree
Colchester
Essex

David & Charles
Brunel House
Forde Road
Newton Abbot
Devon TQ12 4PO

Guild of Master Craftsman
Publications Ltd
166 High Street
Lewes
East Sussex BN7 1XU

Hodder & Stoughton Services
PO Box 6
Dunton Green
Sevenoaks
Kent TN13 2XX

Macmillan Press
Houndsmills
Basingstoke
Hants RG21 2XS

John Murray
50 Albermarle Street
London W1X 4BD

Newnes Technical Books
84-88 The Centre
Feltham
Middlesex TW13 3BH

Orbis
Orbis House
22 Bedforbury
London WC2N 4BL

Stobart Davies Ltd
67-73 Worship Street
London EC2A 2EL

Unwin Hyman
Denmark House
37-39 Queen Elizabeth Street
London SE1 2QB

BOOKS

As the literature of woodworking is now so extensive, a list of essential basic books is given below.

Furniture restoration, boatbuilding, wood machining, joinery and carpentry have not been included for individual colleges will wish to make their own recommendations.

CABINETMAKING

Wearing, Robert
The essential woodworker. Batsford – £15.95
No longer can it be assumed that students commencing college courses come equipped with the necessary woodworking skills. This book will overcome the problem.

Jackson, Albert and Day, Robert
Collins Complete Woodworker's Manual. Collins – £19.95

Martensson, Alf
The Woodworker's Bible. Black – £12.95 pbk
Both these titles provide amateur woodworkers and those contemplating a professional course with most of the background information needed. Martensson is more biased towards the professional craftsman.

Joyce, Ernest
The Technique of Furniture Making. 4th revised. Batsford – £25.00
This new edition revised by Alan Peters is the standard textbook of cabinetmaking.

Frid, Tage
Tage Frid Teaches Woodworking. 3 vols. Taunton Press – £17.95 each
1. Joinery
2. Shaping, veneering, finishing
3. Furniture making
Largely a photographic presentation, this Danish cabinetmaker author has taught in America for many years and explains the techniques using both hand tools and machines.

Peters, Alan
Cabinetmaking: The Professional Approach. Stobart – £14.95 pbk
Essential reading for all considering setting up their own professional cabinet workshop.

TIMBER TECHNOLOGY

Hoadly, R Bruce
Understanding Wood: A Craftsman's Guide to Wood Technology. Taunton Press – £19.95
Required reading for all who aim to understand the material they work.

Lincoln, William A
World Woods in Colour. Stobart – £22.50
The only reasonable priced book that includes timbers currently commercially available. The excellent colour plates also include indigeous timbers.

SPECIAL TECHNIQUES

Leach, Noel Johnson
Wood Finishing. Argus

Phillips, Jim and Perkins, John
Modern Routing Techniques. Unwin Hyman £15.95

Raffan, Richard
Turning Wood with Richard Raffan. Taunton Press – £12.95 pbk

Rowley, Keith
Woodturning: A Foundation Course. Guild of Master Craftsmen – £14.95 pbk

(Either Raffan or Rowley are suitable as an introduction)

REFERENCE BOOKS

Hayward, Charles H
The Woodworker's Pocket Book. Bell & Hyman – £3.50 pbk
Pocket size, but packed with basic information.

*Corkhill, Thomas
A Glossary of Wood. Stobart – £12.95 pbk

*Taylor, Vic
Woodworker Dictionary. Argus pbk

*These two volumes compliment one another. Corkhill is the older and more extensive, while the other contains updated information.

FOR INSPIRATION

Krenov, James
Prentice Hall. Earlier editions: Van Nostrand Reinhold Studio Vista
A Cabinetmaker's Notebook.
The Fine Art of Cabinetmaking.
The Impractical Cabinetmaker.

Read these in the order indicated. Krenov is internationally known and these three volumes provide an insight into his work, philosophy and techniques. Now teaches in America. These are books to be enjoyed.

Unpriced titles indicate that the book is no longer in print, but can be readily consulted in colleges and larger public libraries. Except where indicated, pbk, all books listed are hardback.

ACCESSORIES

Ashford Tool Centre
14 Elwick Road, Ashford, Kent (Tel: 0233 623010)
Stockists of industrial, semi-industrial and hobbyist machines. Hand and power tools, cutters, blades, router bits, turning chisels and finishes can all be found here.

Architectural Components
Locks and Handles of South Kensington, 8 Exhibition Road, London SW7 2HF
(Tel: 071 581 2401)
Immediate delivery on ranges of fine English period and modern door and window furniture. Also supplied are: bathroom accessories; radiator grilles; ventilation panels; fireplace furnishings; decorative brassware; safes and security equipment. Over 6,000 items stocked.

Asles Woodworker Centre
Vineyard Road, Wellington, Telford, Shropshire TF1 1HB (Tel: 0952 40456)
Complete selection of machinery for the specialist manufacturer, tradesman and enthusiast. Stocked items include Dewalt, Kity, Elu, Multico, Nu-Tool, Triton, Hitachi, Ashley Iles and many others. Special promotions every month.

Axminster Power Tool Centre
Chard Street, Axminster, Devon EX13 5DZ
(Tel: 0297 33656)
We stock and sell, both from our shop premises and by mail order, a large selection of woodworking machinery and power tools, together with many other items associated with the woodworking industry (abrasives, bandsaw blades, finishes, router cutters and chucks – including our own 4 jaw self-centring chuck).

BEL Products
Units 1-3 Erdington Ind Park, Chester Road, Erdington, Birmingham B73 0RD
(Tel: 021 377 8414)
Comprehensive ranges of door furniture and architectural ironmongery – encompassing brass, porcelain, wood, gold and silver, aluminium, nickel, pastel aluminium and bronze. Full brass electrics.

Any security ranges available.
Many products are available as contract boxed. Complete cabinet fittings, ranges have been introduced this year.

John Boddys Fine Wood & Tool Store
Riverside Sawmills, Boroughbridge, North Yorkshire YO5 9LJ (Tel: 0423 322370)
A woodworker's superstore retailing over 7,500 items, ranging from tools, finishes, requisites to books and plans, together with 125 species of timber in boards, squares and blanks. Available by self selection or by mail order, plus a full range of woodworking courses and free demonstrations. Easy access from A1.

Bostik
Ulverscroft Road, Leicester LE4 6BW
(Tel: 0533 510015)
A full range of adhesives.

Buck & Ryan
101 Tottenham Court Road, London W1P 0DY
(Tel: 071 636 7475)
We stock handtools, electric tools, cutlery and hardware. We also offer a repair service for electric tools, handsaws, scissors, lawnmowers and cutlery. We pride ourselves as having the widest range of tools in London. Our range of engineers precision tools, taps and dies and drills is excellent.

Burch & Hills Machinery
374 High Street, Aldershot, Hampshire GU12 4NA
(Tel: 0252 334422) and 98 Shirley High Street, Southampton, Hampshire SO1 4FB
(Tel: 0703 704477)
At Aldershot and Southampton our showrooms display a wide range of hand and power tools, woodworking machinery, tooling and accessories. Aldershot have their own workshop facilities and are repairing agents for most manufacturers' products. Both branches have easy parking with a private car park behind the shop at Southampton.

Charltons Timber Centre
Frome Road, Radstock, Bath, Avon BA3 3PT
(Tel: 0761 36229)
Specialising in English hardwoods but also offering

255

a full range of imported and exotic hardwoods, including turning and carving blanks and bargain offcuts. A machining service is available. Complementing this stock we have quality products, including mouldings; sheet materials; joinery softwood; veneers; waxes; finishes; cabinet fittings; adhesives; turning; carving and general tools; portable and static machinery; clock movements; books; plans etc. Together with woodturning accessories.

Peter Child

Woodturning Supplies, The Old Hyde, Little Yeldham, Halstead, Essex CO9 4QT
(Tel: 0787 237291)
We supply everything for the woodturner including lathes, chucks, lathe accessories, turning tools, carving tools, drills and drill chucks, wood blanks, grindstones and sharpening equipment, abrasives, polishes and finishing materials, glass dishes, peppermill inserts, clocks, tiles and weather instruments, cutlery blades, books, safety equipment, electrical fittings, pyrography machines. Callers/mail order welcome.

Crofts & Assinder

Lombard Street, Birmingham B12 0QX
(Tel: 021 622 1074)
Crofts & Assinder are manufacturers and suppliers of handles and fittings. Available in brass, zinc diecast and porcelain.

We have over 100 years experience in designing, manufacturing and finishing both to our designs and those specified by our customers.

Euromail (Tools)

PO Box 13, 65 Low Street, Keighley, West Yorkshire BD21 3QP (Tel: 0535 663325)
We supply nationally through mail order most makes of hand and power tools, not just woodworking but mechanics tools, welding, electrical, spraying, etc. A 260 page discount tool catalogue is available free on request. Our self service shop has over 6,000 lines at the address above.

European Industrial Services

Woden Road West, Kings Hill, Wednesbury, West Midlands WS10 7TT (Tel: 021 556 1991)
Manufacturers and suppliers of Nettlefolds woodscrews and allied products.

Fercell Pollution Control

Unit 60, Swaislands Drive, Crayford Ind Est, Crayford, Kent DA1 4HU
(Tel: 0322 53131/555976).
Wall, ceiling or bench mounted extractor range.

Forgeries

Old Butchery, High Street, Tingford, Hampshire SO21 1RF (Tel: 0962 712196).
Handmade reproduction ironmongery. 'T' hinges, various furniture hinges, handles, latches and hammered-head nails.

G A Woodworking Supplies

6 Rose Street, Newport, Gwent NP9 5FD
(Tel: 0633 266481)
Specialists in two products: router cutters (about 600 in the range) and Hitachi Power Tools. Mail order sales also catered for.

Gill and Hoxby

131-137 St Marks Road, Bush Hill Park, Enfield, Middlesex EN1 1BA (Tel: 081 363 2935)
Power and hand tool specialists including service, repairs and sales to trade and industry. Also large stocks of ironmongery and general products.

The Goport Company

York House, Empire Way, Wembley, Middlesex HA9 0QH (Tel: 081 903 2065)
Goport brings together in one range the tools of independent specialist manufacturers from 10 countries. These include the extensive range of Riss wood drills, auger bits and specialist cutters. Other products include Poldi HSS twist drills, Hindusthan files and rasps, Beargrip hex keys and screwdriver bits, and VEM bench grinders.

Graham Engineering

Alpine House, Roebuck Lane, West Bromwich B70 6QP (Tel: 021 525 3133)
We have over forty years of expertise in engineering

and woodworking and carry over 10,000 stock lines off the shelf.

A full new catalogue and price list is now available at a cost of £3.00 giving over 150 pages of useful machinery and small tool information.

Harlech Power Tools

6 Fleming Close, Wellingborough, Northants NN8 3UF (Tel: 0933 678757)

The full range of Hanning power tools are shown including the 70,80 and 100 bar powerwashers and an extensive selection of power washer accessories. Also shown are Alfer profiles, edgings and Hooks, Felo screwdrivers, Harlech hammers. Lux hand and power tool accessories and Novus staplers. All distributed exclusively by Harlech.

W Hobby

Knights Hill Square, London SE27 0HH (Tel: 081 761 4244)

Toy and model makers will find the Hobby mail order catalogue contains just about everything you need, especially all those bits and pieces which

seem to have disappeared from other sources these days.

Alan Holtham

Old Stores Turnery, Wistaston Road, Willaston, Nantwich, Cheshire CW5 6QJ (Tel: 0270 67010)
Specialist retailers to the woodworking trade with particular emphasis on woodturning and carving. As well as handling small, hand wood lathes we also cater for the needs of the production woodturner and sell the Hapfo range of industrial copy lathes. Our timber section is fast gaining a reputation for quality and variety of woods, and will soon be a major part of our business.

Humbrol

Marfleet, Hull, North Humberside HU9 5NE (Tel: 0482 701191)

Humbrol's well established range of wood adhesives includes Cascamite powdered resin wood glue, Cascophen resorcind adhesive, which is totally water proof, and the new Cascorez water resistant wood adhesive, a ready mixed PVA product.

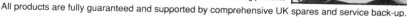

SUPPLIERS

Isaac Lord

Unit 5, Desborough Industrial Park, Desborough Park Road, High Wycombe, Bucks HD12 4B2 (Tel: 0494 459191)

Isaac Lord have been supplying the furniture industry of High Wycombe for 100 years and are a good source for all those pieces which can be hard to find – fittings, hinges, fasteners, handles, castors, abrasives, etc. A Mail order catalogue is available.

Janik Enterprises

Brickfield Lane, Ruthin, Clwyd LL15 2TN (Tel: 082 422096)

A comprehensive range of pyrographs and equipment. Single and dual outlet heat controlled models – solid pint and hot wire, brands, lettering, numbers, etc.

Wood related craft supplies and sundries, craft design books and a wide range of whitewood articles for various crafts.

JKO Cutters

Hughenden Avenue, High Wycombe, Buckinghamshire HP13 5SQ (Tel: 0494 21051)

High quality tools for jointing, gluing, clamping and trimming available through distributors. The range includes Lamello biscuit jointing machines, jointing plates and hinges.

PVA Glue applicators – easy to fill bottles with interchangeable nozzles. Uniclamps, to clamp cabinets, spanner system for difficult shapes, Holzher 2350 trimmer for veneered and laminated boards.

Kingswoode Clocks (WI)

14 Riverside, Eynsford, Kent DA4 0AE (Tel: 0322 864487)

Widest range of clock movements – quartz, mechanical, long case, etc. Barometers, thermometers and music box movements. Dials, chapter rings and brassware. Plans, etc. Send a SAE for free lists.

Loctite UK

Watchmead, Welwyn Garden City, Hertfordshire AL7 1JB (Tel: 0707 331277)

A wide range of adhesives.

E W Lucas

7 Washwood Heath Road, Birmingham B8 1RL (Tel: 021 327 1806)

Retailer of power tools, hardware and timber.

M & M Distributors

56 Haslam Crescent, Bexhill on Sea, Sussex TN40 2QT (Tel: 0424 216897)

Famous for the Triton Mkiii Workcentre and Arbortech Woodcarver blade. Also Titan TCT router cutters.

MSR Power Engineering

30 Redfern Road, Tyseley, Birmingham B11 2BH (Tel: 021 708 2811)

Phase converters to enable you to use three phase machinery off single phase supply. Operation of 3-PH 415V machines (½HP – 20HP) is possible off 1-PH 240V supply.

Machine Sales & Services (Poole)

23 Cowley Road, Nuffield Ind Estate, Poole, Dorset BH17 7UJ (Tel: 0202 686238)

Woodworking machinery, dust extraction, power tools, safety equipment, transformers, generators.

D Mackay

85 East Road, Cambridge CB1 1BY (Tel: 0223 63132)

We offer from our extensive range of products everything from chisels to lathes. This includes products from Bosch, Elu, Ashley Iles, Multico, Sorby, Tyme, Coronet, Henry Taylor, EAC, Emco and Burgess. We have a large showroom where customers can look and handle products or watch one of the various videos we have.

Martin & Co (AI)

97 Camden Street, Birmingham, West Midlands B1 3DG (Tel: 021 233 2111)

A comprehensive range of cabinet hardware for reproduction furniture/antique restorers. The range includes handles, castors, locks and hinges – all of the highest English authentic quality. All these products are on display in Birmingham or Brighton from Richard Barry Ltd Tel: 0273 419471 or Boroughbridge from John Boddy Timber Tel: 0423 322370.

F T Morrell & Co

214 Acton Lane, London NW10 7NH
(Tel: 081 965 1782)

We manufacture and supply a comprehensive range of materials to provide every type of finish required for timbers and MDF.

The most modern techniques and substrates are covered by our products and we back them up with a fine technical service department as well as educating wood finishers in our Woodley Training School.

Norfolk Saw Service

Dog Lane, Horsford, Norwich, Norfolk
(Tel: 0603 898695)

We are a family business offering sales of woodworking machinery and accessories and also a comprehensive saw service to both industry and the enthusiast. Sales also include TCT blades, SHSS blades, TCT rota cutters, bandsaw blades, planer knives and whitehill cutters.

Nylonic Engineering

Woodcock Hill Ind Est, Harefield Road, Rickmansworth, Herts WD3 1PN (Tel: 0923 778111)

Nylon rod and engineering plastic in rod and sheet form. Also with depots near Glasgow, Birmingham and Warrington. Mail order service available. Boxes of off-cuts (roughly 10kg) at £10 each.

The Power Tool Centre

54-58 Victoria Road, Widnes, Cheshire WA8 7RJ
(Tel: 051 424 4545/7965)

Our mail order department specialises in spare parts for Black & Decker, Elu and Dewalt machines. Many obsolete models covered.

Racal Health & Safety Group

Beresford Avenue, Wembley, Middx HA0 1QJ
(Tel: 081 902 8887).

Powered respiratory protection, including the Dustmaster battery-powered face mask.

Richards of Burton
Woodhouse Clockworks, Swadlincoter, Woodville,
Burton-on-Trent DE11 8DA (Tel: 0283 219155)
Long case clock movements and dials, handmade
to traditional styles.

SMS (Woodworking Machinery)
Danesforde, Pamber Road, Silchester, Nr Reading,
Berkshire RG7 2NU (Tel: 0734 700921)
Leigh adjustable dovetail jig, used with portable
routers to produce joints of hand-crafted appearance
with speed and precision. Onsrud inverted pin
routing machines.

Sawclamps (UK)
56 Greevegate, Hunstanton, Norfolk PE36 6AE
(Tel: 0485 533702).
Possibly the only company left producing saw
clamps, used for sharpening saws.

Scott & Sargeant
Unit 4, Forgewood Industrial Estate, Gatwick Road,
Crawley, W Sussex RH10 2PG (Tel:0293 565959)
Image the machinery and tools you would expect
to find in a cabinet maker's or joiner's shop and
you will probably find an example of it at Scott &
Sargeant. It also sells secondhand machinery. Write
for a catalogue or call in.

Specialised Assemblies (W'boro)
Unit 6, Bradfield Close, Finedon Road Industrial
Estate, Wellingborough, Northants NN8 4RQ
(Tel: 0933 76077).
If you need a special bracket or fixing made for
you give us a call. We also make the Snapfix
versatile fixing system, originally developed to hold
the heaviest of wall panels in place.

Speedwell Tool Co
62-70 Meadow Street, Preston, Lancashire PR1
1SU (Tel: 0772 52951)
We are engineers hand and machine tool suppliers,
woodworking machines and woodworking hand
tools. Also model engineering supplies including
bronze and brass bar and sheet.

Stig Ravn (UK)
Unit 4 Rockfort Ind Estate, Hithercroft Road,
Wallingford, Oxon OX10 9DA (Tel: 0491 34486)
Suppliers of small parts storage equipment:
drawers, tool boxes, key storage, portable workbench, hinged small part boxes, tube building
system, bin storage system, storage cabinets, first
aid boxes, cash boxes, security boxes, post boxes.

Timecraft
Unit 19 Sefton Lane Ind Estate, Maghull, Liverpool
L31 8BX (Tel: 051 526 2516)
Importers and exporters of mechanical clock works,
clock dials and clock accessories.

Timms Tools
102/4 Liverpool Road, Patricroft, Eccles,
Manchester M30 0WZ (Tel: 061 789 0909)
Stockists of all leading brands: Elu, Elektra,
Beckum, Dewalt, Myford, Record, Marples, Triton,
Trend, Scheppack, Multico, Coronet, Warco,
Naerok, Black & Decker, Bosch, AEG and Makita.

Titman Tools
Kennedy Way, Valley Road, Clacton on Sea, Essex
CO15 4AB (Tel: 0255 220123)
Manufacture and stock nearly 2,000 standard TCT
router cutters, as well as drills, boring bits and
grooving saws.

Toolmail (GMC) Ltd
170 High Street, Lewes, East Sussex BN7 1YE
(Tel: 0273 477009)
An exclusive range of top quality Japanese and
American tools along side the best of British,
European and other well known branded tools and
accessories.

The Turning Point
British Gates & Timber Ltd, Biddenden, Nr
Ashford, Kent TN27 8DD (Tel: 0580 291555)
The sawmill at British Gates converts large
quantities of homegrown timbers, providing
materials for cabinet-makers, woodturners and
woodcarvers. Stock also includes imported and
exotic types, a wide range of hand tools, lathes and
accessories, chucks, polishes and finishes,
adhesives, and a wide range of craft accessories.

Wealden Tool Co
97 Tudeley Lane, Tonbridge, Kent TN9 2ER
(Tel: 0622 872725)
The best known range of Wealdon cutting tools is
the router cutters, available in ¼in and ½in shank

sizes, but the whole range of cutting tools can be seen in a catalogue available from Wealdon.

Weaves & Waxes

53 Church Street, Bloxham, Banbury, Oxon OX15 4ET (Tel: 0295 721535)

Veneering, polishing, caning, rushing, gilding, clock repairs and upholstery, veneers, brass cabinet fittings, desk top leathers. As experienced restorers we are able to advise our customers who wish to undertake their own restoration. They can of course purchase the appropriate materials from us.

Westward Building Services

Lister Close, Newnham Trading Estate, Plympton, Plymouth, Devon PL7 4HG (Tel: 0752 330303)

WBS are a local company offering a comprehensive service in power tools, fixings, ironmongery and woodworking machinery. Our sales team cover the region, and in addition we offer regular van deliveries. Also we provide full repair and maintenance facilities for the machinery we supply.

K R Whiston

New Mills, Stockport SK12 4PT (Tel: 0663 42028)

A good range of unusual fasteners and metal profiles as bars for those who want to make their own fasteners or special metal fittings. Products are available mail order from a catalogue available on request.

Willis Woodworking

157 West Street, Bedminster, Bristol, Avon BS3 3PN (Tel: 0272 667013)

Wood, aluminium and UPVC machinery, large stock of Trend router cutters, Bosch power tools, saw blades, abrasives, bandsaw blades. Advice on dust extraction and installation. Woodworking lathes and accessories. Machinery servicing and installations carried out. Large stock of lightweight plant and access equipment for hire or sale.

Wokingham Tool Company

99 Wokingham Road, Reading, Berkshire RG6 1LH (Tel: 0734 661511)

Electric tool repair service, saw blade etc sharpening service. Hire of small electric tools.

Woodcutter Services

Mersey Road, Stockport, Cheshire SK4 3BJ (Tel: 061 432 4294)

Special-purpose router cutters produced to order within 10 days. Cutters can be high speed steel or TC-tipped. Price quotations are given on receipt of drawings.

Woodfit

Chorley, Lancashire PR6 7EA (Tel: 02572 6642)

A mail order company selling just about everything for the home handyman from hinges to kitchen units.

Woodpine Machinery Sales

Stream House, Furnace Place, Haslemere, Surrey GU27 2EJ (Tel: 0428 642169/651853)

Specialising in sales, service and spares of a full range of woodworking machinery in the South of England, mainly the full SCM and SAMCO range.

Direct imports include machines from the Surface Group, Alternax mortisers and Conver tenoners.

Used machinery/part exchange/finance available.

Woodrat

The Old School, Godney, Wells, Somerset BA5 1RY (Tel: 0453 32744)

A tool for cutting dovetails and other joints precisely. Fully adjustable.

CARVING

Alan Holtham

Old Stores Turnery, Wistaston Road, Willaston, Nantwich, Cheshire CW5 6QJ (Tel: 0270 67010)

Specialist retailers to the woodworking trade with particular emphasis on woodturning and carving. As well as handling small, hand wood lathes we also cater for the needs of the production wood-turner and sell the Hapfo range of industrial copy lathes. Our timber section is fast gaining a reputation for quality and variety of woods, and will soon be a major part of our business.

FINISHING

Future Finishes

Sabre House, 1A Reedham Street, London SE15 4PG (Tel: 071 732 3528)
Specialist effect spray paints – marbling, graining, crackle glaze, etc.

House of Harbru

101 Crostons Road, Elton, Bury, Lancs BL8 1AL (Tel: 061 764 6769).
French polish, spirit sealers, friction polish, tung oil, Danish oil, lemon oil, waxes, grain filler, stains, dyes, etc.

Mr Jamiesons

10 Whitemyres Avenue, Mastrick Industrial Estate, Aberdeen AB2 6HQ (Tel: 0224 681877)
All kinds of finishes, from the traditional, such as French polish and waxes, to the modern, such as polyurethane. Dyes, lacquers, varnishes and oils also available.

W S Jenkins

Jeco Works, Tariff Road, Tottenham, London N17 0EN (Tel: 081 808 2336)
French polish, spirit varnish, cellulose and synthetic lacquers, stains, waxes, paint removers and sundry materials for the antique restoration and reproduction market.

Jocasta Innes

9 Heneage Street, London E1 5LJ (Tel: 071 377 9262)
DIY specialist finish kits (stippling, marbling, graining, etc). Each kit includes materials, tools and instructions

Langlo

PO Box 32, Asheridge Road, Chesham, Bucks HP5 2QF (Tel: 0494 784 866)
A good selection of finishes, traditional shellac and modern.

John Myland

80 Norwood High Street, London SE27 9NW (Tel: 081 670 9161)
All kinds of French polishes, varnishes and paints.

Rustins

Waterloo Road, Cricklewood, London NW2 7TX (Tel: 081 450 4666)
Danish oil, sanding sealer, plastic coating and a complete selection of finishes.

Sterling Roncraft

15 Churchfield Court, Churchfield, Barnsley S70 2LJ (Tel: 0226 207676)
All kinds of wood finishes.

HAND TOOLS

Abrasive Tools

80 Colne Road, Twickenham, Middlesex TW2 6QE (Tel: 081 894 1273)
Tension files (sawing wires) for hacksaw frames, round and square files up to 6mm (steel and tungsten carbide).

Allmodels Engineering

91 Manor Way, Ruislip, Middlesex HA4 8HW (Tel: 0895 674126)
Wood working machinery, tools, etc. Woodcarving and turning, tools for individuals and also industrial users.

Ashley Iles (Edge Tools)

East Kirkby, Spilsby, Lincolnshire PE23 4DD (Tel: 07903 372)
Ashley Iles Ltd is an independent company, offering as manufacturers a specialist service to woodturners and woodcarvers. Mail order catalogue available on request. Callers welcome. Large selection of honed carving tools and large range of handled and unhandled turning tools including wide range of high speed steel tools.

Asles Woodworker Centre

Vineyard Road, Wellington, Telford, Shropshire TF1 1HB (Tel: 0952 40456)
Complete selection of machinery for the specialist manufacturer, tradesman and enthusiast. Stocked items include Dewalt, Kity, Elu, Multico, Nu-Tool, Triton, Hitachi, and many others. Special promotions every month.

Atkinson-Walker (Saws)

Bower Street, Sheffield, South Yorkshire S3 8RU (Tel: 0742 724748)

Specialist manufacturer of high quality saw blades and TCT saws, from 5in Dia. to 36in Dia. for the woodworking and allied industries. Ranges of hand saws and tenon saws from the disposable DIY quality up to the best quality hand made saws for the craftsman. Saw re-conditioning service available.

Axminster Power Tool Centre

Chard Street, Axminster, Devon EX13 5DZ (Tel: 0297 33656)

We stock and sell, both from our shop premises and by mail order, a large selection of woodworking machinery and power tools, together with many other items associated with the woodworking industry (abrasives, bandsaw blades, finishes, router cutters and chucks – including our own 4 jaw self-centring chuck).

John Boddys Fine Wood & Tool Store

Riverside Sawmills, Boroughbridge, North Yorkshire YO5 9LJ (Tel: 0423 322370)

A woodworker's superstore retailing over 7,500 items, ranging from tools, finishes, requisites to books and plans, together with 125 species of timber in boards, squares and blanks. Available by self selection or by mail order, plus a full range of woodworking courses and free demonstrations. Easy access from A1.

Bristol Design (Tools)

14 Perry Road, Bristol BS1 5BG (Tel:0272 291740)

A continuously altering selection of antique and second hand tools. They are intended mostly for people who want to use them, although occasionally poorer condition collectors pieces are on sale if they are very rare items.

Buck & Ryan

101 Tottenham Court Road, London W1P 0DY (Tel: 071 636 7475)

We stock handtools, electric tools, cutlery and hardware. We also offer a repair service for electric tools, handsaws, scissors, lawnmowers and cutlery.

We pride ourselves as having the widest range of tools in London. Our range of engineers precision tools, taps and dies and drills is excellent.

Burch & Hills Machinery

374 High Street, Aldershot, Hampshire GU12 4NA (Tel: 0252 334422) and 98 Shirley High Street, Southampton, Hampshire SO1 4FB (Tel: 0703 704477)

At Aldershot and Southampton our showrooms display a wide range of hand and power tools, woodworking machinery, tooling and accessories. Aldershot have their own workshop facilities and are repairing agents for most manufacturers' products. Both branches have easy parking with a private car park behind the shop at Southampton.

Clarke International

Lower Clapton Road, London E5 0RN (Tel: 081 986 8231)

Clarke International, one of Britain's largest privately owned manufacturers of electrical and mechanical power products, supplies a wide range of woodworking equipment for DIY and professional use.

The range includes belt and disc sanders, table saws, scroll saws, electric and manual mitre saws, band saws and woodturning lathes.

Euromail (Tools)

PO Box 13, 65 Low Street, Keighley, West Yorkshire BD21 3QP (Tel: 0535 663325)

We supply nationally through mail order most makes of hand and power tools, not just woodworking but mechanics tools, welding, electrical, spraying, etc. A 260 page discount tool catalogue is available free on request. Our self service shop has over 6,000 lines at the address above.

Freud UK

Unit 2 Treefield Ind Estate, Gildersome, Leeds, West Yorkshire LS27 7JU (Tel: 0532 527377)

Freud manufacture a wide range of accessories and power-tools for the woodworking industry. The range comprises laser-cut TCT saw blades, router bits, TCT cutter blocks and hand tools. The power tools include a 3¼ hp router for which a new router table has been designed and a small edge banding machine. Catalogues and price lists available on request.

Gill and Hoxby

131-137 St Marks Road, Bush Hill Park, Enfield, Middlesex EN1 1BA (Tel: 081 363 2935)
Power and hand tool specialists including service, repairs and sales to trade and industry. Also large stocks of ironmongery and general products.

The Goport Company

York House, Empire Way, Wembley, Middlesex HA9 0QH (Tel: 081 903 2065)
Goport brings together in one range the tools of independent specialist manufacturers from 10 countries. These include the extensive range of Riss wood drills, auger bits and specialist cutters. Other products include Poldi HSS twist drills, Hindusthan files and rasps, Beargrip hex keys and screwdriver bits, and VEM bench grinders.

Graham Engineering

Alpine House, Roebuck Lane, West Bromwich B70 6QP (Tel: 021 525 3133)
We have over forty years of expertise in engineering and woodworking and carry over 10,000 stock lines off the shelf.

A full new catalogue and price list is now available at a cost of £3.00 giving over 150 pages of useful machinery and small tool information.

Harlech Power Tools

6 Fleming Close, Wellingborough, Northants NN8 3UF (Tel: 0933 678757)
The full range of Hanning power tools are shown including the 70,80 and 100 bar powerwashers and an extensive selection of powerwasher accessories. Also there are Alfer profiles, edgings and hooks, Felo screwdrivers, Harlech hammers. Lux hand and power tool accessories and Novus staplers. All distributed exclusively by Harlech.

Alan Holtham

Old Stores Turnery, Wistaston Road, Willaston, Nantwich, Cheshire CW5 6QJ (Tel: 0270 67010)
Specialist retailers to the woodworking trade with particular emphasis on woodturning and carving.

As well as handling small, hand wood lathes we also cater for the needs of the production woodturner and sell the Hapfo range of industrial copy lathes. Our timber section is fast gaining a reputation for quality and variety of woods, and will soon be a major part of our business.

JKO Cutters

Hughenden Avenue, High Wycombe, Buckinghamshire HP13 5SQ (Tel: 0494 21051)
High quality tools for jointing, gluing, clamping and trimming available through distributors. The range includes Lamello biscuit jointing machines, jointing plates and hinges.

PVA Glue applicators – easy to fill bottles with interchangeable nozzles.

Uniclamps, to clamp cabinets, spanner system for difficult shapes, Holz-her 2350 trimmer for veneered and laminated boards.

Layburn Tools

Boothferry Road, Goole, North Humberside DN14 6AF (Tel: 0405 720300)
Suppliers of a large range of power and hand tools and safety clothing.

Luna Tools and Machinery

20 Denbigh Hall, Bletchley, Milton Keynes, Buckinghamshire MK3 7QT (Tel: 0908 370771)
Luna is a leading UK company specialising in the supply of machinery, hand and power tools for everyone involved in processing wood. The product range is primarily directed toward the professional craftsman and small business, but the Luna programme also includes equipment used by enthusiasts and the hire industry. Supply is through a nationwide dealer network.

D Mackay

85 East Road, Cambridge CB1 1BY
(Tel: 0223 63132)
We offer from our extensive range of products everything from chisels to lathes. This includes products from Bosch, Elu, Ashley Iles, Multico, Sorby, Tyme, Coronet, Henry Taylor, EAC, Emco and Burgess. We have a large showroom where customers can look and handle products or watch one of the various videos we have.

Neill Tools

Handsworth Road, Sheffield, South Yorkshire S13 9BR (Tel: 0742 449911)

Manufacturer of quality hand tools including: bandsaws, builders tools, cold chisels, DIY/retail range (which includes a range of wood working tools), hacksaw blades, saw frames, engineers hand tools, precision measuring tools, pliers.

Well known for the Spear & Jackson, Eclipse, Moore & Wright and Elliott Lucas brand names.

Paramo Tools Group

Rockingham Street, Sheffield, South Yorkshire S1 3NW (Tel: 0742 725262)

A full range of hand tools under the Paramo Clay and Ibbotson trade marks. Vices, planes, G cramps, turnscrews, chisels, squares, gauges, hand saws, etc. Manufactured in UK factories in Sheffield and Birmingham areas.

The Power Tool Centre

54-58 Victoria Road, Widnes, Cheshire WA8 7RJ (Tel: 051 424 4545/7965)

Our mail order department specialises in spare parts for Black & Decker, Elu and Dewalt machines. Many obsolete models covered.

Richard Sarjent

136 Cowley Road, Oxford OX4 1HU (Tel: 0865 798777)

Hand tools, power tools, machinery, abrasives, finishes, books and videos.

Sanderson Kayser

Newhall Road, Sheffield, South Yorkshire S9 2SD (Tel: 0742 449994)

SK Ltd manufacture a range of industrial and hand saws from steel produced in its own facilities in Sheffield.

A full sharpening and repair service is available based in Sheffield and our operation in Gateshead.

Scott & Sargeant

Unit 4, Forgewood Industrial Estate, Gatwick Road, Crawley, W Sussex RH10 2PG (Tel: 0293 565959)

A catalogue details what is in offer for those who are not local. Mail order sales are accepted. The professional and larger scale production wood-worker would find a lot of interest from Scott & Sargeant, but there is also plenty to interest the hobbyist.

Speedwell Tool Co

62-70 Meadow Street, Preston, Lancashire PR1 1SU (Tel: 0772 52951)

We are engineers hand and machine tool suppliers, woodworking machines and woodworking hand tools. Also model engineering supplies including bronze and brass bar and sheet.

Spiralux Tools

Bredgar Road, Gillingham, Kent ME8 6PN (Tel: 0634 373951)

Under the Tyzack-Turner brand name is a range of saws and woodworking tools. There are also builders and other tools sold.

Stanley Tools

Woodside, Sheffield, South Yorkshire S3 9PD (Tel: 0742 768888)

Stanley Tools manufacture a wide range of top quality hand tools for both the keen woodworker and the craftsman alike. The current range of Stanley and Rabone branded products includes many world renowned tools, all of which share the same high attention to detail which ensures that a job is well done.

Henry Taylor (Tools)

The Forge, Lowther Road, Sheffield, South Yorkshire S6 2DR (Tel: 0742 340282)

Henry Taylor (Tools) Ltd established 1834, manufactures a wide range of woodcarving, woodturning and specialist woodworking tools. In addition, the company produces work holding devices and accessories for use with woodturning lathes. The company is a brand leader and exports to all corners of the world.

Thor Hammer Company

Highlands Road, Shirley, Nr Birmingham, West Midlands B90 4NJ (Tel: 021 705 4695)

Manufacturers of soft faced hammers and soft impact mallets in copper, aluminium, lead, rawhide, rubber, plastics and wood.

Timms Tools
102/4 Liverpool Road, Patricroft, Eccles, Manchester M30 0WZ (Tel: 061 789 0909)
Stockists of all leading brands: Elu, Elektra, Beckum, Dewalt, Myford, Record, Marples, Triton, Trend, Scheppack, Multico, Coronet, Warco, Naerok, Black & Decker, Bosch, AEG and Makita.

Toolmail (GMC)
170 High Street, Lewes, East Sussex BN7 1YE (Tel: 0273 477009)
An exclusive range of top quality Japanese and American tools along side the best of British, European and other well known branded tools and accessories.

The Turning Point
British Gates & Timber Ltd, Biddenden, Nr Ashford, Kent TN27 8DD (Tel: 0580 291555)
The sawmill at British Gates converts large quantities of homegrown timbers, providing materials for cabinet-makers, woodturners and woodcarvers. Stock also includes imported and exotic types, a wide range of hand tools, lathes and accessories, chucks, polishes and finishes, adhesives, and a wide range of craft accessories.

Tyzak Tool Company
81 Kingsland Road, Shoreditch, London E2 8AG (Tel: 0923 50305)
Large range of hand tools from names such as Stanley, Footprint and Nippex. Also power tools and machinery are sold.

Westward Building Services
Lister Close, Newnham Trading Estate, Plympton, Plymouth, Devon PL7 4HG (Tel: 0752 330303)
WBS are a local company offering a comprehensive service in power tools, fixings, ironmongery and woodworking machinery. Our sales team cover the region, and in addition we offer regular van deliveries. Also we provide full repair and maintenance facilities for the machinery we supply.

Willis Woodworking
157 West Street, Bedminster, Bristol, Avon BS3 3PN (Tel: 0272 667013)
Wood, aluminium and UPVC machinery, large

stock of Trend router cutters, Bosch power tools, saw blades, abrasives, bandsaw blades. Advice on dust extraction and installation. Woodworking lathes and accessories. Machinery servicing and installations carried out. Large stock of lightweight plant and access equipment for hire or sale.

Wokingham Tool Company
99 Wokingham Road, Reading, Berkshire RG6 1LH (Tel: 0734 661511)
Electric tool repair service, saw blade etc sharpening service. Hire of small electric tools.

The Woodworks
The Field, Shipley, Nr Heanor, Derbyshire DE7 7JJ (Tel: 0773 719842)
Retailers of all kinds of woodworking tools, equipment and sundries. Leading brands stocked. Mail orders accepted and catalogue available.

LIGHTING

Eterna Lighting
Emily Place, Queensland Road, London N7 7DQ (Tel: 071-609 9011)
Eterna Lighting has the largest range of fittings available to the furniture industry and, with over 50 years experience, can solve any lighting problem.

MACHINES AND POWER TOOLS

A-Z Tools Sales
Kettlebrook Road, Tamworth, West Midlands B77 1BB (Tel: 0827 56767)
DIY and professional tools sales, (B&D, Bosch, etc) plus plant hire.

AEG (UK)
217 Bath Road, Slough, Berkshire SL1 4AW (Tel: 0753 872101)
AEG is meeting the needs of the woodworking industry with its wide range of electrical equipment. The tools include from the stationary woodworking range the new RD 26 and RD 31 planer/thicknesser multifunction machines plus bandsaws and circular saw benches. From the portable range, circular saws, plunge saws, jig saws and reciprocating saws,

drills, planers, sanders and routers are available, as well as the latest dust extraction equipment. All tools are available with a full range of accessories.

Allmodels Engineering
91 Manor Way, Ruislip, Middlesex HA4 8HW (Tel: 0895 674126)
Wood working machinery tools, etc. Woodcarving and turning tools for individuals and also industrial users.

Apollo Products
100 Stone Road, Toftwood, Dereham, Norfolk (Tel:0362 693515)
Manufacturers of lathes from the Woodpecker (the smallest) at around £480 up to the Professional at over £1,000. Also manufacturers of a pantograph copying attachment, made to order and specifically designed for each customer's lathe.

Asles Woodworker Centre
Vineyard Road, Wellington, Telford, Shropshire TF1 1HB (Tel: 0952 40456)
Complete selection of machinery for the specialist manufacturer, tradesman and enthusiast. Stocked items include Dewalt, Kity, Elu, Multico, Nu-Tool, Triton, Hitachi, Ashley Iles and many others. Special promotions every month.

Axminster Power Tool Centre
Chard Street, Axminster, Devon EX13 5DZ (Tel: 0297 33656)
We stock and sell, both from our shop premises and by mail order, a large selection of woodworking machinery and power tools, together with many other items associated with the woodworking industry (abrasives, bandsaw blades, finishes, router cutters and chucks – including our own 4 jaw self-centring chuck).

Black & Decker
Westpoint, The Grove, Slough, Berkshire SL1 1QQ (Tel: 0753 74277)
A wide range of professional and DIY power tools.

John Boddys Fine Wood & Tool Store
Riverside Sawmills, Boroughbridge, North Yorkshire YO5 9LJ (Tel: 0423 322370)
A woodworker's superstore retailing over 7,500 items, ranging from tools, finishes, requisites to books and plans, together with 125 species of timber in boards, squares and blanks. Available by self selection or by mail order, plus a full range of woodworking courses and free demonstrations. Easy access from A1.

Brimarc
PO Box 100, Leamington Spa, Warwickshire CV31 3LS (Tel: 0926 450370)
Suppliers of Veritus tools, from Canada, for the serious woodworker. The Veritus range includes some interesting tools not usually available in the UK. Also Tormek whetstone grinders and Sjoberg workbenches.

R S Brookman
Parkside Works, Rothley, Leicester, Leicestershire LE7 7NS (Tel: 0533 302323)
British built multi-spindle dovetailing machines in both fully automatic and hand lever versions. Dowel boring machines, cluster, spindle, single and multi-head types. Micro-processor controlled linear locator chain morticers, also available in boring version. Selfeedrils – a unit head multiple drilling system for all types of drilling.

Buck & Ryan
101 Tottenham Court Road, London W1P 0DY (Tel: 071 636 7475)
We stock handtools, electric tools, cutlery and hardware. We also offer a repair service for electric tools, handsaws, scissors, lawnmowers and cutlery. We pride ourselves as having the widest range of tools in London. Our range of engineers precision tools, taps and dies and drills is excellent.

Burch & Hills Machinery
374 High Street, Aldershot, Hampshire GU12 4NA (Tel: 0252 334422) and 98 Shirley High Street, Southampton, Hampshire SO1 4FB (Tel: 0703 704477)
At Aldershot and Southampton our showrooms display a wide range of hand and power tools, woodworking machinery, tooling and accessories. Aldershot have their own workshop facilities and are repairing agents for most manufacturers' products. Both branches have easy parking with a private car park behind the shop at Southampton.

Charnwood

1-3 Rowan Street, Fosse Road North, Leicester, Leicestershire LE3 9GP (Tel: 0533 511550)

Charnwood manufactures and imports woodworking machinery sold under the "Woodworker Range" including the W250 and W265 marketed by Charnwood for some eight years.

The range has gradually expanded and now includes mortisers, tenoners, panel saws, routers and spindle moulders.

Clarke International

Lower Clapton Road, London E5 0RN (Tel: 081 986 8231)

Clarke International, one of Britain's largest privately owned manufacturers of electrical and mechanical power products, supplies a wide range of woodworking equipment for DIY and professional use.

The range includes belt and disc sanders, table saws, scroll saws, electric and manual mitre saws, band saws and wood turning lathes.

Cutwell Tools

Creech Heathfield, Taunton, Somerset TA3 5EQ (Tel: 0823 443766)

Cutwell Tools supply a full range of tools, cutters and machinery for every aspect of woodworking. They have their own range of TCT router cutters. The range of cutters includes normal blocks, special profiles and turnover systems. Main machine range is Artisan, a selection of saws, spindles and other standards that give the medium size manufacturer many features normally only found in larger, more expensive equipment.

Euromail (Tools)

PO Box 13, 65 Low Street, Keighley, West Yorkshire BD21 3QP (Tel: 0535 663325)

We supply nationally through mail order most makes of hand and power tools, not just woodworking but mechanics tools, welding, electrical, spraying, etc. A 260 page discount tool catalogue is available free on request. Our self service shop has over 6,000 lines at the address above.

Freud UK

Unit 2 Treefield Ind Estate, Gildersome, Leeds, West Yorkshire LS27 7JU (Tel: 0532 527377)

Freud manufacture a wide range of accessories and power-tools for the woodworking industry. The range comprises laser-cut TCT saw blades, router bits, TCT cutter blocks and hand tools. The power tools include a 3¼ hp router for which a new router table has been designed and a small edge banding machine. Catalogues and price lists available on request.

Gill and Hoxby

131-137 St Marks Road, Bush Hill Park, Enfield, Middlesex EN1 1BA (Tel: 081 363 2935)

Power and hand tool specialists including service, repairs and sales to trade and industry. Also large stocks of ironmongery and general products.

The Goport Company

York House, Empire Way, Wembley, Middlesex HA9 0QH (Tel: 081 903 2065)

Goport brings together in one range the tools of independent specialist manufacturers from 10 countries. These include the extensive range of Riss wood drills, auger bits and specialist cutters. Other products include Poldi HSS twist drills, Hindusthan files and rasps, Beargrip hex keys and screwdriver bits, and VEM bench grinders.

Graham Engineering

Alpine House, Roebuck Lane, West Bromwich B70 6QP (Tel: 021 525 3133)

We have over forty years of expertise in engineering and woodworking and carry over 10,000 stock lines off the shelf.

A full new catalogue and price list is now available at a cost of £3.00 giving over 150 pages of useful machinery and small tool information.

Griffiths Woodworking Supplies

6 Rose Street, Newport, Gwent NP9 5FD (Tel: 0633 266481)

Mail order supply of industrial quality tungsten carbide carb-i-tool, router cutters and Hitachi power tools. We offer 25% discount on Hitachi power tools. Delivery often within 24 hours of ordering. A range of over 550 cutters, all ex-stock. Free mail order brochure.

Harlech Power Tools

6 Fleming Close, Wellingborough, Northants NN8 3UF (Tel: 0933 678757)

The full range of Hanning power tools are shown including the 70,80 and 100 bar powerwashers and an extensive selection of powerwasher accessories. Also there are Alfer profiles, edgings and hooks, Felo screwdrivers, Harlech hammers. Lux hand and power tool accessories and Novus staplers. All distributed exclusively by Harlech.

Hegner

Wymondly House, Ersham Road, Hailsham, Sussex BN27 3LE (Tel: 0323 442440)

The Hegner Universal fretsaw range and the Hegner Table Workshop, a small, freestanding sawbench.

George Higgins (Sidcup)

77 Station Road, Sidcup, Kent DA15 7DN (Tel: 081-300 4936)

Retailer of all kinds of woodworking machinery and hand tools.

Hitachi Power Tools (UK)

Precedent Drive, Rooksley, Milton Keynes, Buckinghamshire MK13 8PJ (Tel: 0908 660663)

Hitachi Power Tools manufacture an extensive range of quality power tools. For the woodworker the range includes: mains and cordless drills and screwdrivers, sabre saws, jigsaws, circular saws, mitre saws, disc, belt and orbital sanders, polishers, routers, planers, trimmers, accessories.

Alan Holtham

Old Stores Turnery, Wistaston Road, Willaston, Nantwich, Cheshire CW5 6QJ (Tel: 0270 67010)

Specialist retailers to the woodworking trade with particular emphasis on woodturning and carving. As well as handling small, hand wood lathes we also cater for the needs of the production wood-turner and sell the Hapfo range of industrial copy lathes. Our timber section is fast gaining a reputation for quality and variety of woods, and will soon be a major part of our business.

Kendal Tools & Machinery

Unit 12 Chancel Place, Shap Road Industrial Estate, Kendal, Cumbria LA9 6NZ (Tel: 0539 733774)

An excellent selection of all kinds of woodworking machinery – lathes, spindle moulders, planer-thicknessers, radial arm saws, etc.

Layburn Tools

Boothferry Road, Goole, North Humberside DN14 6AF (Tel: 0405 720300)

Suppliers of all kinds of power tools across the whole spectrum, also hand tools and safety clothing.

Luna Tools and Machinery

20 Denbigh Hall, Bletchley, Milton Keynes, Buckinghamshire MK3 7QT (Tel: 0908 370771)

Luna is a leading UK company specialising in the supply of machinery, hand and power tools for everyone involved in processing wood. The product range is primarily directed toward the professional craftsman and small business, but the Luna programme also includes equipment used by enthusiasts and the hire industry. Supply is through a nationwide dealer network.

Machine Mart

211 Lower Parliament Street, Nottingham NG1 1GN (Tel: 0602 587666)

A good selection of woodworking machinery and tools. A catalogue is produced for mail order sales.

Machine Sales & Services (Poole)

23 Cowley Road, Nuffield Ind Estate, Poole, Dorset BH17 7UJ (Tel: 0202 686238)

Woodworking machinery, dust extraction, power tools, safety equipment, transformers, generators.

D Mackay

85 East Road, Cambridge CB1 1BY (Tel: 0223 63132)

We offer from our extensive range of products everything from chisels to lathes. This includes products from Bosch, Elu, Ashley Iles, Multico, Sorby, Tyme, Coronet, Henry Taylor, EAC, Emco and Burgess. We have a large showroom where customers can look and handle products or watch one of the various videos we have.

SUPPLIERS

Makita Electric (UK)

"Finway", Dallon Road, Luton, Bedfordshire LU1 1TR (Tel: 0582 455777)

Makita Electric, the leading industrial power tool company, have a reputation within woodworking for being the best. We have an extensive range of routers, sanders, planers and saws that will make easy work of any woodworking job.

Micom

Industrial Estate, The Street, Maldon, Essex CM9 7XP (Tel: 0621 856324)

Copy routing machines, up to the large capacity 20-copy Mark V. This is a versatile alternative to CNC equipment for those involved in small scale and varied production.

Multico Machinery

Brighton Road, Salfords, Redhill, Surrey RH1 5ER (Tel: 0293 820250)

Suppliers of the world's only **a la carte** woodworking system in the Scheppach Kombi System, now available direct from Multico.

Myford

Chilwell Road, Beeston, Nottinghamshire NG9 1ER (Tel: 0602 254222)

The design of the new Myford-Mystro is based on 42 years of manufacturing wood-lathes. It offers heavy duty 2mt spindle; taper roller bearings; reversing feature; 3/4hp motor; headstock swivels through 180°, all steel hand rests; sturdy bowl turning attachment. Vari-speed model optional.

Neville M Oldham

Dale Streetmills, Longwood, Huddersfield, Yorkshire HD3 4TG (Tel: 0484 641219)

Neville M Oldham are suppliers of new and secondhand woodworking machinery, tooling and accessories to the trade and DIY market. We stock over 160 secondhand machines at our factory in Huddersfield and more than 50 new machines. Our price list can be supplied free by 'phoning or writing with your full address.

Norfolk Saw Service

Dog Lane, Horsford, Norwich, Norfolk (Tel: 0603 898695)

We are a family business offering sales of woodworking machinery and accessories and also a comprehensive saw service to both industry and the enthusiast. Sales also include TCT blades, SHSS blades, TCT rota cutters, bandsaw blades, planer knives and whitehill cutters.

Norwood Woodworking Machinery

The Bridge, Milford, Derbyshire DE5 0QF (Tel: 0773 828101)

This is where the Norwood Universal Woodworking Machine comes from.

Peugeot Power Tools

6 Churchbridge, Oldbury, West Midlands B69 2AP (Tel: 021 552 4580)

A comprehensive range of power tools and dust extraction systems.

Pollards Woodworking Machines

1 Cannons Road, Old Wolverton, Milton Keynes, Buckinghamshire MK12 5TL (Tel: 0908 222272)

The Hapfo AP5000 lathe has a twist attachment which makes spiral twistwork and fluting easy. Inca brand bandsaws and other machines also supplied.

The Power Tool Centre

54-58 Victoria Road, Widnes, Cheshire WA8 7RJ (Tel: 051 424 4545/7965)

Our mail order department specialises in spare parts for Black & Decker, Elu and Dewalt machines. Many obsolete models covered.

Rawdon Machine Sales

6 Acorn Park, Charlestown, Shipley, West Yorkshire BD17 7SW (Tel: 0274 597826)

Mechanical and hydraulic copy turning lathes across a price range from £1,500 to £40,000.

Record Power

Parkway Works, Sheffield, South Yorkshire S9 3BL (Tel: 0742 449066)

Record Power are the UK's largest volume suppliers of quality woodturning lathes, turning tools and accessories, selling under the brand names of Coronet, Arundel and Drillmaster.

In addition, Record Power manufacture and supply over 60 woodworking machines including bandsaws, dust extractors, circular saws, planer thicknessers and drilling machines and complement this with a full range of tooling and accessories.

Sanlin Leisure Marketing

Unit 1, 24 High Street, Toddington, Bedfordshire LU5 6BY (Tel: 05255 2259)
Suppliers of the Felder range of woodworking tools – bandsaws, universal machines, spindle moulders, etc. Send for a brochure.

Richard Sarjent Tools

116 Manchester Road, Swindon, Wiltshire (Tel: 0793 513005)
Hand tools, power tools, machinery, abrasives, finishes, books and videos.

J Simble & Sons

The Broadway, Queens Road, Watford, Hertfordshire (Tel: 0923 226052)
Retailers of woodworking machinery and tools.

Robert Sorby

Athol Road, Sheffield, South Yorkshire S8 0PA (Tel: 0742 554231)
Manufacturers of top quality woodturning and woodworking tools.
Range includes over 100 woodturning tools in carbon steel and high speed steel – many products unique to Sorby.

Our chisel range includes top quality gilt edge chisels with choice of CAB boxwood or rosewood handles.

Also specialist range of registered, paring, corner and heavy duty chisels.

SMS (Woodworking Machinery)

Danesforde, Pamber Road, Silchester, Nr Reading, Berkshire RG7 2NU (Tel: 0734 700921)
Low-cost vertical panel saws, precision-built for high cutting accuracy. Ross 380mm and 660mm wide power drum sanders, for sanding materials up to 175mm thick.
Leigh adjustable dovetail jig, used with portable routers to produce joints of hand-crafted appearance with speed and precision.

Onsrud inverted pin routing machines.

Speedwell Tool Co

62-70 Meadow Street, Preston, Lancashire PR1 1SU (Tel: 0772 52951)
We are engineers hand and machine tool suppliers, woodworking machines and woodworking hand tools. Also model engineering supplies including bronze and brass bar and sheet.

Startrite Machine Tool Co

Waterside Lane, Gads Hill, Gillingham, Kent ME7 2SF (Tel: 0634 281281)
We offer a range of woodworking machinery including bandsaws, sawbenches, planer thicknessers, universal woodworkers, lathes and dust extractors. Panel saws with scoring are also available to handle 8ft and 10ft boards. We offer quality machinery at competitive prices with a comprehensive after sales service from our factory in Kent.

Timms Tools

102/4 Liverpool Road, Patricroft, Eccles, Manchester M30 0WZ (Tel: 061 789 0909)
Stockists of all leading brands: Elu, Elektra, Beckum, Dewalt, Myford, Record, Marples, Triton, Trend, Scheppack, Multico, Coronet, Warco, Naerok, Black & Decker, Bosch, AEG and Makita.

Toolmail (GMC)

170 High Street, Lewes, East Sussex BN7 1YE (Tel: 0273 477009)
An exclusive range of top quality Japanese and American tools along side the best of British, European and other well known branded tools and accessories.

Trend Machinery & Cutting Tools

Unit N, Penfold Works, Imperial Way, Watford, Hertfordshire WD2 4VF (Tel: 0923 249911)
Trend specialise in tools and machines for routing wood, plastics and non-ferrous metals.
Router cutters in 600 types and profiles are described on a wall chart illustrating the wood shapes obtained from the tools. All profiles are drawn to exact size.

The Turning Point

British Gates & Timber Ltd, Biddenden, Nr Ashford, Kent TN27 8DD (Tel: 0580 291555)

The sawmill at British Gates converts large quantities of homegrown timbers, providing materials for cabinet-makers, woodturners and woodcarvers. Stock also includes imported and exotic types, a wide range of hand tools, lathes and accessories, chucks, polishes and finishes, adhesives, and a wide range of craft accessories.

Tyme Machines (Bristol)

Halls Road, Kingswood, Bristol, Avon BS15 2JD (Tel: 0272 603726)

Tyme Machines manufacture the popular Avon and Cub woodturning lathes together with full range of attachments and accessories. The experience gained by our manufacturing department working with the aerospace industries has resulted in products being manufactured to high specifications. While compact in design, these swivel headstock machines, made from cast-iron, steel and aluminium, have the rigidity and capacity of more expensive machines.

Tyzak Tool Company

81 Kingsland Road, Shoreditch, London E2 8AG (Tel: 0923 50305)

All major makes of drills for the hobby and professional market. Machinery mainly Tyme, Coronet, Kity. Also hand tools.

Westward Building Services

Lister Close, Newnham Trading Estate, Plympton, Plymouth, Devon PL7 4HG (Tel: 0752 330303)

WBS are a local company offering a comprehensive service in power tools, fixings, ironmongery and woodworking machinery. Our sales team cover the region, and in addition we offer regular van deliveries. Also we provide full repair and maintenance facilities for the machinery we supply.

Willis Woodworking

157 West Street, Bedminster, Bristol, Avon BS3 3PN (Tel: 0272 667013)

Wood, aluminium and UPVC machinery, large stock of Trend router cutters, Bosch power tools, saw blades, abrasives, bandsaw blades. Advice on dust extraction and installation. Woodworking lathes and accessories. Machinery servicing and installations carried out. Large stock of lightweight plant and access equipment for hire or sale.

Wokingham Tool Company

99 Wokingham Road, Reading, Berkshire RG6 1LH (Tel: 0734 661511)

Electric tool repair service, saw blade etc sharpening service. Hire of small electric tools.

Woodpine Machinery Sales

Stream House, Furnace Place, Haslemere, Surrey GU27 2EJ (Tel: 0428 642169/651853)

Specialising in sales, service and spares of a full range of woodworking machinery in the South of England, mainly the full SCM and SAMCO range.

Direct imports include machines from the Surface Group, Alternax mortisers and Conver tenoners.

Used machinery/part exchange/finance available.

The Woodworks

The Field, Shipley, Nr Heanor, Derbyshire DE7 7JJ (Tel: 0773 719842)

Suppliers of a wide range of leading brands of woodworking machinery, tools, materials and accessories. Mail orders accepted and catalogue available.

MUSICAL INSTRUMENTS

D H Bolton

44 Church Lane, Acklam, Middlesbrough, Cleveland TS5 7EB (Tel: 0642 817097)

Kits for harpsichords, etc, specially suited to experienced woodworkers who can make the case themselves and need only the inner parts, plans and instructions. Though not essential, there are 1-week summer courses for Bolton kit builders.

Six models: Italian harpsichord, English spinet, English and Flemish virginals, French double harpsichord, clarichord.

Lothian Tree Services

Whitehill Sawmill, Thornton, Rosewell, Midlothian EH24 9EF (Tel: 031 440 4175)

Stocks of figured sycamore for musical instruments.

Sydney Evans

45 Regent Place, Birmingham, West Midlands B1 3NB (Tel: 021 233 1741)

We are suppliers of wood, tools and accessories for makers of stringed musical instruments (ie. violin, viola, cello and guitar). Manufacturer and supplier of various specialist tools, violin makers brass planes, reamers, peg shapers, etc.

PLANS

Craft Design Plans

4 Grassfield Way, Knutsford, Cheshire WA16 9AF (Tel: 0565 51681)

Design plans for spinning wheels, looms, period furniture and toys on large AO sheets, fully dimensioned, parts lists etc. Brochure available on request.

PYROGRAPHY

Peter Child

Woodturning Supplies, The Old Hyde, Little Yeldham, Halstead, Essex CO9 4QT (Tel: 0787 237291)

We supply everything for the woodturner including lathes, chucks, lathe accessories, turning tools, carving tools, drills and drill chucks, wood blanks, grindstones and sharpening equipment, abrasives, polishes and finishing materials, glass dishes, peppermill inserts, clocks, tiles and weather instruments, cutlery blades, books, safety equipment, electrical fittings, pyrography machines. Callers/ mail order welcome.

Janik Enterprises Ltd

Brickfield Lane, Ruthin, Clwyd LL15 2TN (Tel: 082 422096)

A comprehensive range of pyrographs and equipment. Single and dual outlet heat controlled models – solid pint and hot wire, brands, lettering, numbers, etc.

Wood related craft supplies and sundries, craft design books and a wide range of whitewood articles for various crafts.

RESTORATION

Weaves & Waxes

53 Church Street, Bloxham, Banbury, Oxon OX15 4ET (Tel: 0295 721535)

Veneering, polishing, caning, rushing, gilding, clock repairs and upholstery, veneers, brass cabinet fittings, desk top leathers. As experienced restorers we are able to advise our customers who wish to undertake their own restoration. They can of course purchase the appropriate materials from us.

STORAGE

Stig Ravn (UK) Ltd

Unit 4 Rockfort Ind Estate, Hithercroft Road, Wallingford, Oxon OX10 9DA (Tel: 0491 34486)

Suppliers of small parts storage equipment: drawers, tool boxes, key storage, portable workbench, hinged small part boxes, tube building system, bin storage system, storage cabinets, first aid boxes, cash boxes, security boxes, post boxes.

TIMBER

Dryers

Arrowsmiths

74 Wilson Street, Darlington, Co Durham DL3 6QZ (Tel: 0325 481970/381204)

Manufacturers of economical timber dryers, also suppliers of moisture meters at discount prices.

TIMBER

Arborcraft

Unit 5 Kingsdown Industrial Estate, Kingsdown, Swindon, Wiltshire (Tel: 0793 823646)

Mainly stocking mahogany, oak and ash.

Acorn Hardwoods

Harlstone Firs Sawmill, New Duston, Northampton NN5 6UJ (Tel: 0604 581445)

English oak, ash, elm, yew, beech, lime, etc. Available kiln dried and air dried.

Small order department – selected orders 7 days notice.

Harry Adcock

Saw Mills, Corby Glen, Grantham, Lincolnshire (Tel: 0476 84231)

Just about all the home grown hardwoods plus some softwood.

Ailstone Hardwoods

The Brickyard, Preston-on-Stour, Stratford-on-Avon, Warwickshire CV37 8BN (Tel: 0789 87345)

Suppliers of most English hardwoods ie. oak, ash, elm, walnut (kiln dried and air dried). Beams cut to order.

Altham Hardwood Centre

Altham, Accrington, Lancashire (Tel: 0282 71618)

Stock includes English oak, ash, beech, elm and sweet chestnut. The Centre will only supply timber from sustainable, managed sources and aims to plant 10 whips for every tree it uses.

Amalgamated Hardwoods

Englemere Sawmills, London Road, Ascot, Berks SL5 8DG (Tel: 0344 885451)

A good selection of British and imported hardwoods. The world's hardwoods from one telephone number.

Antique Pine Suppliers

Unit 27 Healey Hall Mills, Healey Den, Shawclough, Rochdale, Lancashire OL12 6BG (Tel: 0706 523091)

Specialist sawmillers in reclaimed 18th and 19th century American pines. Advice given. Self-selection invited.

Barchards

Gibson Lane, Melton, North Ferriby, East Yorkshire HU14 3HF (Tel: 0482 633388)

Oak, larch, iroko for boatbuilding. Opele, Douglas fir etc, for marine work and civil engineering. Beech and birch for chair frame makers. All species of home grown timber which can be sawn to any thickness in our sawmill.

Bath House Crafts

South Place, Chesterfield, Derby (Tel: 0246 270322)

Supplier of British and imported hardwoods, specialising in English and American Walnut.

John Boddys Fine Wood & Tool Store

Riverside Sawmills, Boroughbridge, North Yorkshire YO5 9LJ (Tel: 0423 322370)

A woodworker's superstore retailing over 7,500 items, ranging from tools, finishes, requisites to books and plans, together with 125 species of timber in boards, squares and blanks. Available by self selection or by mail order, plus a full range of woodworking courses and free demonstrations. Easy access from A1.

British Gates & Timber

Biddenden, Nr Ashford, Kent TN27 8DD (Tel: 0580 291555)

A whole selection of all kinds of timber, including many blanks and specialist wood for turning.

Jean Burhouse Farmhouse

The Old Sawmill, Iver, Dunkeld, Perth PH8 0JR (Tel: 0350 2723)

A good stock of home grown and imported hardwoods. Oak, Walnut, lime, Sycamore, etc in lengths up to 4m and 1-5in thickness. Many exotics. Over 80 different species stocked altogether.

Charltons Timber Centre

Frome Road, Radstock, Bath, Avon BA3 3PT (Tel: 0761 36229)

Specialising in English hardwoods but also offering a full range of imported and exotic hardwoods, including turning and carving blanks and bargain offcuts. A machining service is available.

Clark Taylor (Timber)

Kingsway North, Team Valley, Gateshead, Tyne & Wear NE11 0EE (Tel: 091 482 5151)

Home grown softwood. Pallet, fencing, carcassing, rough sawn softwood.

Craft Supplies

The Mill, Millers Dale, Buxton, Derbyshire SK17 8SN (Tel: 0298 871636)

Craft Supplies offers the complete package for the woodturner. A complete novice or experienced professional can purchase from the 115 page colour catalogue. Six tutors take woodturning courses, structured to suit the beginner or advanced turner. 140 woods are now housed in converted farm buildings to speed the process of storing, drying and machining. A good range of machinery, plus chucks and other accessories, as well as finishing materials, books and videos, plans, clocks and barometers. Many other household components are available, a selection of which are displayed in the newly designed showroom.

Craftwoods

Thatchways, Thurlestone, Kingsbridge, Devon TQ7 3NJ (Tel: 0548 560721)

Mostly exotic timbers, although some home grown, for cabinet making and blanks for turning.

Crown Hardwoods

63 Union Street, Newport Pagnell, Buckinghamshire MK16 8ET (Tel: 0908 618167)

A good selection of hardwoods.

Crown Hill Timber Yard

Halberton, Tiverton, Devon (Tel: 0884 820152)

A good selection of timber to choose from.

Darby Bros

Bridge Wharf, Beccles, Suffolk NR34 0PA (Tel: 0502 712119)

Stocks of English air dried and kiln dried hardwoods available, also a good selection of kiln dried imported hardwoods and joinery quality softwoods. A selection of veneers and inlays etc.

R E & R Duffield & Sons

Green Lane, Melmerby, Ripon, North Yorkshire HG4 5JB (Tel: 0765 84564)

Specialists in the supply of home-grown and european hardwoods in particular kiln dried oak, quarter sawn oak, ash, elm, sycamore, sweet chestnut and beech.

Ecological Trading Company

1 Lesbury Road, Newcastle-upon-Tyne NE6 5LB (Tel: 091 276 5547)

Homegrown and imported timber, but care is taken that only wood from sustainably managed forests is stocked.

Eco Timber

Unit 5, Gibson Business Centre, 800 High Road, Tottenham, London N17 0DH (Tel: 081 365 0222)

Specialists in the supply of timber from sustainable sources, mostly hardwoods from the UK, Europe and the USA. A planing and moulding service is available. Good quality spalted woods and burrs a speciality.

English Timbers

1a Main Street, Kirkburn, Driffield, North Humberside YO25 9DU (Tel: 0377 89301)

English oak, ash, elm, cherry, sycamore, holly, fruitwoods, chestnut, yew, etc. American – maple, cherry, walnut. French – Oak, cherry, beech and fruitwoods etc.

Machining service run by experienced cabinet makers. All cutting lists prepared, tops jointed, components prepared, etc.

A wide range of hardwood flooring, mouldings, skirtings, architraves, doors, panelling, etc, made to order.

Bulk sales of timber direct from Europe to the customer.

Febjade

Downs Estate, Ruden Way, Epsom Downs, Surrey KT17 3LR (Tel: 0737 358918)

Fox English Hardwoods

The Old Cheese Factory, Reapsmoor, Longnor, Nr Buxton, Derbyshire SK17 0LG (Tel: 0298 84467)

Ash, beech, elm, oak and sycamore.

Suppliers of kiln-dried English hardwoods, sawn through-and-through, in lengths up to 12ft. Customers may select their own boards at no extra cost. Write or ring for price list and availability. Timber planed all round to order. Ask for a quotation. Bowl blanks stocked.

Henry Venables Hardwoods

Doxey Road, Stafford, Staffordshire ST16 2EN (Tel: 0785 55115)

Suppliers of temperate hardwoods from Europe and North America (all from sustainable forest). Specialists in restoration timbers and machined hardwood components.

SUPPLIERS

Holmes (Wragby)
Units 1 & 2 Sadler Road, Doddington Road Ind Estate, Lincoln, Lincolnshire LN6 3RS (Tel: 0522 500510)
Brazilian mahogany, utile, lauan, meranti, agba, idigbo, iroko, teak, yellow pine, American ash, oak and cherry.

We can offer any of these species sawn roughly to length, in any quantity, at competitive prices. Delivery can be arranged.

Alan Holtham
Old Stores Turnery, Wistaston Road, Willaston, Nantwich, Cheshire CW5 6QJ (Tel: 0270 67010)
Specialist retailers to the woodworking trade with particular emphasis on woodturning and carving. As well as handling small, wood lathes we also cater for the needs of the production woodturner and sell the Hapfo range of industrial copy lathes. Our timber section is fast gaining a reputation for quality and variety of woods, and will soon be a major part of our business.

Hoyle Hardwoods
27 Church Road, Coalbrookdale, Telford, Shropshire TF8 7NT (Tel: 0939 33006)

Kilnwood
Unit 18 Gaza Trading Estate, Scabharbour Road, Hildenborough, Tonbridge, Kent TN11 8PL (Tel: 0732 452059)
Ash, beech, Brazilian mahogany, Lebanon cedar, cherry, chestnut, elm, lime, European oak, American white oak, pear, south American yellow pine, sycamore.

We offer all the above from stock and a comprehensive, versatile machining service.

James Latham
Leeside Wharf, Mount Pleasant Hill, Clapton, London E5 9NG (Tel: 081 806 3333)
Around 30 different temperate and tropical hardwoods are stocked together with a further six species of UK hardwoods.

James Latham, with its strategically placed depots across the country, offers a large selection of hardwoods, softwoods and panel products in a variety of sizes and thicknesses. A number of specialist items are included in the range of timber and timber-based products.

Limehouse Timber
3 Oak Industrial Park, Chelmsford Road, Great Dunmow, Essex CM6 1XN (Tel: 0371 876361)

Lothian Tree Services
Whitehill Sawmill, Thornton, Rosewell, Midlothian EH24 9EF (Tel: 031 440 4175)
Stocks of native British hardwoods for craftsmen. No tropical timbers as firm policy, occasional imported European timbers. Most timber from local small scale sources. Small customers welcome, large customers need to be patient. Excellent stocks of figured sycamore for musical instruments.

Mackintosh Craft Wood
Unit 7 Fort Fareham Industrial Estate, Newgate Lane, Fareham, Hampshire, PO14 1AH (Tel: 0329 221925)

Medomsley Sawmills
Manor Road, Medomsley, Consett, Co Durham DH8 6QS (Tel: 0207 560266/560278)
Specialists in pressure treatment, fencing and accessories. Forestry management services.

MHL Specialwoods
Unit 3 Water Lane Industrial Estate, Willenhall, Wolverhampton WV13 3SU (Tel: 0902 712436)

Northwood Timber
Burcott Road, Hereford HR4 9LW (Tel: 0432 265071)

Pennine Abrasive and Timber Co
Unit 0 Springfield Trading Estate, Samuel Street, Failsworth, Manchester (Tel: 061 688 4099)

Project Timber Supplies
Burlais Works, Approach Road, Cwmbwrla, Swansea SA5 8NN (Tel: 0792 642728)
Homegrown and exotic timbers. Project timber was set up in January '89 for woodworkers, woodturners and carvers and antique restorers. We stock veneers, hardwoods, woodturning and carving woods, tools, finishes, Record machines (lathes and bandsaws).

We are also running a woodturning club with

over 70 members. Since the set up in July we have organised trips, demonstrations, videos and hands-on help to budding woodturners.

Shrewsbury Timber

Peplow, Nr Hodnet, Shropshire TF9 3JF (Tel: 0630 84777/8/9)

Large stocks of home grown hardwoods. Kiln and air dried English oak, burr oak, brown oak, chestnut, ash, sycamore, ripple sycamore, cedar of Lebanon, cherry, larch, walnut, yew, lacewood, lime, beech, spalted beech.

Stockists of imported timbers and restoration oak. Our "timber cave" for bowl blanks, turnery blocks and woodworkers' materials.

Stockists of a wide range of finish and restoration products.

Machinery and delivery service available. Large or small quantities welcome.

Smee Timber Importers

Winsford Sawmills, Smoke Hall Lane, Winsford, Cheshire CW7 3BE (Tel: 0606 861062)

Ternex (London)

27 Ayot Green, Welwyn, Hertfordshire AL6 9BA (Tel: 0707 324606)

Stockist of English and imported commercial hard and softwoods.

Machining service available. Contract saw-milling.

Timberline

Unit 7 Munday Works, 58-66 Morley Road, Tonbridge, Kent TN9 1RP (Tel: 0732 355626)

Treske Sawmills

Station Works, Thirsk, North Yorkshire YO7 4NY (Tel: 0845 522770)

British home grown hardwoods – oak, ash, elm, beech, cherry, sycamore, yew etc.

Specialist supplier of home grown English hardwoods. Timbers available fresh sawn, air dried or kiln dried. Have machine shop and can prepare cutting lists. Specialists in ash, elm (still available) and oak.

The Turning Point

British Gates & Timber Ltd, Biddenden, Nr Ashford, Kent TN27 8DD (Tel: 0580 291555)

The sawmill at British Gates converts large quantities of homegrown timbers, providing materials for cabinet-makers, woodturners and woodcarvers. Stock also includes imported and exotic types, a wide range of hand tools, lathes and accessories, chucks, polishes and finishes, adhesives, and a wide range of craft accessories.

Whitmore's Timber Co

Main Road, Claybrooke Magna, Lutterworth, Leicestershire LE17 5AQ (Tel: 0455 209121)

Quality English, Continental and North American temperate hardwoods. Whitmore's Timber Co Ltd's 17 acre site comprises a sawmill, considerable drying sheds and three vacuum kiln driers and is able to offer from stock a comprehensive range of fresh sawn, air dried and kiln dried timber for uses such as building restoration; furniture; joinery; river, canal and coastal defence work; construction; fence and gate manufacture; and for musical instruments.

Bill Wilder

Church Farm, Easton Grey, Malmesbury, Wiltshire SN16 0PF (Tel: 0666 840254)

Yandle & Sons

Hurst Works, Martock, Somerset TA12 6JU (Tel: 0935 822207)

VENEERS AND MARQUETRY

Abbey Marquetry

14/15 Fiddlebridge Ind Centre, Lemsford Road, Hatfield, AL10 0DE (Tel: 0707 276444)

Manufacturers of marquetry kits, stockists of exotic veneers for marquetry and cabinet making. Banding, stringing and motifs.

Manufacturers of special marquetry motifs, laminated block for bobbins, thimbles and window jewellery.

Books related to veneering and marquetry. Hot pressing up to 8ft x 4ft.

The Art Veneers Co

Chiswick Avenue Ind Estate, Mildenhall, Suffolk IP28 7AY (Tel: 0638 712550)

We supply rare and exotic veneers for cabinet making, reproduction work and DIY projects, from full leaf lengths down to smaller pieces for repairs or marquetry work.

We manufacture a range of over 90 marquetry craft kits.

Through our mail order service you can order these items along with an extensive range of inlay bandings and motifs, tools, glues, polishes, clock movements, leather skives, beech legs and much more!

Full details in our manual/catalogue – cost £1.75.

Designer Marquetry

125a Bevan Street East, Lowestoft, Suffolk NR32 2AQ (Tel: 0502 563701)

Suppliers of marquetry kits and equipment and veneers.

Weaves & Waxes

53 Church Street, Bloxham, Banbury, Oxon OX15 4ET (Tel: 0295 721535)

Veneering, polishing, caning, rushing, gilding, clock repairs and upholstery, veneers, brass cabinet fittings, desk top leathers. As experienced restorers we are able to advise our customers who wish to undertake their own restoration. They can of course purchase the appropriate materials from us.

WALKING STICKS AND CANES

4-Shot Ltd (Theo Fossel)

119 Station Road, Beaconsfield, Buckinghamshire HP9 1LG (Tel: 0494 672349)

Britains specialist supplier for all kinds of sticks, crooks, books, videos, components and weekend residential training courses in several countries. Special commissions gladly undertaken. Mail order catalogue £1 (in stamps) from the address above (callers strictly by appointment).

WOODTURNING

Allmodels Engineering

91 Manor Way, Ruislip, Middlesex HA4 8HW (Tel: 0895 674126)

Wood working machinery, tools, etc. Woodcarving and turning, tools for individuals and also industrial users.

John Boddys Fine Wood & Tool Store

Riverside Sawmills, Boroughbridge, North Yorkshire YO5 9LJ (Tel: 0423 322370)

A woodworker's superstore retailing over 7,500 items, ranging from tools, finishes, requisites to books and plans, together with 125 species of timber in boards, squares and blanks. Available by self selection or by mail order, plus a full range of woodworking courses and free demonstrations. Easy access from A1.

Charltons Timber Centre

Frome Road, Radstock, Bath, Avon BA3 3PT (Tel: 0761 36229)

Specialising in English hardwoods but also offering a full range of imported and exotic hardwoods, including turning and carving blanks and bargain offcuts. A machining service is available. Complementing this stock we have quality products, including mouldings; sheet materials; joinery softwood; veneers; waxes; finishes; cabinet fittings; adhesives; turning; carving and general tools; portable and static machinery; clock movements; books; plans etc. Together with woodturning accessories.

Peter Child

Woodturning Supplies, The Old Hyde, Little Yeldham, Halstead, Essex CO9 4QT (Tel: 0787 237291)

We supply everything for the woodturner including lathes, chucks, lathe accessories, turning tools, carving tools, drills and drill chucks, wood blanks, grindstones and sharpening equipment, abrasives, polishes and finishing materials, glass dishes, peppermill inserts, clocks, tiles and weather instruments, cutlery blades, books, safety equipment, electrical fittings, pyrography machines. Callers/ mail order welcome.

Clarke International

Lower Clapton Road, London E5 0RN
(Tel: 081 986 8231)
Clarke International, one of Britain's largest privately owned manufacturers of electrical and mechanical power products, supplies a wide range of woodworking equipment for DIY and professional use.

The range includes belt and disc sanders, table saws, scroll saws, electric and manual mitre saws, band saws and woodturning lathes.

Craft Supplies

The Mill, Millers Dale, Buxton, Derbyshire SK17 8SN (Tel: 0298 871636)
Craft Supplies offers the complete package for the woodturner. A complete novice or experienced professional can purchase from the 115 page colour catalogue. Six tutors take woodturning courses, structured to suit the beginner or advanced turner. 140 woods are now housed in converted farm buildings to speed the process of storing, drying and machining. A good range of machinery, plus chucks and other accessories, as well as finishing materials, books and videos, plans, clocks and barometers. Many other household components are available, a selection of which are displayed in the newly designed showroom.

Fylde Woodturning Supplies

255 Church Street, Blackpool, Lancashire FY1 3PB (Tel: 0253 28262)
A comprehensive supply of woodturning tools, lathes, finishes and associated items. Also woodcarving chisels, mallets, timber, slipstones rifflers, etc. Friendly efficient service for woodturners, by woodturners.

Alan Holtham

Old Stores Turnery, Wistaston Road, Willaston, Nantwich, Cheshire CW5 6QJ (Tel: 0270 67010)
Specialist retailers to the woodworking trade with particular emphasis on woodturning and carving. As well as handling small, hand wood lathes we also cater for the needs of the production woodturner and sell the Hapfo range of industrial copy

lathes. Our timber section is fast gaining a reputation for quality and variety of woods, and will soon be a major part of our business.

Multistar Machine & Tools

Ashton House, Wheatfield Road, Colchester, Essex CO3 5YA (Tel: 0206 549944)
Suppliers of the Superchuck Mk2 woodturning chuck which comes in a seven size jaw range, each providing five options in compression or expansion. The Duplex Chuck System caters for all kinds of turning.

Myford

Chilwell Road, Beeston, Nottinghamshire NG9 1ER (Tel: 0602 254222)
The design of the new Myford-Mystro is based on 42 years of manufacturing wood-lathes. It offers heavy duty 2mt spindle; taper roller bearings; reversing feature; 3/4hp motor; headstock swivels through 180°; all steel hand rests; sturdy bowl turning attachment. Vari-speed model optional.

Project Timber Supplies

Burla's Works, Approach Road, Cwm Bwrla, Swansea SA5 8NN (Tel: 0792 642728)
Project Timber was set up in 1989 especially to supply woodworkers, including woodturners.

Record Power

Parkway Works, Sheffield, South Yorkshire S9 3BL (Tel: 0742 449066)
Record Power are the UK's largest volume suppliers of quality woodturning lathes, turning tools and accessories, selling under the brand names of Coronet, Arundel and Drillmaster.

In addition, Record Power manufacture and supply over 60 woodworking machines including bandsaws, dust extractors, circular saws, planer thicknessers and drilling machines and complement this with a full range of tooling and accessories.

Robert Sorby

Athol Road, Sheffield, South Yorkshire S8 0PA (Tel: 0742 554231)
Manufacturers of top quality woodturning and woodworking tools.

Range includes over 100 woodturning tools in

carbon steel and high speed steel – many products unique to Sorby.

Our chisel range includes top quality gilt edge chisels with choice of CAB boxwood or rosewood handles.

Also specialist range of registered, paring, corner and heavy duty chisels.

Startrite Machine Tool Co
Waterside Lane, Gads Hill, Gillingham, Kent ME7 2SF (Tel: 0634 281281)
Startrite offer a range of woodworking machinery including bandsaws, sawbenches, planer thicknessers, universal woodworkers, lathes and dust extractors.

Panel saws with scoring are also available to handle 8ft and 10ft boards.

We offer quality machinery at competitive prices with a comprehensive after sales service from our factory in Kent.

The Turning Point
British Gates & Timber Ltd, Biddenden, Nr Ashford, Kent TN27 8DD (Tel: 0580 291555)
The sawmill at British Gates converts large quantities of homegrown timbers, providing materials for cabinet-makers, woodturners and woodcarvers. Stock also includes imported and exotic types, a wide range of hand tools, lathes and accessories, chucks, polishes and finishes, adhesives, and a wide range of craft accessories.

Tyme Machines (Bristol)
Halls Road, Kingswood, Bristol, Avon BS15 2JD (Tel: 0272 603726)
Tyme Machines manufacture the popular Avon and Cub woodturning lathes together with full range of attachments and accessories. The experience gained by our manufacturing department working with the aerospace industries has resulted in products being manufactured to high specifications. While compact in design, these swivel headstock machines, made from cast-iron, steel and aluminium, have the rigidity and capacity of more expensive machines.

Willis Woodworking
157 West Street, Bedminster, Bristol, Avon BS3 3PN (Tel: 0272 667013)
Wood, aluminium and UPVC machinery, large stock of Trend router cutters, Bosch power tools, saw blades, abrasives, bandsaw blades. Advice on dust extraction and installation. Woodworking lathes and accessories. Machinery servicing and installations carried out. Large stock of lightweight plant and access equipment for hire or sale.

Yandle & Sons
Hurst Works, Martock, Somerset TA12 6JU (Tel: 0935 822207)
A timber merchant who has set up a woodturning centre selling just about all requirements, from blanks to machinery. There is also a gallery selling work.

Contact	Tel	Address

Contact	Tel	Address

Contact	Tel	Address

Contact	Tel	Address

Contact	Tel	Address

Contact	Tel	Address